KAROLINSKA SYMPOSIA
on Research Methods in Reproductive Endocrinology

ORGANIZED BY

Karolinska Institutet, Stockholm

WITH THE COLLABORATION OF

The World Health Organization

AND WITH A GRANT FROM

The Ford Foundation
New York

ORGANIZING COMMITTEE:

E. Diczfalusy, Sweden (Chairman)
E. Baulieu, France
J. Ferin, Belgium
P. Hubinont, Belgium
B. Lunenfeld, Israel
L. Martini, Italy
K. J. Ryan, U.S.A.

In vitro Methods
in
Reproductive Cell Biology

Transactions of the third Symposium held in Geneva
on January 25 – 27, 1971

EDITOR
E. Diczfalusy

EDITORIAL ASSISTANT
A. Diczfalusy

Stockholm 1971

A limited number of copies of this publication
are available for distribution from
The Reproductive Endocrinology Research Unit
Karolinska sjukhuset
104 01 Stockholm 60, Sweden
Tel. 34 05 00 / 2461 · Cables: Kirix

This volume is also published as Supplementum No. 153
of Acta endocrinologica (Kbh.)

Printed in Denmark
by Bogtrykkeriet Forum
Copenhagen

CONTENTS

OPENING REMARKS

Dr. H. Mahler
Assistant Director General
World Health Organization
Geneva

On behalf of the World Health Organization, I have great pleasure in welcoming you to the Third Karolinska Symposium on Research Methods in Reproductive Endocrinology. I would like to take this opportunity to emphasize the positive value we have found in being involved collaboratively in these meetings. The Symposia have added another element to WHO's programme in reproductive biomedicine. The aims of this particular programme are to promote research in this field through stimulation, co-ordination, and financial assistance for research work and research training. It is quite clear that great research efforts are needed both at the fundamental and applied level if we are to improve our ability to promote reproductive health, provide adequate means to regulate fertility, and alleviate reproductive disease.

The experience with the first two meetings in the series of Symposia has clearly established several points: first, standards of scientific excellence by the participants in the analysis of the current state of knowledge of specific subjects and in the formulation of problems requiring further research; second, the stimulation of ideas through the interchange of information and concepts during the meeting itself, and on a much broader scale, as a result of the unprecedented rapidity with which the proceedings were printed and widely distributed; and third, the value of applying the approaches of various scientific disciplines to research problems in the field of reproduction. One bit of evidence of the multi-disciplinary impact of the Symposia is the feedback being received from scientists who have been sent a copy of the proceedings and from additional requests continuously received from research workers representing a wide range of scientific fields.

The papers you have prepared for the present Symposium indicate that the high quality and usefulness of the Karolinska Symposia will be maintained. In a sense, this conference on »In vitro methods in reproductive cell biology« presents a particular challenge: the biological materials involved are themselves highly intricate; the preservation of function *in vitro* demands delicate experimental handling; the complexity of the systems magnifies the methodological problems.

Besides the intrinsic value of a better understanding of the fundamental processes and mechanisms involved at the level of the cell in relation to reproductive physiology, such insights should produce further leads with potential applicability to a variety of problems in this field. The importance of developing new research methodology and techniques towards these ends should permit more rapid advances to be made, and represents vital objectives of your discussions.

The organizing committee is to be congratulated for an agenda which avoids familiar beaten paths and which provides ample scope for inventive and creative thinking. Your agenda is a full one, and I shall no longer delay the beginning of your discussions. It remains for me to wish you every success and a pleasant stay in Geneva.

Case Western Reserve University, School of Medicine,
Cleveland, Ohio, U. S. A.

TECHNIQUES FOR THE ISOLATION OF CELLS OF THE ADRENAL CORTEX, THE ANTERIOR PITUITARY AND THE CORPUS LUTEUM: MORPHOLOGICAL AND FUNCTIONAL EVALUATION OF THE ISOLATED CELLS[1]

By

*George Sayers, Ronald Portanova, Robert J. Beall,
Steven Seelig and Sasha Malamed*[2]

ABSTRACT

A trypsin technique for the isolation of cells of the rat adrenal, the rat anterior pituitary and the bovine corpus luteum is described. The isolated cells have been characterized in morphological and functional terms.

Knowledge of the secretion and action of hormones has been derived in large measure from studies in the whole animal, the tissue slice and the tissue homogenate. Isolated cells of the endocrine glands or of the target tissues of the hormones represent a new approach to such studies. These preparations retain the advantages of the intact cell, yet eliminate problems of penetration of diffusion barriers inherent in the tissue slice.

Explants of normal tissue and more frequently of malignant tissue have been dispersed and the cells carried through repeated culture. Isolated cells from

---

[1] This work has been supported by grants from the National Science Foundation (GB 8427) and the United States Public Health Service (AM 13820-01 and 5 T01 GM00899).
[2] Department of Anatomy, Rutgers University, Rutgers, New Jersey.

culture have been used to great advantage and this will be the subject of Dr. Sato's presentation at this symposium. We have been interested in cells freshly isolated from the organism. The animal is sacrificed, the endocrine gland removed and dispersed, the freed cells collected, the pellets suspended in medium; aliquots of the suspension are incubated with and without hormone and the end point of response measured. The sequence of events from sacrifice of the animal to measurement of response of the isolated cells is completed in one day and without attention to sterile conditions.

The isolation of living cells from animal tissues is more an art than a science. As stated by *Rinaldini* (1958),

>»Many successful methods in biology and biochemistry are the product of empiricism, but a long series of trials in this and other laboratories has shown that there may be no short cut to the preparation of suspensions of undamaged cells from different tissues in sufficient quantities for chemical estimations, and that a more rational approach to the problem is needed. This must be based on an appraisal of (1) the nature and structure of the intercellular materials to be disaggregated, (2) the action of the agents used for this purpose, and (3) the response of the cells under the particular conditions employed. The task is rendered more arduous by the insufficiency of our present knowledge on these points.«

We will focus attention on the dispersion of endocrine tissue or of tissue sensitive to the action of hormones. However, the basic techniques for dispersion have been developed by workers in the field of tissue culture, the story of which is presented in the article by *Rinaldini* (1958).

A contribution of greatest impact has been that of *Rodbell* (1964) who developed a simple and highly reproducible technique for the isolation of adipocytes. Collagenase combined with gentle agitation frees the cells of the epididymal fat pad of the rat; the isolated cells synthesize and release fatty acids, processes which are exquisitely sensitive to the addition of insulin, epinephrine and other hormones to the incubation medium. The metabolic activities of the isolated adipocytes and the regulation of these activities by insulin and other hormones appear to be a close representation of the events as they occur in the animal.

The collagenase technique was applied to rat adrenal tissue with a modicum of success. At the suggestion of Dr. Swallow we switched from collagenase to trypsin with rewarding results (*Swallow & Sayers* 1969). Modifications and refinements of the trypsin technique have led to the preparation of isolated cells of the rat adrenal which respond with increased production of corticosterone to the addition of less than a picogram of ACTH. The trypsin technique has been successful in the isolation of cells of the rat anterior pituitary (*Portanova et al.* 1970); the isolated pituitary cells maintain a high concentration of ACTH when incubated under appropriate conditions. More recently we have been able to isolate cells of the bovine corpus luteum with this same technique (*Beall & Sayers,* unpublished observations). In this report we shall describe the technique in detail and present criteria for the evaluation of the »quality« of the isolated cells; the goal is the isolation of viable endocrine cells whose metabolic activities, and responsiveness to added hormones reflect the physiological activity of these cells *in situ.*

THE TRYPSIN TECHNIQUE FOR THE ISOLATION OF CELLS OF THE RAT ADRENAL

1. *Introduction*

Collagenase has been used for the preparation of isolated cells of the rat adrenal (*Kloppenborg et al.* 1968). As stated above, we had little success with this enzyme. We turned to trypsin for a number of reasons. First, *Moscona* (1952) had demonstrated that embryonic tissue could be dispersed with trypsin and the isolated cells grew and differentiated in culture. Second, *Tong et al.* (1962) had been able to prepare isolated cells of thyroid of ovine and of bovine origin (*Tong* 1964). Third, trypsin can be obtained commercially in a high state of purity. We have used numerous lots of trypsin, all with uniform success. It has been stated that it is not collagenase in collagenase preparations that is effective in breaking the cement that binds the cells; some have ascribed the action to a contaminating proteolytic enzyme. In the case of trypsin, the high purity of the preparations employed suggests that it is this enzyme which is the effective agent in dispersion. However, one cannot be absolutely certain since a report has appeared (*Steim et al.* 1968) to the effect that commercial preparations of trypsin are contaminated with ribonuclease. Finally, inhibitors of trypsin are available. Despite repeated washes of cell suspensions, some trypsin is carried over from the dispersion process; ACTH is an excellent substrate for trypsin and is destroyed when incubated with cell suspension contaminated with the enzyme. Destruction of the hormone is avoided by the addition of an appropriate quantity of lima bean trypsin inhibitor.

2. *The Trypsin Technique*

Sixteen male Sprague-Dawley rats (300 to 450 g) are anaesthetized with ether and bled by section of the abdominal aorta. The adrenals are removed, freed of fat, quartered and transferred to a cold (4°C), siliconized 50 ml Erlenmeyer flask which contains 20 ml of KRBG and trypsin (TRL, Worthington Biochemical Corporation; 0.25 g per 100 ml). A siliconized glass rod with a paddle shaped end is inserted into the flask, the flask placed in a water bath (37°C), and the rod driven at a constant rate, 500 rpm (Waco-Supreme Power Stirrer; Wilkens-Anderson Co., Chicago, Illinois). A gas mixture of 95 % O_2, 5 % CO_2 is blown into the flask via a small-bore plastic tube. After 20 min the stirrer is stopped and the quarters settle. The fluid containing the freed cells is transferred with a siliconized pasteur pipette to a cold (4°C), siliconized 250 ml Erlenmeyer flask. Twenty ml of fresh trypsin-KRBG solution is added and the process repeated. A pool of cell suspensions (about 100 ml of volume from five 20 min dispersions) is distributed between two siliconized 50 ml centrifuge tubes and centrifuged at $100 \times g$ for 30 min at 4°C. The final speed is attained gradually through a period of 10 min. The total time in the centrifuge is 40 min. After centrifugation, the supernatant is removed and the pellet is resuspended in 34 or 60 ml (*vide infra*) of KRBG to which has been added BSA (0.5 g per 100 ml), lima bean trypsin inhibitor (LBI, Worthington Biochemical Corporation, 0.1 g per 100 ml), and calcium chloride (to bring final concentration to 7.65 mM). The few large stringy particles which settle out are removed with a siliconized pasteur pipette. Aliquots of 0.9 ml of the resuspended cells[3] are added to each of 36 or 64 teflon beakers (10 ml capacity). The suspension of cells is gently rocked between removal of each 0.9 ml to ensure uniformity of cell count in each aliquot. Standard ACTH in a volume of 0.1 ml or in the case of blanks, 0.1 ml of vehicle, is added to the beakers. The teflon beakers are placed in a Dubnoff shaker and incubated (66 oscillations per min) for 2 hours in an atmosphere of 95 % O_2, 5 % CO_2 at 37°C. The quantity of fluorescent steroid in each incubate (cells plus medium) is measured by a modification of the method of *Silber et al.* (1958).

ACTH is the U. S. P. Standard (Third International Standard, 1962) which has a stated potency of 5 Subcutaneous Units or 1.5 Intravenous Units per vial (*Bangham et al.* 1962). The quantities of ACTH employed in this study are expressed in Intravenous Units. The vehicle for ACTH is a solution of 0.1 N HCl to which has been added sodium chloride (0.9 g per 100 ml) and BSA (0.5 g per 100 ml).

Corticosterone in each incubate is measured by the procedure of *Silber et al.* (1958) with the following modifications: 1) To each incubate (cells plus medium) are added 5.0 ml of methylene chloride and the mixture is shaken vigorously for 30 seconds and centrifuged at 2000 rpm, room temperature, for 2 minutes; 2) the upper aqueous layer is aspirated off and an aliquot of the

---

[3] Wet weight of the cells in a 0.9 ml aliquot is approximately 20 % of wet weight of a rat adrenal for 34 ml final volume and 10 % for 60 ml final volume of cell suspension.

methylene chloride extract is interacted with 2.0 ml of H_2SO_4:EtOH reagent (65:35 v/v) by vigorous shaking on a Vortex mixer for 20 to 30 seconds. The mixture is allowed to stand at room temperature for 60 to 80 minutes; 3) fluorescence of each sample is determined on an Aminco-Bowman spectrofluorometer with an exciting wave length of 470 mμ and an emitting wave length of 535 mμ.

Methylene chloride extracts of several incubates were combined and evaporated to dryness. Labelled corticosterone (Mann Research Laboratories) was added. Fluorescence and radioactivity were measured on the combined extract before and after Thin Layer Chromatography (Kodak silica plates) using three different solvent systems: $CHCl_3$:MeOH (95:6), CH_2Cl_2:Acetone (80:20), and Benzene:EtOH (90:10). On the basis of these studies, we conclude that corticosterone accounts for at least 90 % of the fluorescence in the methylene chloride extracts of incubates of isolated rat adrenal cells.

3. Morphology

Electron micrographs of suspensions show intact cells with well defined plasma membranes. The features are characteristic of steroid secreting cells: 1) large round mitochondria in which vesicular membranous structures are imbedded in the matrix, 2) extensive smooth endoplasmic reticulum, 3) rich supply of ribosomes scattered throughout the cells and 4) large lipid droplets. After two hours of incubation with or without ACTH the cells maintained their morphological features of integrity and viability. In particular, 2 hours of incubation of the cells with a quantity of ACTH that induced maximum rate of secretion of ACTH did not induce an observable change in the lipid droplets or in the mitochondria. The medium of the cells does contain some particulate material (*Malamed et al.* 1970a). We plan to estimate cell destruction with estimates of the concentration of an intracellular enzyme in the medium.

4. Function

1. *Rate of corticosterone production in the presence of ACTH.* After a 3 to 5 minute lag period, corticosterone production reaches a steady rate which is maintained for about 90 minutes of incubation. This is illustrated in Fig. 1.

2. *Maximum rate and »basal« rate of corticosterone production.* The 0.9 ml aliquots of the suspension of cells of the adrenal cortex contain 250 000 to 500 000 cells. The number of cells varies with the preparation and with the dilution factor. We estimate that the cells in a 0.9 ml aliquot are equivalent in mass to 1/5th to 1/10th of a single rat adrenal. Maximum rates of corticosterone production by 0.9 ml aliquots of the isolated cells may range from 1

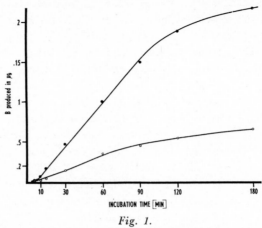

Fig. 1.

Corticosterone (B) produced plotted against time for aliquots of isolated adrenal cells treated with 100 μU of ACTH. Upper curve is for isolated cells from adrenals of intact rats, lower curve, for cells from hypophysectomized rats.

to 6 μg/h or in terms of a mass equivalent to one adrenal, 0.15 to 1.0 μg/min. Studies in which corticosterone in adrenal vein blood of the hypophysectomized rat has been measured indicate a maximum rate of secretion of the gland *in situ* of about 0.5 μg/min (*Liddle et al.* 1962; *Garren et al.* 1965). It would appear that the isolated cells are functionally similar to cells *in situ*. In the presence of an excess of ACTH, rate of corticosterone production is high and of the same order of magnitude as the cells *in situ*. Furthermore, in the absence of ACTH, rate of corticosterone production is very low (about 1/50th of the maximum rate). The combination, high maximum rate in the presence of excess of ACTH and low basal rate of steroidogenesis in the absence of ACTH is, in our opinion, one of the truly distinguishing features of a viable cell under hormonal control.

In preliminary experiments we have compared the responses of isolated adrenal cells to NADPH and to ACTH. The results suggest that this may be an approach to the characterization of the quality of a cell suspension. A good preparation with few leaky cells should exhibit a small increase in steroidogenesis upon addition of NADPH and a large increase upon addition of an excess of ACTH. (See *Halkerston et al.* for a discussion of this aspect of the problem).

3. *ACTH receptor interaction.* We have devised what we consider to be a new and unique approach to the evaluation of an isolated adrenal cell preparation. It is derived from the interaction of ACTH with receptors on the

16

isolated adrenal cells. The approach may be of limited usefulness, requiring as it does, that the system be characterized by a well defined kinetic relationship.

The relation between quantity of ACTH added and net corticosterone production by the isolated adrenal cells is expressed by the equation

$$\frac{B}{B_{max}} = \frac{[A]}{[A] + [A_{50}]} \tag{1}$$

where B is the net production of corticosterone per unit of time, B_{max} is the maximum rate of production of B, $[A]$ is the concentration of ACTH (the quantity added to each ml aliquot of cell suspension) and $[A_{50}]$ that quantity of ACTH which will induce half maximal rate of corticosterone production. It is convenient to transform equation (1) to the form

$$\frac{[A]}{B} = \frac{[A]}{B_{max}} + \frac{[A_{50}]}{B_{max}} \tag{2}$$

The slope of the line is the reciprocal of B_{max} and the intercept on the ordinate is $\dfrac{[A_{50}]}{B_{max}}$. We have attained a degree of perfection of preparation and incubation of the isolated cells such that $\dfrac{[A]}{B}$ plotted against $[A]$ yields a

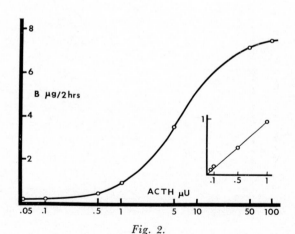

Fig. 2.

Net corticosterone (B) produced by aliquots of isolated adrenal cells in response to various quantities of ACTH. The small plot at the lower right shows that at low doses of ACTH the response and the quantity of ACTH added, both plotted as arithmetic values, are related by a straight line. This follows from the relation

$$B = \frac{[A]}{[A] + [A_{50}]} B_{max} \ ([A] \ll [A_{50}]).$$

17

straight line over a remarkably great range of [A] (0.1 to 220.0 femtomoles). Such a plot is presented in Fig. 3.

B_{max} is a measure of the total number of receptors in the preparation (or the total number of active cells in the suspension) and [A_{50}] is a measure of the apparent affinity of the cell receptors for ACTH.

The usefulness of estimates of [A_{50}] in assessing the quality of an isolated cell preparation is illustrated by the data of an experiment in which the conditions of incubation were less than optimal. The samples were incubated in polyethylene, rather than teflon beakers. The data are plotted as [A]/B vs [A] in Fig. 4. [A_{50}] has an estimated value of 57 fmoles, a value about four times greater than that of the experiment presented in Fig. 3. Note that at the low concentrations of ACTH, the experimental points lie significantly above the line (Fig. 4). Cell destruction may have occurred at a relatively fast rate when suspensions were incubated in polyethylene as against teflon beakers. Cellular debris, we believe, elevates [A_{50}] by degrading ACTH and/or by providing nonfunctional interacting sites. In addition, polyethylene may bind more ACTH than teflon.

To test the hypothesis that cellular debris elevates the observed [A_{50}] value, a suspension of isolated cells was divided into 2 equal parts and to one part was added a volume of homogenate of rat adrenals and to the other part an

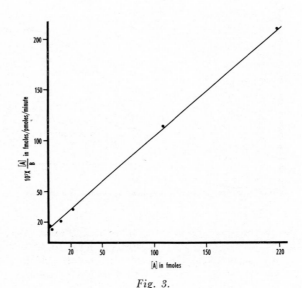

Fig. 3.
[A]/B plotted against [A]. [A] is expressed as fmoles (1.0 μU of ACTH = 10 picograms = 2.2 fmoles). Incubation carried out in teflon beakers.

18

equal volume of buffer. ACTH was added to aliquots of both suspensions. The data are plotted in Fig. 5. First, addition of homogenate to the cell suspension increases the value of the vehicle blank, a result to be expected since a homogenate of rat adrenal tissue, when incubated for 2 hours in KRB buffer, is characterized by high basal level of corticosterone production and no response to ACTH (*Sayers & Ma*, unpublished observation). Net production of corticosterone was most significantly reduced in the cell suspensions to which homogenate had been added at quantities of ACTH of 2.2, 22 and 220 fmoles. B_{max} was not influenced by addition of homogenate as shown by the fact that 2200 fmoles induced a response equal to that of the B_{max} for suspensions to which no homogenate was added. The results support the hypothesis that the value of $[A_{50}]$ is determined to some degree by the presence of cell fragments in the cell suspensions.

TRYPSIN TECHNIQUE FOR THE ISOLATION OF CELLS OF THE RAT ANTERIOR PITUITARY

1. *Introduction*

A suspension of isolated cells of the adenohypophysis is obviously an excellent tool for the solution of certain problems in the area of pituitary physiology. We have demonstrated that such a preparation is an exceedingly

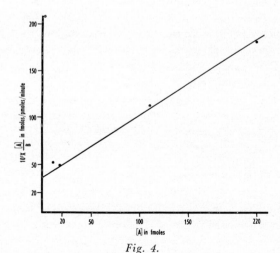

Fig. 4.

Same as Fig. 4 but incubation carried out in polyethylene rather than teflon beakers.

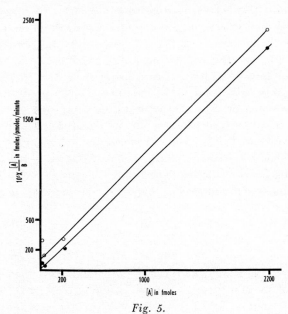

Fig. 5.

[A]/B vs [A] for two isolated cell preparations. The lower curve is for a regular isolated cell suspension, the upper curve for these same cells to which broken cells (a homogenate) had been added.

sensitive test object for the assay of corticotrophin releasing factor (CRF). The isolated cells are probably of value in the assay of the other releasing factors elaborated in the median eminence of the hypothalamus. A suspension of isolated cells, composed of a mixture of cell types, would be the starting material for sedimentation methods designed to prepare homogenous populations of adenohypophysial cells, *e. g.,* corticotrophs.

Fortunately, the trypsin technique described above for the dispersion of adrenal tissue with slight modification is effective in the dispersion of rat anterior pituitary tissue (*Portanova et al.* 1970).

2. *The Trypsin Technique*

In each experiment, 6 to 12 male rats of the Sprague-Dawley strain, 250 to 450 g, were decapitated, and the anterior pituitaries were removed, quartered, and placed in a siliconized 50 ml Erlenmeyer flask with 20 ml of a Krebs-Ringer bicarbonate buffer containing 0.2 % glucose (KRBG) and 0.25 % trypsin (Worthington Biochemical Corporation). The KRBG was previously gassed for 10 min with a 95 % O_2 : 5 % CO_2 mixture and adjusted to pH 7.35

to 7.40. The pituitary tissue was mechanically agitated for 20 min by a siliconized glass paddle driven by a constant speed motor at 500 rpm (Waco Supreme Power Stirrer, Wilkens Anderson), while kept at 37°C under a 95 % $O_2 : 5$ % CO_2 atmosphere. At the end of the 20 min period, the supernatant containing dispersed cells was drawn off with a siliconized pasteur pipette and placed in a siliconized, iced, 250 ml Erlenmeyer flask. An additional 20 ml of KRBG containing trypsin was added to the tissue, and the mechanical agitation was continued for another 20 min. After three such dispersion periods, the combined cell suspensions were placed in two siliconized 50 ml centrifuge tubes and centrifuged at 100 g (gradually accelerated to speed during a 10 min period) for 30 min at 4°C. The supernatant was aspirated.

For incubation, the pituitary cells were resuspended to a concentration of two pituitaries per ml of KRBGA without LBI. Aliquots of 0.5 ml of the suspension were placed in the incubation flasks and preincubated for 10 min at 37°C under 95 % $O_2 : 5$ % CO_2 with shaking (66 oscillations/min). Between 4 and 8 mg of LBI was added to the flasks in 0.5 ml KRBGA and the cells preincubated for an additional 5 min. KRBGA (0.1 ml) containing test substance or 0.1 ml of KRBGA alone for controls was then added, and the cells were incubated for 20 min. The cells were removed by centrifugation at 600 g for 5 min at room temperature. Aliquots of the supernatant were taken and the ACTH activity was determined as previously described.

3. *Morphology*

Electron micrographs of the suspensions of isolated anterior pituitary cells reveal intact rounded or ovoid cells which contain a rich array of organelles including secretory granules. Forty minutes of incubation was not associated with detectable necrosis or disruption of the plasma membrane.

Five different adenohypophysial cell types have been identified in the suspensions. Identification has been on the basis of size and distribution of the secretory granules: 1) thyrotrophs; granules 1500 Å maximal diameter, 2) corticotrophs; granules distributed peripherally and of 2000 Å maximal diameter, 3) gonadotrophs; granules 2000 Å maximal diameter plus pale spheroidal bodies of about 7000 Å diameter, 4) somatotrophs; granules approximately 3500 Å in diameter, 5) mammotrophs; granules irregular in shape and about 6000 Å maximal diameter (*Malamed et al.* 1970*b*).

4. *Function*

The isolated pituitary cells contain ACTH in a concentration per cell mass approximately equal to that of pituitary tissue (2500 to 5000 microunits per 100 000 cells). Under control conditions of incubation only 1 % of the ACTH is released into the medium. Release of ACTH is promoted by the addition

21

of extracts of rat hypothalamic median eminence tissue. The isolated cells catalyze the incorporation of radioactive amino acids into protein. Omission of glucose from, or addition of puromycin to the incubation medium inhibits this process.

TRYPSIN TECHNIQUE FOR THE ISOLATION OF CELLS OF THE BOVINE CORPUS LUTEUM

The trypsin technique for the dispersion of cells of the rat adrenal cortex is effective for the dispersion of cells of the corpus luteum. Corpora lutea from cows in the early stage of pregnancy (foetus less than 30 cm in length) are cut into small sections, each weighing about 10 mg. The sections are incubated in Krebs-Ringer bicarbonate buffer and agitated as described for adrenal quarters. The freed cells are collected as a pellet by centrifugation; the pellet is suspended in 32 ml of KRB which contains glucose, bovine serum albumin and lima bean trypsin inhibitor. Approximately 15 million cells are obtained from each gram of corpus luteum. Examination under the phase microscope reveals cells of 30 to 50 microns in diameter surrounded by a well defined plasma membrane and containing numerous large lipid droplets.

Aliquots (0.9 ml) containing approximately 500 000 cells have been incubated for 2 hours with and without the addition of luteinizing hormone (LH) or human chorionic gonadotrophin (HCG). These hormones induce production of cyclic 3',5'-adenosine monophosphate and of progesterone. We are in the process of modifying the conditions of incubation to increase sensitivity of the system to LH and to HCG.

ACKNOWLEDGMENTS

We would like to acknowledge the assistance of Rose-Marie Ma, Beth Wiblin, Mary Vegh and Nick Giordano.

REFERENCES

Bangham D. R., Mussett M. V. & Stack-Dunne M. P.: Bull. Wld Hlth Org. 27 (1962) 395.

Garren L. D., Ney R. L. & Davis W. W.: Proc. Natl Acad. Sci. (U. S. A.) 53 (1965) 1443.

Halkerston I. D. K., Feinstein M. & Hechter O.: Endocrinology 83 (1968) 61.

Kloppenborg P. W. C., Island D. P., Liddle G. W., Michelakis A. M. & Nicholson W. D.: Endocrinology 82 (1968) 1053.

Liddle G. W., Island D. & Meador C. K.: Recent Progr. Hormone Res. *18* (1962) 125.

Malamed S., Sayers G. & Swallow R. L.: Z. Zellforsch. *107* (1970a) 447.

Malamed S., Portanova R. & Sayers G.: J. Cell Biol. *47* (1970b) 128 A.

Moscona A.: Exp. Cell Res. *3* (1952) 535.

Portanova R., Smith D. K. & Sayers G.: Proc. Soc. exp. Biol. Med. *133* (1970) 573.

Rinaldini L. M. J.: Int. Rev. Cytol. 7 (1958) 587.

Rodbell M.: J. biol. Chem. *239* (1964) 375.

Silber R. H., Busch R. D. & Oslapas R.: Clin. Chem. *3* (1958) 278.

Steim J. M., Edner O. J. & Bargoot F. G.: Science *162* (1968) 912.

Swallow R. L. & Sayers G.: Proc. Soc. exp. Biol. Med. *131* (1969) 1.

Tong W., Kerkof P. & Chaikoff I. L.: Biochim. biophys. Acta (Amst.) *60* (1962) 1.

Tong W.: Endocrinology *74* (1964) 304.

DISCUSSION

Hansel: Dr. Sayers, your calculations are based on current dogma, which suggests that the trophic hormones, LH and ACTH, need not enter the cell to produce their effects. Have you any evidence that ACTH and LH in fact do not enter these trypsinized cells, or normal cells of the adrenal or corpus luteum?

Sayers: We have no experimental data on that point. However, Dr. Gordon Sato and his colleagues (*Schimmer et al.* 1968) found that ACTH chemically linked to a large, insoluble polymer retains its ability to stimulate steroidogenesis when added to the medium of cultured adrenal slices. Since such a large molecule would hardly be expected to cross the plasma membrane, it was concluded that ACTH acts on the outer surface of the cell.

Kohler: Dr. Sayers, have you come across modifications of your dispersion techniques where the response of the cells to ACTH or releasing factors was obliterated or decreased in sensitivity? The reason why I ask this is that a few years ago, Dr. O'Malley and I (*O'Malley & Kohler* 1967) were working on a chick oviduct system where the tissue in explant cultures responded to progesterone with an induction of avidin synthesis. However, when we attempted to completely disperse the cells with trypsin, we usually obtained no induction of avidin by progesterone. We were never sure whether the trypsin had destroyed a receptor, which seems unlikely in a steroid-responsive system, or whether we had disrupted an important cell:cell interaction.

Sayers: We were interested in that particular point. It is quite possible that trypsin destroys some receptors which interact with ACTH on the cell surface. That is a possibility, I don't see how you can rule it out entirely. Since maximum steroid production in the isolated adrenal cells approaches that *in situ*, we are inclined to think that trypsin is not damaging the receptors. Of course, you are aware of the work of *Kono* (1968) in which it was demonstrated that trypsin acting on adipocytes obliterates the response to insulin.

Stumpf: Did you study the tinctorial and ultrastructural properties of the isolated pituitary cells? One might expect a functional transformation, especially in the absence of hypothalamic tissues.

Sayers: We have not studied the tinctorial qualities, the classical approach to the distinction of the various adenohypophysial cell types. We have used the electron microscope to characterize the isolated pituitary cells before and after incubation. We have been able to distinguish five distinct types on the basis of the size of the secretory granules and the location of these granules in the cell. I cannot answer your question about a functional transformation. We have not recognized such a transformation, but I should point out that the longest period of incubation with and without CRF has been 40 minutes.

Baulieu: Dr. Sayers, could you tell us what is known about the adrenal arterial plasma concentration of ACTH? How does it compare with the ACTH concentration you have to use, and is there any known concentration of ACTH in adrenal tissue? Also, I was looking at your ACTH response curve of corticosterone production versus ACTH amount, not after two hours' production, but after a shorter incubation – did you get the same curve shape?

Another question deals with the evaluation of your isolated responsive cells. Did you have a possibility to test some compounds, for instance cyclic AMP, in this system? And what about other parameters of cell function, for instance protein synthesis?

Sayers: The concentration of ACTH in rat plasma (»basal« level) (*Giordano & Sayers* 1971) is definitely greater than the minimum effective concentration of ACTH necessary to stimulate steroidogenesis in suspensions of isolated adrenal cells.

I have no data on the concentration of ACTH in adrenal tissue of normal rats either at »basal« or at elevated levels of endogenous ACTH. The information we have concerns the quantity of ACTH in adrenal tissue following the intravenous administration of a large quantity of ACTH (*Richards & Sayers* 1951).

We have observations on times of incubation other than 2 hours. First, for maximum or near maximum quantities of ACTH, constant rate of corticosterone production is attained after a lag period of 3 to 5 minutes; constant rate is maintained for about an additional 90 minutes after which it slows. Second, the shape of the dose-response curve is the same for 30, 45, 60 and 120 minutes of incubation. I am pleased to have holds for periods of incubation in which the rate of corticosterone production is constant.

$$\frac{B}{B_{max}} = \frac{[A]}{[A] + A_{50}}$$

holds for periods of incubation in which the rate of corticosterone production is constant.

Cyclic 3′,5′-AMP stimulates steroidogenesis when added to suspensions of isolated adrenal cells dibutyryl cyclic AMP is more effective (*Sayers et al.* 1971). Lag period onset of constant rats of corticosterone production is the same for dibutyryl cyclic AMP as for ACTH (3 to 5 minutes). It would appear that the lag period after addition of ACTH is not related to the interaction of ACTH with receptors. In support of this conclusion is the fact that increased production of cyclic AMP by isolated adrenal cells starts immediately following addition of ACTH (*Beall & Sayers* 1971).

As to protein synthesis, I have nothing to report.

Lerner: Why do you use 7.65 mM of calcium? Other authors, for example *McLimans et al.* (1957) have shown that cells in suspension grow indefinitely in the absence of added calcium, although small amounts of calcium might be provided by the bovine serum albumin which you use in your system. Do you think that this may have some connection with the action of cyclic AMP, since in some enzyme systems, calcium would act similarly to the adenyl cyclase-cyclic AMP system (by converting »inactive phosphorylase-b-kinase« into »active phosphorylase kinase«, or the glucose-6-phosphate independent glycogen synthetase into the glucose-6-phosphate dependent one (*Krebs et al.* 1959; *Krebs & Fischer* 1962; *Meyer* 1962; *Belocopitow* 1961; *Appleman et al.* 1964))? So that this might also be the first part of the messenger and the hormone action through the cell membrane?

Sayers: A_{50} and B_{max} have been determined for concentrations of calcium of 2.55 mM and 7.65 mM, and of zero in the Krebs-Ringer bicarbonate incubation medium. B_{max} is the same for 2.55 and 7.65 mM calcium; B_{max} is reduced by 50 % when no calcium is added to the medium. A_{50} is less, the higher the concentration of calcium (for 7.65 mM calcium, A_{50} is 1×10^{-14} moles for 2.55 mM calcium, A_{50} is 1.5×10^{-14} moles; for 0 calcium, A_{50} is 38×10^{-14} moles). Calcium concentration of the medius is obviously most important for the response of the isolated cells to ACTH; the effect may be on »binding« of ACTH to receptors, to activation of adenyl cyclase or to the action of cyclic AMP on steroidogenesis. We are attempting to delineate sites of action of calcium in the isolated cell system.

I am interested in the report by *Lefkowitz et al.* (1970) which concerns the influence of calcium on the binding of ACTH to »subcellular cell membrane particles from a line of steroid-producing ACTH-sensitive adrenal tumours, grown in LAF_1 mice . . .«. When the calcium ion concentration was greater than 2 mM, a striking inhibition of ACTH binding to receptors was noted. Furthermore, 2 mM (as compared to 1 mM) calcium inhibited ACTH-sensitive cyclase on the membrane particles. As previously noted, 7.65 mM calcium as compared to 2.55 mM is not inhibitory (actually slightly stimulatory) in our isolated cell system. The »subcellular cell membrane particles« and the isolated adrenal cells are complex, making it difficult to explain the difference in the actions of calcium in the two systems.

Rodbell: Calcium ion is required for the actions of hormone on the adenyl cyclase system (*Birnbaumer & Rodbell* 1969); it is also a potent inhibitor of adenyl cyclase (*Birnbaumer et al.* 1969). Calcium is probably also involved in stabilizing the structure of cell membranes. All three actions of calcium ion must be considered as possible candidates for effects on adrenal cells.

Hamberger: As far as I can understand it, Dr. Sayers, you are dealing with a mixture of cells from the adrenal cortex. Have you made any attempts to separate the various adrenal cortical cells to see if the metabolic capabilities in the various cell types are different in your systems?

Sayers: In the experiments that I have presented, rat adrenal quarters were dispersed. No attempt was made to separate the various zones of the cortex. In the case of the rat adrenal, cells of the medulla do not appear in the suspensions. If you are interested, a paper by *Haning et al.* (1970) just appeared in Endocrinology on the matter of dispersion of capsular tissue.

Wira: Have you had an opportunity to explore the specificity of your glucocorticoid secretion, perhaps by the addition of other pituitary hormones, or even by direct addition of other pituitary hormones, or even by direct addition of CRF?

Sayers: Crude and purified fractions of hypothalamus do not induce steroidogenesis in the isolated adrenal cell suspensions. Furthermore, glucagon, oxytocin, insulin and vasopressin do not act in the isolated cell system. It looks highly specific.

Eshkol: Couldn't it be that the difference of response in adrenal cells of hypophys-ectomized and intact animals is due to a difference in the ratio of the various cell populations and not to a different responsiveness of the cells? You might not have the same ratio of cells since hypophysectomy affects the various zones to a different degree.

Sayers: I agree that it is a distinct possibility. However, we have so arranged it that the cell count that we used in suspensions of cells from the adrenals of hypophys-ectomized rats was equal or greater than in the case of cells from the adrenals of intact rats.

Diczfalusy: You mentioned that with the improved purification of the preparation the recovery of ACTH is increasing. Could you tell us, Dr. Sayers, what is your best recovery of ACTH, when the system works at its best?

Sayers: Adding the natural porcine ACTH[1-39], we have been able to recover, in a 30 minute incubation period, 90 % of the ACTH added. It is possible that ACTH activates the receptor without simultaneous or subsequent degradation.

References:

Appleman M. M., Belocopitow E. & Torres H. N.: Biochem. biophys. Res. Comm. *14* (1964) 550.

Beall R. & Sayers G.: Fed. Proc. (1971) April.

Belocopitow E.: Acta Biochem. Biophys. *93* (1961) 458.

Birnbaumer L. & Rodbell M.: J. biol. Chem. *244* (1969) 3477.

Birnbaumer L., Pohl S. L. & Rodbell M.: J. biol. Chem. *244* (1969) 3468.

Giordano N. & Sayers G.: Proc. Soc. exp. Biol. Med. *136* (1971) 623.

Haning R., Tait S. A. S. & Tait J. F.: Endocrinology *87* (1970) 1147.

Kono T.: Fed. Proc. *27* (1968) 495.

Krebs E. G. & Fischer E. H. In: Nord F. F., Ed. Advances in Enzymology Vol. 24, Interscience Publishers, Inc. New York (1962) p. 263.

Krebs E. G., Graves D. J. & Fischer E. H.: J. biol. Chem. *234* (1959) 2867.

Lefkowitz R. J., Roth J. & Pastan I.: Nature (Lond.) *228* (1970) 864.

McLimans W. F., Davis E. V., Glover F. L. & Rake G. W.: J. Immunol. *76* (1957) 428.

Meyer W. L.: Fed. Proc. *21* (1962) 83.

O'Malley B. W. & Kohler P. O.: Proc. Nat. Acad. Sci. (U. S. A.) *58* (1967) 2359.

Richards J. B. & Sayers G.: Proc. Soc. exp. Biol. Med. *77* (1951) 87.

Sayers G., Ma R. & Giordano N.: Proc. Soc. exp. Biol. Med. *136* (1971) 619.

Schimmer B. P., Uede F. & Sato G. H.: Biochem. biophys. Res. Commun. *32* (1968) 806.

Department of Obstetrics and Gynecology,
University of Tokyo School of Medicine,
Hongo, Bunkyo-ku, Tokyo, Japan

IN VITRO METHODS FOR THE STUDY OF THE ADENOHYPOPHYSIAL FUNCTIONS TO SECRETE GONADOTROPHIN

By

T. Kobayashi, T. Kigawa, M. Mizuno
and T. Watanabe

ABSTRACT

There are several *in vitro* methods to analyse the function of the adeno-hypophysis or the mechanisms of its regulation. The present paper deals with single cell culture, organ culture and short term incubation techniques by which the morphology and gonadotrophin-secreting function of the adenohypophysis were studied. In trypsin-dispersed cell culture, the adenohypophysial cells showed extensive propagation to form numerous cell colonies and finally develop into a confluent mono-layer cell sheet covering completely the surface of culture vessels. Almost all of the cultured cells, however, became chromophobic, at least at the end of the first week of cultivation, when gonadotrophin was detectable neither in the culture medium nor in the cells themselves. After the addition of the hypothalamic extract, gonadotrophin became detectable again, and basophilic or PAS-positive granules also reappeared within the cells, suggesting that the gonadotrophs were stimulated by the extract to produce gonadotrophin. In organ culture and short term incubation, the incorporation of [³H] leucine into the adenohypophysial cells in rela-tion to the addition of hypothalamic extract was examined. It was obvious that the ability to incorporate [³H] leucine into the gonadotrophs *in vitro* was highly dependent upon the presence of the hypothalamic extract.

27

During past decades, *in vitro* methods have been applied widely to analyse the structures and the functions of the adenohypophysis or the mechanisms of its regulation. These methods included short term incubation, organ culture or single cell culture, etc. The authors have performed *in vitro* studies of the adenohypophysis mainly in relation to the mechanisms of the control of gonadotrophin secretion and have reported the results obtained (*Kobayashi et al.* 1963, 1964, 1965, 1967). A part of these studies will be presented in this paper.

MATERIALS AND METHODS

Animals

Mature female rats of Wistar strain weighing 120 to 200 g were used.

Preparation of cell suspensions from adenohypophysial tissue

The anterior lobes were collected from 50 rats and cell suspensions were prepared following the method of *Youngner* (1954), using 0.1 % trypsin solution (Fig. 1). The culture medium consisted of 10 % human serum, 5 % calf serum, 0.5 % lactalbumin hydrolysate, 100 μg/ml of penicillin and 100 μg/ml of streptomycin in Hank's balanced salt solution with a pH of 7.6. Viable cell count was done with the aid of nigrosin (*Kaltenbach et al.* 1958).

Microscopic observation of the adenohypophysial cells cultivated in vitro

A drop of a cell suspension prepared to contain 1 to 2×10^5 cells/ml of medium was put on a coverslip which had been placed in a Petri dish and incubated at 37°C with 5 % CO_2 in air. After the first one or two days of incubation, 4 ml of fresh medium was added and incubation was continued with renewal of the medium every two days. Staining was done with Giemsa or periodic acid-Schiff (PAS) reagent during the days following inoculation. Phase contrast microscopy was also performed to observe the viability of the cultured cells.

Detection of gonadotrophin secretion from the adenohypophysial cells cultivated in vitro

Two to 3×10^6 cells in 5 ml of culture medium were inoculated into a square bottle of 200 ml and cultured at 37°C. The medium was renewed every two days and all the media were stored at –30°C. At the end of cultivation, the cultured cells were detached from the surface of the culture vessel, using 0.1 % trypsin solution, collected by centrifugation at 3000 rpm for 20 min and stored at –30°C. Both stored media and cultured cells were subjected to

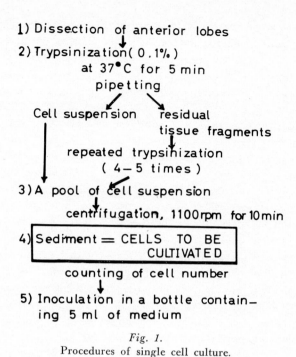

1) Dissection of anterior lobes

2) Trypsinization(0.1%)
at 37°C for 5 min
pipetting

Cell suspension → residual
tissue fragments
repeated trypsinization
(4—5 times)

3) A pool of cell suspension
centrifugation, 1100 rpm for 10 min

4) Sediment = CELLS TO BE CULTIVATED
counting of cell number

5) Inoculation in a bottle containing 5 ml of medium

Fig. 1.
Procedures of single cell culture.

gonadotrophin assay by the mouse uterine weight method (*Wilkins* 1957), after the stored media were extracted with absolute ethanol and the stored cells were homogenized in physiological saline.

Preparation of hypothalamic and brain cortical extracts

On the seventh day after castration the rats were killed by decapitation under ether anaesthesia. The basal part of the hypothalamus and a part of the brain cortex were cut out, pooled, respectively, homogenized in 1/10 M acetic acid and centrifuged at 10 000 rpm for 10 min. The supernatants obtained were freed of lipid by repeated treatment with petroleum ether and freeze-dried. These extracts were designated hypothalamic extracts (HE) and brain cortical extracts (CE), respectively.

Autoradiographic observation in vitro

Each of the adenohypophyses were dissected into 8 to 10 pieces, put into a test tube, attached to its side wall and then 1 ml of Eagle's solution was added without leucine. Incubation was carried out at 37°C, using a roller drum which rotated 6 times per h. On the second or fourth day of cultivation, 10 μCi of [³H] leucine (specific activity 215 mCi/mM, the Radiochemical Center, Japan) was added. After this, incubation was continued for 4, 8 or 12 h.

Another experiment was carried out with short term incubation. The dissected fragments of the adenohypophyses from three rats were pooled and put into a flask containing 10 ml of saline F composed of 1.2 g of $NaHCO_3$, 7.4 g of NaCl, 0.285 g of KCl, 0.17 g of anhydrous Na_2HPO_4, 0.083 g of KH_2PO_4, 0.154 g of $MgSO_4 \cdot 7H_2O$, 0.016 g of $CaCl_2$, 1.1 g of glucose, and 0.0012 g of phenol red in one l of double distilled water. Two μCi of [³H] leucine was added and incubation started in a shaker at 37°C. When the time of incubation with [³H] leucine reached 2 h, the media were discarded and the pituitary fragments were taken out and rinsed twice with physiological saline. They were fixed in Bouin's fluid for two days. Then they were washed, dehydrated, embedded in paraffin, sectioned at 4 μm and stained with PAS reagent. The stained preparations were covered with Sakura's liquid emulsion by a dipping method (*Kopriva & Leblond* 1962). Finally, they were stained again with methanil yellow and toluidine blue after being developed and air-dried (*Siperstein* 1963).

Autoradiographic grain counts were done under a light microscope (a 100 × oil immersion objective lens and 10 × eye-piece). A micrometer disc was adopted in the eye-piece to demarcate a field of 2500 μm².

RESULTS

Cell culture of the adenohypophysis

Proliferation of culture cells began to take place on the surface of the coverslips within two days following inoculation. Mitosis could be observed in a relatively large number. With the increase in population, the cells began forming colonies. As seen in Fig. 2, the cells belonging to a colony showed close contact with each other. There were large cells with pseudopoda at the peripheral area of the colonies and small cells at the central area. Intracellular granules were generally located close to the nuclei. With progress of culture age, the cell population became greater and the cultures formed a confluent monolayer covering completely the surfaces of the coverslip in about eight days after inoculation. Fig. 3 shows a part of a stained preparation of an 8 day old culture in which identification of cell types by staining was difficult; almost all cells were homogeneously chromophobic. However, when HE was added to the culture medium at the concentration of 0.1 % from the third to tenth day of cultivation, basophil cells appeared in relatively great number and eosinophils in small number, as shown in Fig. 4. PAS-staining

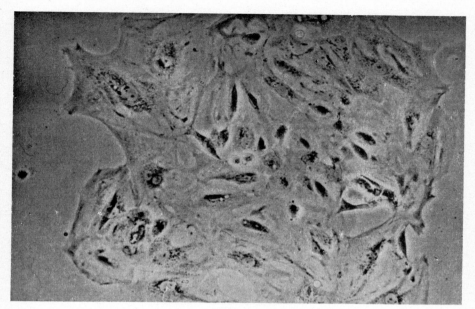

Fig. 2.
Phase contrast micrograph of a cell colony which appeared in a cell culture of the rat adenohypophysis on the 8th day of cultivation (400 ×).

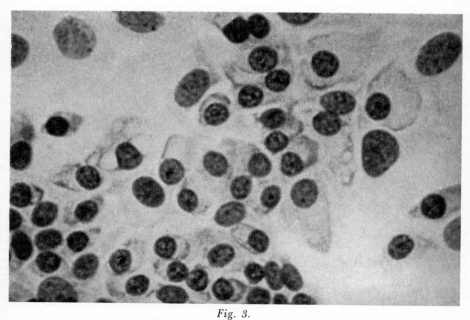

Fig. 3.
Photomicrograph of a part of the stained preparation of an 8 day old cell culture of the rat adenohypophysis (Giemsa stain, 400 ×). Almost all cells are homogeneously chromophobic.

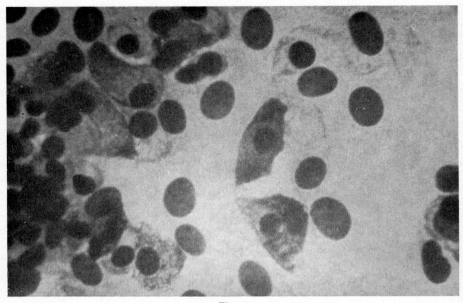

Fig. 4.
Photomicrograph of a part of the stained preparation of an 8 day old cell culture of
the rat adenohypophysis which had the addition of HE (Giemsa stain. 400 ×). Many
basophilic cells are observed.

became also positive in the culture with HE, while it was negative in the
control culture with CE.

Gonadotrophin secretion from adenohypophysial cells cultivated in vitro

All media replaced during the first and second weeks were pooled separately
and at the end of each week, culture cells were also collected. These were
subjected to gonadotrophin assay. Two bottles of culture were used for each
assay. As presented in Fig. 5, a considerable amount of gonadotrophin was
released during the first week, and at the end of this week, the cultured cells
lost their gonadotrophic activity almost completely. Thereafter, gonadotrophin
was not detectable either in the media or in the cells. On the first day of the
third week, HE was added at a concentration of 0.1 % and cultivation was
continued for a week. The media replaced during that week were pooled and
assayed (Fig. 6). It was found that the addition of HE induced significant increase ($P < 0.01$) of gonadotrophic activity in culture cells as well as in culture
media. However, it dropped to an undetectable level on the tenth day following termination of the addition of HE, as estimated in another series of

cultures. Control experiments with CE did not show any increase in gonado-trophic activity.

[³H] leucine uptake by the adenohypophysial cells in vitro

Three different types of cells could be identified by staining characteristics of their cytoplasms in double-stained autoradiographic sections of the adeno-hypophysis; these were PAS-positive cells, acidophils with yellowish colour, and chromophobes, respectively.

It was found that in organ-cultured adenohypophysis the uptake of [³H]-leucine was much less in PAS-positive cells as compared with the other two types of cells, irrespective of culture age or time of exposure to [³H] leucine (Table 1).

HE was added to the incubation medium at a dose of 5 mg per ml (1 mg is equivalent to 1 – 1½ hypothalami). CE was used as a control. It was demon-strated that the addition of HE markedly accelerated the uptake of PAS-positive cells (Figs. 7 and 8). No change was observed in chromophobes. In

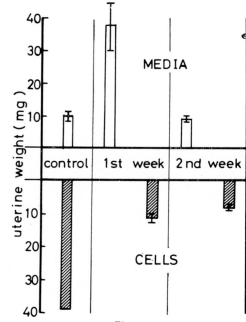

Fig. 5.

Changes of gonadotrophic activities in cell cultures of the rat adenohypophysis. Almost the whole amount of gonadotrophin contained initially in the cells is released to the medium within the 1st week of cultivation. The assay of gonadotrophin was performed by the mouse uterine weight method.

33

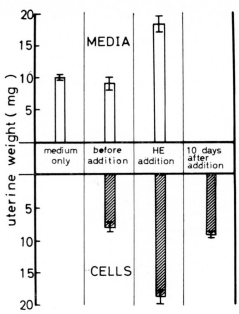

Fig. 6.

The effect of hypothalamic extract (HE) on the production and release of gonado-trophin. Undetectable level of gonadotrophin in the culture (see the column »Before addition«) became significantly higher after the addition of HE in both cells and media.

Table 1.

The rate of [³H] leucine uptake by various types of adenohypophysial cells in organ culture.

Age of culture	Incubation time with [³H] leucine in hours	Mean grain counts per cell		
		PAS-positive	Acidophil	Chromophobe
	4	2.9 ± 2.0*	8.8 ± 4.4	10.0 ± 3.2
2nd day	8	5.4 ± 2.7	14.6 ± 4.2	13.2 ± 4.2
	24	14.0 ± 4.4	26.9 ± 5.2	24.6 ± 5.6
4th day	4	4.2 ± 2.0	10.1 ± 3.3	11.7 ± 3.4

* Mean ± standard error.
The total number of grains contained in 50 cells of the same type was counted and mean value per cell was calculated for each type.

Table 2.

The effect of hypothalamic extract on the rate of [³H] leucine uptake by various types of adenohypophysial cells in short term incubation of 2 h*.

Series of incubations	Mean grain counts per cell		
	PAS-positive	Acidophil	Chromophobe
HE added	21.3 ± 7.0**	7.4 ± 2.7	11.6 ± 3.2
CE added	8.8 ± 5.1	8.9 ± 3.6	12.1 ± 3.7
Without addition	4.2 ± 3.0	10.2 ± 3.7	12.1 ± 4.2

* In this experiment castrated rats were used.
** Mean ± standard error.
The total number of grains contained in 50 cells of the same type was counted.

acidophils, a slight decrease in the rate of uptake was observed following addition of HE. CE did not show any effect (Table 2).

DISCUSSION

As already stated, no detectable amount of gonadotrophin existed even inside the cell body in trypsin-dispersed cell cultures older than eight days following inoculation. However, the addition of HE induced a marked restoration of gonadotrophic activities in these cultures. It might be concluded that HE has a gonadotrophin-producing activity. Histochemical observations indicating that gonadotrophs, as identified by the intracellular presence of PAS-positive or basophilic granules, appeared in the cultures following the addition of HE support this conclusion and further suggest that differentiation of adeno-hypophysial cells is conducted under the influence of HE. Isolation from hypo-thalamic influence seems to affect gonadotrophs to a greater extent compared with other types of adenohypophysial cells, since the autoradiographic studies revealed that the uptake of [³H] leucine by that type of cells decreased most markedly under such conditions, while the greatest augmentation of [³H]-leucine was also observed in the same type of cells after replacement with HE.

Organ culture and short term incubation are two tools which have been generally applied and considered to be reliable methods for the *in vitro* assess-ment of so-called gonadotrophin-releasing substances (*Guillemin & Vale* 1970). It is believed, however, that cell culture would be better for the solution of

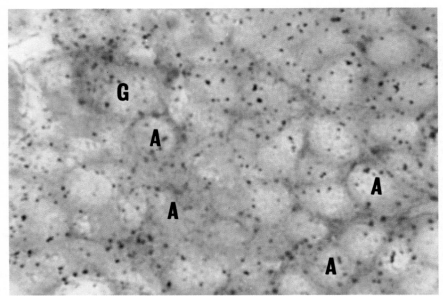

Fig. 7.

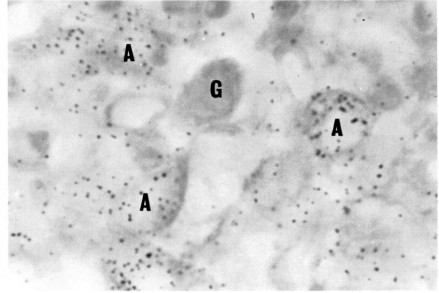

Fig. 8.

such problems as whether or not HE stimulates synthesis of gonadotrophin by the adenohypophysis. With the other two methods, the influence of the initial level of gonadotrophin content cannot be avoided and may complicate the evaluation of the results obtained.

ACKNOWLEDGMENTS

This work was supported by grants from the Population Council, New York, from 1964 to 1971.

REFERENCES

Guillemin R. & Vale W. In: Meites J., Ed. Hypophysiotrophic Hormones of the Hypothalamus: Assay and Chemistry, The Williams & Wilkins Co., Baltimore (1970) 21.

Kaltenbach J. P., Kaltenbach W. B. & Lyons W. B.: Exp. Cell Res. *15* (1958) 112.

Kobayashi T., Kobayashi T., Kigawa T., Mizuno M. & Amenomori Y.: Endocr. jap: *10* (1963) 16.

Kobayashi T., Kigawa T., Mizuno M. & Sato H.: Gunma Symposium on Endocrinology *1* (1964) 249.

Kobayashi T., Kobayashi T., Kigawa T., Mizuno M., Amenomori Y. & Watanabe T.: Endocr. jap. *12* (1965) 47.

Kobayashi T., Kobayashi T., Kigawa T., Mizuno M., Amenomori Y., Watanabe T. & Ichikawa H.: Endocr. jap. *14* (1967) 101.

Kopriwa B. M. & Leblond C. R.: J. Histochem. Cytochem. *10* (1962) 269.

Siperstein E. R.: J. Cell Biol. *17* (1963) 521.

Wilkins L.: The Diagnosis and Treatment of Endocrine Disorders in Childhood and Adolescence, Charles C. Thomas (1957) 52.

Youngner J. S.: Proc. Soc. exp. Biol. (N. Y.) *85* (1954) 202.

Fig. 7.
Photomicrograph of an autoradiographic preparation of the rat adenohypophysis incubated with [³H] leucine plus hypothalamic extract (double stain with PAS, methanil yellow and toluidine blue, 1000 ×). Small black grains within cells show the uptake of [³H] leucine, which is significantly increased in PAS-positive cells.
G = PAS-positive cell. A = acidophil cell.

Fig. 8.
Photomicrograph of an autoradiographic preparation of the rat adenohypophysis incubated with [³H] leucine for 2 h (double stain with PAS, methanil yellow and toluidine blue, 1000 ×). Only PAS-positive cells have no grains.
G = PAS-positive cell. A = acidophil cell.

DISCUSSION

Leleux: In 1963, *Pasteels*, using human foetal pituitary cell cultures, but also rat pituitary cell cultures, demonstrated that during the first week of these cultures, all adenohypophysial cells seemed to become chromophobes, as you have found. However. by the use of histochemical staining specific for the pituitary, these chromophobic cells appeared to be very similar to the prolactin producing cells. In parallel, those cells disconnected from the hypothalamus were secreting large amounts of prolactin in the medium. In your controls, did you test your cultured cells by histochemical staining specific for their prolactin secreting characteristics? When considering the morphogenetic effect of hypothalamic extracts it is indeed important to know whether the cells which become PAS positive and gonadotrophin secreting are really »de-differentiated« chromophobes or whether they are transforming from prolactin se-creting cells to gonadotrophin producing cells.

Kobayashi: Unfortunately, we didn't perform histochemical staining specific for pro-lactin. I have no idea of the change of prolactin secreting chromophobes to PAS positive cells.

Stumpf: It is noteworthy that Dr. Leleux in quoting *Pasteels* seems to adhere to the »pluripotentiality theory« regarding anterior pituitary cell functions, which challenges – in agreement with our view – the currently prevailing »one-cell-one-hormone« theory.

Dr. Kobayashi, from which part of the cortex did you take your control extracts? From our steroid hormone localization data we would expect hypophysiotrophic ac-tivity in extracts from »cortex« that contains such areas as the amygdala, the hippo-campus.

Kobayashi: The cortical extracts were from the frontal part of the brain and were prepared by the same procedure as the hypothalamic extract.

Hamberger: You mentioned that you used hypophyses from mature female rats for your cultures. Did you choose any special phase in the ovarian cycle when you took these hypophyses? Does it in that case make any difference if you start with hypo-physes from animals in pro-oestrous or di-oestrous phase?

Kobayashi: We did not check the cycle of the rat ovary.

Hansel: Dr. Kobayashi, did you interpret the apparent stimulation of prolactin pro-duction shown in one of your slides as evidence for a prolactin stimulatory factor (PSF) in addition to the prolactin inhibitory factor (PIF)? If I remember correctly, you got an inhibition with one-half hypothalamus, but with one-tenth you apparently got a stimulation. Does this suggest the existence of a PSF as well as that of a PIF?

Kobayashi: The slight increase of prolactin production with one-fiftieth hypothalamus was not statistically significant. I have not yet confirmed any PSF activity in hypo-thalamic extracts.

Lunenfeld: For the gonadotrophin assays you extracted your media with abs. ethanol and your cells with saline. Do you know anything about the recovery by these methods? I note from your paper that you make two point assays. Did you attempt to quantitate more precisely your gonadotrophic potencies? Thirdly, did you ever attempt to measure gonadotrophins by specific methods, like FSH by the Steelman-Pohley method or LH by the ovarian ascorbic acid depletion or any other method?

Kobayashi: I have carried out specific assays both for FSH and LH in our later experiments, using the Steelman-Pohley and OAAD methods, respectively (*Kobayashi et al.* 1966).

Hamberger: In your hypothalamic extracts you may have a very different concentration of monoamines, depending on the various phases from which you take your extracts. I don't know if you destroy the monoamines or their activity by your extraction procedure, but do you know whether the monoamine content of the extract can influence the responses? Have you tested the effects of various monoamines on the responses you get?

Kobayashi: I didn't test such effects. However, it has been shown by Dr. McCann's group (*Schneider & McCann* 1969) that neither various catecholamines nor serotonin were effective at the pituitary level *in vitro* in doses known to be present in the hypothalamus. There appears to be no indication that these monoamines are the LRF itself.

Sayers: Dr. Kobayashi, do you consider there to be two general categories of factors from the hypothalamus acting on the adenohypophysis, that is, one group which brings about release of the trophic hormones, and another group which has a nurturing effect? Do you believe that the releasing factors are one and the same as the factors which you describe, which appear to bring about differentiation of the cells?

Kobayashi: I think there are two actions, but I don't know if these two actions are dependent on two substances, or whether one substance has two actions. In our *in vivo* method, 15 minutes after injection of hypothalamic extract into the carotid artery, the pituitary contents of gonadotrophins increased, then decreased, and 30 minutes later almost nothing was found. However, the blood concentration increased, so this increase after injection indicates that the hypothalamic gonadotrophin-releasing factor may not only release, but also produce the gonadotrophin.

Nakane: Last year you reported that if you add synthetic thyreotrophin-releasing factor (TRF) to pituitary glands *in vitro*, it promptly releases TSH, with a maximum after about 15 minutes. However, it increases the rate of synthesis as well. Since we are using synthetic TRF, I believe that at least as far as TRF is concerned, it has a releasing factor as well as an ability to stimulate synthesis.

Stumpf: Dr. Kobayashi, in your system of amino acid incorporation, can you distinguish between the effect of hypophysiotrophic hormones and peripheral hormones, such as oestradiol, testosterone and progesterone? I think we have to consider both factors, because there is a dual effect.

Kobayashi: I have not examined the effect of peripheral hormones on the amino acid incorporation. This would be very interesting to do. In an *in vitro* system, however, oestradiol has been observed in Dr. Meites' laboratory to directly stimulate LH and prolactin (*Nicoll & Meites* 1962; *Piacsek & Meites* 1966). Also, Dr. Kato in my laboratory demonstrated that oestradiol was preferentially taken up by the anterior pituitary.

References:

Kobayashi T., Kobayashi T., Kigawa T., Mizuno M., Amenomori Y. & Watanabe T.:
   Endocr. jap. *13* (1966) 430.
Nicoll C. S. & Meites J.: Endocrinology *70* (1962) 272.
Pasteels J. L.: Arch. biol. (Liège) *74* (1963) 439.
Piacsek B. E. & Meites J.: Endocrinology *79* (1966) 432.
Schneider H. P. G. & McCann S. M.: Endocrinology *85* (1969) 121.

KAROLINSKA SYMPOSIA ON RESEARCH METHODS IN REPRODUCTIVE ENDOCRINOLOGY

3rd Symposium . In Vitro Methods in Reproductive Cell Biology

January 25–27, 1971

From the Departments of Physiology and Neurobiology,
University of Göteborg, Göteborg, Sweden

METHODS FOR METABOLIC STUDIES ON ISOLATED GRANULOSA AND THECA CELLS

By

L. Hamberger, A. Hamberger and H. Herlitz

ABSTRACT

A review is given of methods for biochemical studies on isolated ovarian cells of various origin. Special attention has been paid to the methodological problems involved in the micro-dissection of homogeneous cell samples. The main results on the capacity of granulosa and theca cells to synthetize various steroids are summarized and discussed.

Methods to study respiration, on a micro-scale, of isolated ovarian cells from the rat are described. The techniques which require minute amounts of cells for each determination allow multiple analyses on cells isolated from the same follicle. The application of the techniques for studies on gonadotrophic influence upon ovarian cells from the pre-pubertal rat is illustrated. The effects of various gonadotrophins on succinate and glucose oxidation demonstrate that LH and FSH selectively stimulate oxidative processes in various types of ovarian cells.

Other techniques which are applicable for studies of proteins, enzymatic activities, RNA and electrolyte content in isolated ovarian cells are briefly discussed.

INTRODUCTION

Techniques for isolation of specific endocrine cell types have been sought during recent years as a means of evaluating their biosynthetic capabilities under well-defined experimental conditions. The morphological and functional complexity of the ovary raises specific problems in evaluation of results obtained from biochemical studies of the whole organ or from sliced tissue – the main source of information so far. Up to 1959 only limited attempts had been made to isolate individual ovarian cell types. In that year *Falck* (1959) described an elegant technique for isolation and transplantation of small aggregates of

41

ovarian tissue containing only one endocrine cell type. By means of histo-logical methods it was possible to demonstrate that both granulosa and theca cells were required for oestrogen formation in the rat.

In biochemical investigations there is generally a demand for relatively large amounts of cellular material and hence studies on isolated ovarian cells have been performed on species with large-sized ovaries, *e. g.* granulosa cells from the pig ovary (*Bjersing & Carstensen* 1964, 1967) and equine ovarian cells (*Ryan & Short* 1965, 1966, see below). Techniques for growing various ovarian cell types in tissue culture have been reported during the last years, con-stituting another promising approach to these problems (*Channing* 1966, 1969*a,b*; 1970*a,b*; *Bergman et al.* 1966; *Cirillo et al.* 1969, see below). Most of the work performed on isolated ovarian cells has so far been focused upon problems involving biosynthesis and secretion of steroid hormones. Not until recently has the gonadotrophic influence on steroidogenesis in isolated ovarian cells been studied (*Channing* 1969, 1970*b*; *Cirillo et al.* 1969).

As steroidogenesis is only one of various capabilities of the ovarian cells, a deeper and extended knowledge of different aspects of ovarian metabolism is essential in this connection. We have used the rat as experimental animal in a number of studies on whole ovaries concerned with gonadotrophic in-fluence upon trans-membrane transport of amino acids, protein and RNA syn-thesis as well as energy and carbohydrate metabolism (*Ahrén et al.* 1969, 1970). There are better possibilities of controlling the endocrine state, the environ-mental conditions, food intake etc. in laboratory animals as compared to larger animals from which ovaries are obtained at the slaughter house. Furthermore, it is possible to work with inbred strains of known age which decreases the variability in the basal experimental conditions. The choice of isolated ovarian cells from the rat in our studies is also due to the fact that observations on isolated cells by necessity must be compared and evaluated in relation to observations on the whole ovary in order to give them a physiological signi-ficance. One obvious disadvantage in studies with rat ovaries is the restricted amount of cells due to the small size of the ovary. In the following, techniques suitable for metabolic studies on isolated ovarian cells on a micro-scale will be presented together with a brief summary of the results obtained so far.

STUDIES ON STEROIDOGENESIS BY ISOLATED GRANULOSA AND THECA CELLS

A. *Acute incubation experiments*

In 1962 *Bjersing* described a technique for isolation of pure granulosa cells from the porcine ovary in amounts large enough for biochemical studies of steroid hormone synthesis. Fresh ovaries from sexually immature sows were obtained from the slaughter house. The specimens were immersed in isotonic Krebs-Ringer bicarbonate buffer, pH 7.3, containing glucose. Each ovary was placed on a cork board under a dissection microscope and the follicles (diameter approximately 4 mm) were punctured with a sharp pointed instrument. The follicle was compressed with a blunt pincette and its content transferred to fresh buffer. After the preparation, which required approximately 10 min per ovary, the cell suspension was centrifuged for 5 min at 3000 rpm, the medium decanted, and the wet weight of the pelleted granulosa cells (25–50 mg per ovary) determined. Approximately 50 mg of granulosa cells were then incubated for 3–4 h in 5 ml of medium in 50 ml flasks gassed with carbogen. Labelled steroids and in some experiments co-factors were added to the medium. The results from these experiments (*Bjersing & Carstensen* 1964, 1967) showed that granulosa cells exhibited efficient 3β-hydroxysteroid dehydrogenase, 20α-hydroxysteroid dehydrogenase and 17β-hydroxysteroid dehydrogenase activities. There were also aromatizing and probably some 21-hydroxylating enzyme activities. The granulosa cells were particularly low in 17α-hydroxylase and side-chain cleaving enzyme activities, although some activity was demonstrated.

In 1965, *Ryan & Short* reported experiments on isolated granulosa and theca cells of the equine ovarian follicle. Equine ovaries were obtained immediately upon slaughter and packed in ice prior to dissection. Developing follicles were carefully dissected free from surrounding connective tissue and could be »shelled out« intact, surrounded by only a thin layer of theca externa cells. The follicular fluid was collected and the follicles measuring 3–5 cm in diameter were incised and inverted. The granulosa cells were removed by careful blunt dissection with the back of a scalpel blade with a sweeping motion taking special pains not to rupture the thecal vessels. The granulosa cells were suspended in buffer and used without further purification. The follicle lining containing theca interna and externa cells was minced with scissors prior to use. The two cell types were incubated for 3 h in 5 ml Krebs phosphate buffer (pH 7.0) containing labelled acetate or labelled steroids and co-factors. The gas phase was air. The dry weights of the fractions after incubation and extraction were, in a typical experiment, 48 mg for the granulosa and 78 mg for the theca cells. The results (*Ryan & Short* 1965, 1966) show that both cell types were capable of converting acetate into cholesterol. No steroid hormone formation from acetate could be demonstrated. Labelled testosterone was converted *in vitro* to oestrone and oestradiol to a greater extent by the granulosa cells than by the theca cells.

In experiments on isolated granulosa and theca cells from human ovaries by the same group (*Ryan & Petro* 1966), a similar dissection and incubation procedure was used. No co-factors were added to the medium in these experiments. In the granulosa cells, essentially the same results were obtained as reported by *Bjersing & Carstensen* (1964, 1967, see above) for porcine granulosa cells and principally equal capacity for steroid synthesis was shown for the isolated theca cells. However, the conversion of pregnenolone to progesterone was carried out to a much greater extent by the granulosa cells than by the theca cells.

In a subsequent study (*Ryan et al.* 1968) isolated granulosa and theca cells were obtained from a woman pretreated with HMG for 12 days followed by a single injection of HCG. The same type of incubation was used as described earlier and labelled acetate was added to the incubation medium. Both cell types were shown to form labelled cholesterol, pregnenolone, progesterone, 17-hydroxyprogesterone, androstenedione and oestrone. These findings are in agreement with those reported by *Channing* (see below) from tissue culture experiments, but in contrast to the results reported by *Ryan & Short* (1966) on equine ovarian cells discussed earlier, where no steroids were formed from labelled acetate.

B. *Tissue culture experiments*

In 1966 the first report on isolated ovarian cells in tissue culture appeared (*Channing* 1966). Granulosa cells from equine follicles were isolated according to *Ryan & Short* (1965). In these experiments 7 and 14 d cultures were tested. Labelled pregnenolone was converted to progesterone and there was evidence for *de novo* synthesis of progesterone by these cells. In the presence of gonadotrophins equine granulosa cells by themselves were capable of some androgen and oestrogen biosynthesis. The cultures were exposed to labelled steroids for 24 h in these experiments. In further studies, *Channing* (1969a) has provided evidence that granulosa cells will undergo luteinization within a few days in culture, if removed from ovaries of mares in oestrus or in the early luteal phase but not from ovaries of mares during the mid-luteal phase. This suggests that exposure *in vivo* to hormonal conditions associated with oestrus is essential in initiating luteinization of these cells.

In experiments on monkeys (*Channing* 1970b), more direct evidence was presented, showing that isolated granulosa cells from all kinds of follicles were luteinized when a mixture of LH and FSH was added to the tissue culture. Evidence that this gonadotrophic effect was mediated by cyclic 3′,5′-AMP in porcine granulosa cells grown in tissue culture has also recently been reported (*Channing & Seymour* 1970). In studies employing labelled precursors and steroids it was found that equine granulosa cells in tissue culture primarily converted acetate, cholesterol and pregnenolone to progesterone. Addition of LH and HCG *in vitro* increased the rate of progesterone synthesis

44

(*Channing* 1969*a*, 1970*a*). A similar stimulatory effect by LH and cyclic 3′,5′-AMP on progesterone synthesis was recently reported for bovine granulosa cells grown in tissue culture (*Cirillo et al.* 1969).

STUDIES ON RESPIRATION BY ISOLATED GRANULOSA AND THECA CELLS

Methodological aspects

Prepubertal female rats of the Sprague-Dawley strain ranging in age between 22–36 days were used. Prior to the experiments the rats were kept in rooms with constant temperature (24–26°C) and relative humidity 50–55 %. They were exposed to controlled illumination 14 h daily.

A semisynthetic diet (*Gustafsson* 1959) was given together with water *ad libitum*. The rats were sacrificed by cervical fracture, the ovaries rapidly removed and placed in ice-cold 0.32 M sucrose solution.

Microdissection

Single follicles, ranging in diameter between 100–500 μm, were carefully dissected free from surrounding tissue under a Zeiss stereomicroscope with a pair of small iris scissors, scalpels and stainless steel needles (50–200 μm diameter) mounted in drawn glass tubes. An isolated follicle was gently transferred to a small drop of incubation medium in a hollow glass cup through which ice-cold water was circulated.

Granulosa cells. – The isolated follicle was punctured with a 70 μm thick stainless steel needle and then gently pressed against the bottom of the dissection cup with a blunt steel needle in order to release the oocyte and the granulosa cells into the medium (Fig. 1). Granulosa cell samples were transferred by a micropipette to glass cups with fresh medium with and without addition of gonadotrophins. In the first report on gonadotrophic influence on the respiratory rate of these cells (*Ahrén et al.* 1965), granulosa cells surrounding the oocyte were used, but later it was observed that there was no difference in respiratory rate or responsiveness to gonadotrophins between granulosa cells close to the oocyte and granulosa cells close to the theca layer. Samples of 50 granulosa cells were used for each determination. The small samples required for determination of oxygen consumption make it possible to compare gonadotrophic effects on cells from the same follicle which is an advantage in view of the variability in development of follicles within an ovary.

Theca cells. – The theca capsule of the follicle was meticulously cleared from adhering granulosa cells by blunt dissection, divided into the requisite

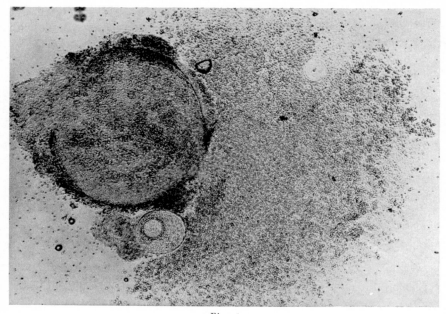

Fig. 1.

Photomicrograph of fresh tissue on a glass preparation slide. Follicle in the moment after bursting with numerous granulosa cells scattered around. Small (diam. 90 μm) intact follicle at bottom. Notice the oocyte.

number (around 10) of small samples and transferred by a micropipette to new cups containing fresh medium with or without gonadotrophins. The theca cell samples represent the whole follicular wall. No attempt was made to separate the theca externa layer from the theca interna layer. A remaining contamination of the samples by granulosa cells was easily revealed by microscopical examination at a high magnification. No staining of the cells could be performed before incubation but the purity of the samples was checked separately in fixed and stained material, and the degree of contamination by interstitial cells was very low.

Determination of dry weight

Granulosa cells. – The number of granulosa cells used for each incubation was carefully counted (see above). The cells are relatively uniform in size and in a sample of 50 cells, the biological variations in cell size are more or less equalized, thus giving comparable masses. For quantitative purposes the dry mass of the granulosa cells was determined by the direct X-ray absorption technique developed by *Rosengren* (1959). Clusters of granulosa cells ranging between 10 and 60 cells were dried in air on a thin supportive formvar film. Each sample was then placed on top of a vaporized gold aperture, 100 μm in diameter, and irradiated with soft X-rays of a wavelength of 8.3 Å. The output of X-rays was constant per unit time. The transmitted radiation was measured by a proportional counter and compared to that of the background of the supporting formvar film to determine the absorption of the granulosa cells. The dry weight of 50 granulosa cells was $(10.2 \pm 1.1) \times 10^{-6}$ mg. No statistical difference in dry weight/50 cells was found comparing cells taken from rats varying in age between 22–35 days.

Theca cells. – In contrast to the granulosa cells it is not possible to obtain a quantitative determination of theca cells by counting the cells in unstained material. Following incubation each cell sample was therefore transferred free of medium to a thin supportive formvar film. After drying in open air, the mass was determined by the direct X-ray absorption technique. As the cell samples were trimmed to comparable sizes, the variations in dry weight were relatively small ($\pm 15 \%$) within each experiment. The dry weights of the theca cell samples varied in various series of experiments between $(5–150) \times 10^{-6}$ mg. The mass determinations were further checked using a commercially available X-ray absorption equipment and another reference system for the masses (*Hagberg et al.* 1967). No significant differences were found between the results obtained with the two techniques.

Measurement of respiration

Micro-divers. – Oxygen uptake by the various cell samples was determined manometrically using the micro-diver technique (*Zeuthen* 1953; *Zaijicek & Zeuthen* 1961). The divers were made by thin-walled Pyrex glass capillaries, approximately 1 mm in diameter. The diver was weighed and fastened in a glass handle by means of a rubber stopper, as described by *Brzin & Zeuthen* (1961). The diver tip was introduced into the incubation medium containing the cell samples. Each diver was filled with one sample together with 0.3–0.5 μl medium, after which the tip was sealed with bees-wax heated to its melting point (about 60°C). The diver was then detached from its handle and adjusted to flotation equilibrium in 0.1 M phosphate buffer, pH 7.4. This implies that the air bubble in the ampoule (the thickest central part of the diver, see Fig. 2) was enclosed by the incubation medium and the biological material in the sealed end and by the phosphate buffer in the open end. The size of the air bubble was such that the diver was just able to remain afloat in the phosphate buffer. The diver was then transferred to a flotation vessel connected with manometers. The time interval between sacrifice of the animals and the introduction of the cell samples into the micro-diver did not exceed 30 min. The flotation vessels were filled with the same phosphate buffer as that used for adjustments of the divers. The vessels were immersed in a thermostatically regulated water bath with extremely good isolation. The

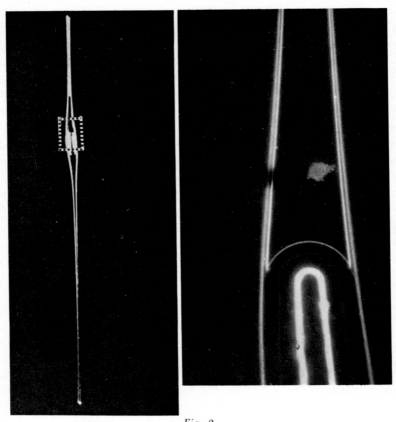

Fig. 2.

Photograph of micro-diver (left). The dotted rectangle represents the part shown to the right. Position of the cell sample in the diver. At bottom, air bubble.

temperature variations measured by a thermistor thermometer placed inside the flotation vessels remained below ± 0.002°C. All determinations were performed at 37°C. After a temperature equilibration period of 30 min, manometric readings of the equilibration pressure were made every 10–20 min for 2–3 h. The pressure was plotted against time and a linear relation was found during the first 3–4 h and often for a longer period. Blank micro-divers, containing incubation medium but no cells showed no oxygen consumption. An automatic recording unit has been described (*Hamberger et al.* 1967) and used in our laboratory since the micro-diver technique requires frequent manometrical adjustments by a trained person for several hours. The continuous registration is an obvious advantage with this technique.

Oxygen consumption was registered in the magnitude of 10^{-3}–10^{-4} μl/h and calculated according to *Zeuthen* (1953). In theoretical calculations and experimentally, *Zajicek & Zeuthen* (1961) found the error of the micro-diver technique to be $\pm$ 5 % in determinations of gas consumption or production in order of magnitude of 10^{-4} μl/h.

Methods for mixing solutions in the micro-diver. – Various methods for addition of substrates or metabolic inhibitors during the experiment have been reported for the micro-diver technique. The micro-diver can be removed from its flotation vessel in the thermostatically controlled bath, opened, and the incubation medium may be replaced by a fortified medium (*Brzin & Zeuthen* 1961). The micro-diver is then sealed and replaced in the flotation vessel and after 30 min of thermoequilibration, the effect of the changed medium added can be recorded. A method for mixing solutions in the micro-diver without removing the diver during the experiment was described by *Chakravarty* (1967). A small drop containing the substrate to be added is placed in the air bubble space of the diver. The drop can be brought to mix with the incubation medium by initiation of an increase of the manometric pressure. Due to the relatively large size of the air bubble space necessary, the sensitivity of the method is of the order of 10^{-2} μl/h.

»Two compartment micro-divers«. – Two methods for addition of reactants without removing the diver or the flotation vessel from the bath have been used in our laboratory. With the first technique (*Hamberger & Tengroth* 1965) Q-switched laser pulses were used to break small capillaries, which had been charged with reactants, sealed and inserted into the diver. The requirement for extreme precision in order to prevent damage to the cells by the laser pulses limits, however, its applicability. The method in use now is shown in Fig. 3 (*Hamberger* 1968*a*). The sensitivity of this technique is of the order of 10^{-4} μl/h, which is enough to measure respiration in single cells (*i. e.* oocytes). A detailed description of the applicability of the technique has been given in studies on isolated ovarian cells (*Hamberger* 1968*b*), isolated testicular cells (*Hamberger & Steward* 1968) and isolated intestinal cells (*Hamberger & Lundgren* 1971).

Standard divers. – This technique, developed by *Linderstrøm-Lang* in 1937, is suitable for measurements of gas consumption in the order of 10^{-1}–10^{-2} μl/h. Recently the method was further developed by *Hellerström* (1967) to enable initiation of reactants and inhibitors during an experiment.

The same type of Pyrex glass is used as for the micro-divers. The divers are cylindrical and coated with silicone in a 2 % solution of toluene before each experiment. At equilibrium pressure, the total gas volume of a charged diver is about 5 μl and the total volume of the diver between 8–11 μl. As can be seen from Fig. 4, each diver is charged with potassium hydroxide (KOH) to absorb the CO_2, which is liberated by the respiring cells into the incubation

49

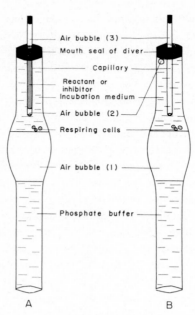

Fig. 3.

Schematic drawing of a two-compartment micro-diver. Dimensions: length between 20 and 25 mm, diameter 0.3–0.5 mm. The micro-diver is filled in its upper part with incubation medium containing cells and in its lower part with phosphate buffer. A small capillary (diameter approx. 70 μm) containing the reactant or inhibitor, the effect of which is to be studied, is introduced into the upper end of the diver and fixed by bees-wax (mouth seal of diver). The small capillary is sealed in its upper end by bees-wax and in both ends there are air bubbles. Air bubble 2 serves as a lock and prevents the content of the capillary to mix with the incubation medium (A). After determination of the control respiratory rate, the pressure around the diver is decreased. This leads to an expansion of air bubble 3 which thus pushes away air bubble 2, allowing the reactant or inhibitor to reach the cells (B). The sizes of air bubble 2 and 3 should be in the ratio 1:4 in order to avoid drastic alterations of the pressure. (From *Hamberger* 1968a).

medium. Below and above the incubation medium small drops containing the test substances are placed on the inside wall of the diver. Above the upper drop paraffin oil is placed to prevent the exchange of water between the aqueous solution in the diver and the strong salt solution (flotation medium) surrounding the diver during the experiment. The flotation medium in the top of the diver serves as a barrier against the escape of gas from the diver. The source of oxygen for the respiring cells is air.

The oxygen uptake of the cell samples is measured manometrically at 37°C in a thermostatically controlled water bath as described above for the micro-diver. In order to bring the small drops of incubation medium containing the test substances into contact with the incubation medium containing the cells, the pressure around the divers is altered. With this technique it is possible to introduce two alterations in the composition of the incubation medium during an experiment, which is an advantage compared to the micro-diver technique, and this is especially useful for studies of *e. g.* dose-response for gonadotrophins. Oxygen uptake is calculated according to *Holter* (1943, 1961). The amount of cells in each sample corresponds to a dry weight between 1–10 μg (determined by an ultramicro balance, Mettler UM7) limiting the applicability of the technique. In studies on granulosa cells from the rat ovary, cells must be collected from more than one follicle. This technique has so far mainly been applied to isolated cells from the human ovary.

Incubation media. – For determination of respiration with succinate as substrate the following medium was used: Na_2HPO_4–KH_2PO_4 buffer, pH 7.4,

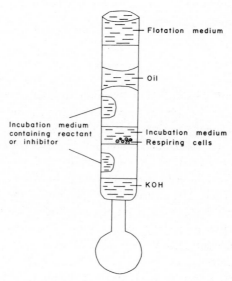

Fig. 4.

Schematic drawing of a cylindrical standard diver. Dimensions: length between 20–30 mm, diameter 0.9–1.1 mm. The diver is filled from the bottom by means of volume-calibrated micropipettes. Small drops of medium containing reactants or inhibitors are placed on the inside wall of the diver above and under the medium containing the cells. After determination of the control respiratory rate the pressure around the diver is either decreased or increased. This procedure leads to mixing of the small drops with the incubation medium. The design makes it possible to introduce two alterations of the composition of the incubation medium during the experiment (modified after *Hellerström* 1967).

37.5 mM; cytochrome C 8.6×10^{-2} mM; $AlCl_3$ 0.5 mM; $MgCl_2$ 0.5 mM; Na succinate 25 mM (*Slater* 1949; *Potter* 1957). In this medium, which is hypotonic to plasma, the penetration of succinate is facilitated and it has been found that the gonadotrophic effects studied were more pronounced in this medium compared to other media tested. The endogenous respiration without added substrate was less than 5 % of the respiration in the medium containing succinate. For determination of glucose oxidation the following medium which is isotonic, was used: Tris-HCl buffer, pH 7.4, 25 mM; NaCl 124 mM; KCl 5 mM; $CaCl_2$ 1.5 mM; $MgSO_4$ 0.5 mM; glucose 6 mM.

Hormones and chemicals. – Bovine luteinizing hormone (NIH-LH-B3) and ovine follicle stimulating hormone (NIH-FSH-S2) were supplied by the Endocrinology Study Section, National Institutes of Health, U. S. A. Human chorionic gonadotrophin (HCG) containing 10 460 IU/mg was a gift from Leo Ltd., Hälsingborg, Sweden. N^6-2^1O-Dibutyryl-adenosin 3′,5′-monophosphat, cyclisch (cyclic-3′,5′-AMP) was purchased from Boehringer Ltd., Mannheim, W. Germany. All other chemicals were reagent grade.

RESULTS

The effect of LH on the oxidation of succinate in isolated granulosa cells from ovaries of rats varying in age between 22 and 36 d is summarized in Fig. 5. The oxygen consumption expressed as μl/h $\times$ dry weight (QO_2) slightly increased with age in the control cell samples. (QO_2 between 20 and 40). The most pronounced stimulatory effect by LH was found around 29 days of age. This stimulatory effect by LH was elicited within 10–15 min after the application of the hormone, as revealed by the use of the »two-compartment micro-diver« (Fig. 6). No influence on the respiration of granulosa cells was observed after addition of FSH *in vitro*. Principally similar results were obtained when the gonadotrophins were injected in one iv dose (100 μg/100 g body weight) 2 h before removal of the ovaries (see Table 1), *i. e.* a stimulatory effect by LH and no effect by FSH. In experiments with *in vitro* addition of cyclic 3′,5′-AMP (1–2 mM) a small stimulatory effect on the oxidation of succinate by isolated granulosa cells (25–30 d old rats) was registered (18.4 $\pm$ 7.2 %). In experiments on granulosa cells from 25–30 d old rats with glucose as substrate, QO_2 was 10.2 in the control group and after addition of LH (50 μg/ml) 17.4.

In experiments on isolated human granulosa cells with succinate as substrate, addition of HCG in a concentration of 100 IU/ml caused a 25–45 % increase in the rate of oxygen uptake (*Hamberger & Swartz*, unpublished data).

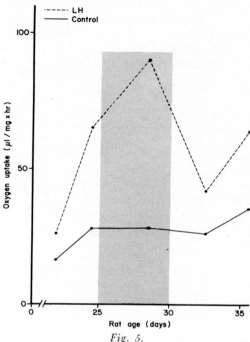

Fig. 5.

Influence of age on the responsiveness of isolated granulosa cells to LH. Granulosa cell samples were obtained from rats varying in age between 22–36 d. Oxygen uptake was determined at 37°C in medium containing succinate with or without addition of LH (50 μg/ml). A peak in sensitivity to LH was found at around 29 d of age. The lines are based upon 58 determinations with cellular material from 14 rats. (From *Hamberger* 1968*b*).

Determinations of oxygen uptake in isolated theca cells from ovaries of rats varying in age between 25–30 d were performed with succinate as substrate. The oxygen uptake of theca cells was slightly lower (QO_2 range 18–27) than that of the granulosa cells. Maximal responsiveness to gonadotrophins occurred at an animal age of approximately 29 d which was similar to that of the granulosa cells. Administration of FSH either *in vitro* or *in vivo* caused an increase in the rate of oxygen uptake (Fig. 7). The most pronounced stimulatory effect was elicited after *in vivo* administration of FSH (QO_2 44.0 ± 6.6). No effect was found by LH, neither *in vitro* nor *in vivo* (see Table 1). Similar results were found in experiments where glucose was used as substrate, *i. e.* a stimulatory effect by FSH both *in vitro* and *in vivo* but no effect by LH.

Table 1.
Summary of results concerning the acute gonadotrophic influence upon oxygen uptake in granulosa and theca cells isolated from prepubertal rat ovaries. The hormones were either added directly to the incubation medium (*in vitro*) or injected in one iv dose 2 h before removal of the ovaries (*in vivo*). Addition of cyclic 3′,5′-AMP *in vitro* caused stimulatory effects in concentrations between 1–2 mM.

		Granulosa cells	Theca cells
LH	*in vitro*	+	—
	in vivo	+	—
FSH	*in vitro*	—	+
	in vivo	—	+
3′,5′-AMP *in vitro*		+	not tested

Symbols: + = stimulatory effect; — = no effect.

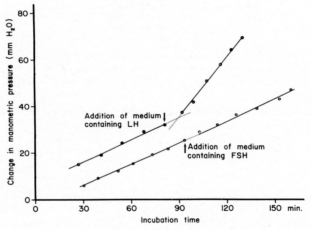

Fig. 6.

Gonadotrophic influence *in vitro* on the oxygen uptake of isolated granulosa cells obtained from prepubertal rat ovaries. Experiments performed with the »two-compartment diver«. The cells were incubated at 37°C in medium containing succinate. The figure shows two different experiments where the oxygen uptake (expressed as change in manometric pressure) is plotted against incubation time. The first 30 min of the incubation period were used for thermoequilibration. Manometric readings were then performed. Addition of LH (upper curve) in a final concentration of 40–60 µg/ml increased the respiratory rate of the granulosa cells by 155 % above the control level within 10–15 min, while addition of FSH (lower curve) in the same amounts as of LH did not change the rate of oxygen uptake during the incubation period.

(From *Hamberger* 1968).

Direct biochemical evidence of the ability of separated granulosa and theca cells of ovarian follicles from the sow, the horse and the human for *de novo* synthesis of cholesterol has been presented. *Bjersing & Carstensen* (1964, 1967) reported that porcine granulosa cells had a particularly low content of 17α-hydroxylase and side-chain cleaving enzyme activities. Other authors have reported that these enzymes are active in equine granulosa cells grown in tissue culture (*Channing* 1966) and in human granulosa cells *in vitro* (*Ryan et al.* 1968), thus enabling them to form oestrogen. However, in both these cases the granulosa cells were pretreated with gonadotrophic hormones. Falck's conclusion (*Falck* 1959) that both theca interna cells and granulosa cells were required to produce oestrogen was based on experiments on cycling albino rats. The discrepance between the results of different authors might be due to species differences, to variations in the experimental procedure or to direct effects by gonadotrophic hormones. Evidence for a direct effect by both LH and HCG on the rate of progesterone synthesis in equine and human granulosa cells grown in tissue culture has been presented (*Channing* 1969a,b).

These data are in agreement with our findings that both LH and HCG have a direct stimulatory effect upon the energy metabolism of granulosa cells isolated from rat or homo. Exactly how these findings are related, if indeed they are, is at present not clear. The hormone specificity obtained in the acute

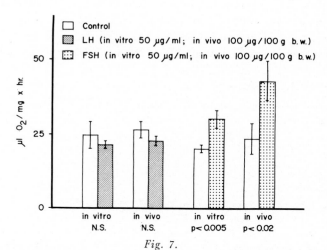

Fig. 7.

Effects of LH and FSH on oxygen consumption of isolated theca cells from perpubertal rat ovaries. The cell samples were incubated with succinate as substrate. Standard errors are indicated on top of the columns.

studies of gonadotrophic influence on the respiration of isolated granulosa and theca cells is exactly opposite to what might be predicted from present views on the physiological functions of LH and FSH. However, further evidence that FSH has a direct effect on theca cells has been put forward in autoradiographic studies (*Rubinstein* 1967; *Hamberger, Sjöstrand* and *Ahrén,* unpublished data). One iv injection of FSH 2–4 h before removal and incubation of ovaries from prepubertal rats in a medium containing [^{3}H] glycine caused an increased incorporation of radioactivity mainly in the theca cells and probably in some of the interstitial cells. No significant increase in radioactivity of the granulosa cells was seen.

Compared for example to the nervous system which, similar to the ovary, displays heterogeneity with respect to cell composition and function, the microchemical exploration of the ovary has been pursued on a limited scale. Methods for RNA analysis at the cellular level described by *Edström* (1953, 1960) have been applied only in a preliminary study on isolated ovarian cells (*Hamberger* and *Jarlstedt,* unpublished data). Protein separation at the cellular level by micro disc electrophoresis (*Hydén et al.* 1966) is likely to give valuable information related *i. a.* to steroidogenesis in granulosa and theca cells. Fluorimetric methods for enzyme measurements in single cells (*Lowry et al.* 1964) would also provide valuable tools to resolve cellular specificity in the ovary. In many studies it is also desirable to correlate changes in enzymatic activities in single cells with the simultaneous total cellular electrolyte content, or electrolyte changes, which can be performed by ultramicro flame photometry (*Haljamäe* & *Waldman* 1970). Another aspect which has received little attention regarding the ovary is the information which can be obtained by subcellular fractionation of small, homogeneous cell samples.

The functional importance of specific metabolic features cannot be resolved until accurate estimates are available as to their localization both between cell types and within the organelles of the single cell.

It seems justifiable to predict that a continuous and expanding use of microtechniques will lead to an increased understanding of the functional interplay in the ovarian follicle.

ACKNOWLEDGMENTS

This study was supported by grants from the Swedish Medical Research Council (B71-14X-2873), Swedish Cancer Society (70:24), US Public Health (1 ROI HD02795-01) and from the Medical Faculty, University of Göteborg (H. H.).

We wish to acknowledge gratefully the expert technical assistance of Mrs. Anita Sjögren and Miss Barbro Berggren.

REFERENCES

Ahrén K., Hamberger A. & Hamberger L.: Endocrinology 77 (1965) 332.

Ahrén K.. Hamberger L. & Rubinstein L. In: McKerns K. W., Ed. The Gonads, Appleton-Century-Crofts, New York (1969) 327.

Ahrén K., Hamberger L., Jarlstedt J. & Nilsson L.: Acta physiol. scand. 74 (1970) 379.

Bergman S., Bjersing L. & Nilsson O.: Acta path. microbiol. scand. 68 (1966) 461.

Bjersing L.: Acta path. microbiol. scand. 55 (1962) 127.

Bjersing L. & Carstensen H.: Biochem. biophys. Acta (Amst.) 86 (1964) 639.

Bjersing L. & Carstensen H.: J. Reprod. Fertil. 14 (1967) 101.

Brzin M. & Zeuthen E.: C. R. Lab. Carlsberg 32 (1961) 139.

Chakravarty N.: Exp. Cell Res. 47 (1967) 278.

Channing C. P.: Nature (Lond.) 210 (1966) 1266.

Channing C. P. In: McKerns K. W., Ed. The Gonads, Appleton-Century-Crofts, New York (1969a) 245.

Channing C. P.: J. Endocr. 45 (1969b) 297.

Channing C. P.: Recent Progr. Hormone Res. 26 (1970a) 589.

Channing C. P.: Endocrinology 87 (1970b) 49.

Channing C. P. & Seymour J. F.: Endocrinology 87 (1970) 165.

Cirillo V. J., Andersen O. F., Ham E. A. & Gwatkin R. B. L.: Exp. Cell Res. 57 (1969) 139.

Edström J.-E.: Biochim. biophys. Acta (Amst.) 2 (1953) 361.

Edström J.-E.: J. biophys. biochem. Cytol. 8 (1960) 39.

Falck B.: Acta physiol. scand. Suppl. 163 (1959).

Gustafsson B. E.: Ann. N. Y. Acad. Sci. 78 (1959) 17.

Hagberg S., Haljamäe H. & Röckert H.: Acta chir. scand. 133 (1967) 265.

Hamberger A. & Tengroth B.: Exp. Cell Res. 37 (1965) 460.

Hamberger A., Hamberger L. & Larsson S.: Exp. Cell Res. 47 (1967) 229.

Hamberger L.: Acta physiol. scand. 74 (1968a) 91.

Hamberger L.: Acta physiol. scand. 74 (1968b) 410.

Hamberger L. & Steward V. W.: Endocrinology 83 (1968) 855.

Hamberger L. & Lundgren O.: Experientia (1970) in press.

Haljamäe H. & Waldman A. In: Glick D. & Rosenbaum R., Eds. Techniques of biochemical and biophysical morphology. John Wiley and Sons Inc., New York (1970).

Hellerström C.: Endocrinology 81 (1967) 105.

Holter H.: C. R. Lab. Carlsberg 24 (1943) 399.

Holter H. In: Danielli J. F., Ed. Gen. Cytochem. Methods vol. 2. Academic Press, New York (1961) 93.

Hydén H., Bjurstam K. & McEwen B.: Analyt. Biochem. 17 (1966) 1.

Linderstrøm-Lang K.: Nature (Lond.) 140 (1937) 108.

Lowry O. H., Passoneau J. V., Hasselberger F. X. & Schultz D. W.: J. biol. Chem. 239 (1964) 18.

Potter V. R. In: Umbreit W. W., Burris R. H. and Stauffer J. F., Eds. Manometric techniques, Burgess, Minneapolis (1957) 170.

Rosengren B. H. O.: Acta radiol. (Stockh.) Suppl. 178 (1959).

Rubinstein L.: Endocrinology 80 (1967) 768.

Ryan K. J. & Short R. V.: Endocrinology 76 (1965) 108.

Ryan K. J. & Short R. V.: Endocrinology 78 (1966) 214.

Ryan K. J. & Petro Z.: J. clin. Endocr. 26 (1966) 46.

Ryan K. J., Petro Z. & Kaiser J.: J. clin. Endocr. 28 (1968) 355.

Slater E. C.: Biochem. J. 44 (1949) 305.

Zaijicek J. & Zeuthen E. In: Danielli J. F., Ed. Gen. Cytochem. Methods vol. 2. Academic Press, New York (1961) 131.

Zeuthen E.: J. Embryol. expr. Morph. 1 (1953) 239.

ADDENDUM

In recent experiments oocytes from rat follicles of various diameters were dissected from ovaries of rats varying in age between 30–100 days. After isolation under a stereomicroscope, each oocyte was surrounded by only 2–3 layers of granulosa cells which could not be removed without damage of the cell membrane of the oocyte. The rate of oxygen consumption of this cellular complex was determined by means of the micro-diver technique in medium containing succinate as substrate (for technical details, see above). Linear respiratory curves were in general elicited for at least 3–4 h. The mean respiratory rate of each sample was found to be in the order of $(20-25) \times 10^{-4}$ μl/h. Twelve oocytes isolated from follicles of six different mature rats were tested by means of the »two-compartment« diver technique for their responsiveness to in vitro addition of LH (NIH-LH-B5). The final hormonal concentration was 10–20 μg/ml medium. After addition of LH there was in all 12 experiments a decreased respiratory rate registered within 15 min after the addition of the hormone. The mean decrease was $49.7 \pm 5.7 \%$ with a total range of 25–78 % (Hillensjö T., Hamberger L. and Ahrén K. To be published).

DISCUSSION

Diczfalusy: At a recent meeting at the Population Center in Bethesda (October 1970), Dr. K. Savard from Miami presented some preliminary data. He incubated isolated entire follicles with labelled acetate and isolated steroids, mainly oestrogens. He found that the addition of minimal amounts of LH greatly stimulated steroid synthesis, whereas FSH had no effect. These findings would seem to parallel very nicely your data on the metabolic effects in granulosa cells.

Means: I believe, Dr. Hamberger, that you alluded to doing studies concerning dose-response relationships of gonadotrophins in vitro. Could you briefly describe those for us, please.

Hamberger: When we started these studies, we chose rather high hormone concentrations. Thirty to fifty μg/ml of luteinizing hormone (NIH-LH-B3) was used, which is a relatively high concentration, but we get stimulatory effects with as little as about 1 μg/ml. Still, the sensitivity is less pronounced than when we incubate whole ovaries, because we get metabolic effects on whole isolated ovaries at hormone concentrations around 0.01 μg/ml. I think that this also depends on the type of medium one is using. With our standard medium, a phosphate buffer with succinate as a substrate, we demonstrate a higher hormone sensitivity than with the tris buffer medium, which we have used in other experiments. So the lowest detectable concentration may be related to the choice of incubation medium.

Lerner: I have a question related to the LH response in the cyanide experiment. Have you done such experiments also with FSH?

Hamberger: These experiments were performed on isolated granulosa cells to which we added large amounts of cyanide; the respiration was stopped immediately.

Lerner: It would be interesting to see the effect of FSH on theca cells. It seems to me that LH may act upon cytochrome oxydase or on the respiratory chain enzyme system. If so, it might be that it would act even on steroid biosynthesis, at least on the pathway involving the cholesterol side chain cleaving enzyme system, which is also correlated to cytochrome P450. This might be a simple way to explain part of the steroidogenic action, and this is why I wonder if you have tried it also in theca cells.

Hamberger: We have not done that so far. The main reason why we chose cyanide for these experiments was that we wanted to check that we had no leakage of reactant from the capillary in the two-compartment micro-diver before we took away the seal, the air bubble, and that was tested just with granulosa cells.

Johannisson: Have you any information about the oocyte? Is there any specific effect of LH or FSH on the oxidative processes in the oocyte?

Hamberger: As a matter of fact, that is one of our main interests at the moment. Our first series of experiments were performed on rats varying in age between 25 and 30 days, *i. e.* prepubertal rats; they mature at 42 days. I got no gonadotrophic influence at all on the respiration of isolated oocytes in these young rats, so I left that subject for the moment. During last year, however, we used oocytes from mature rats, and there we were not able to isolate the oocyte itself, because you always have granulosa cells surrounding it. If you try to remove the granulosa cells, you spoil the plasma membrane of the oocyte. Still, however, the granulosa cells should be stimulated by LH. Where you have the complex of an oocyte and one or two layers of granulosa cells from the cycling rat, you get a dramatic decrease in the respiratory rate after the *in vitro* addition of LH. That decrease is also, we think, correlated to the phase in the ovarian cycle, in such a way that it is more pronounced around prooestrus and less pronounced in dioestrus. What this means, I do not know. It could be one way for the oocyte to save substrate and thus survive longer after it has been released from the follicle. That is just a theory to explain why the metabolic activity of the oocyte is decreasing so much after the administration of LH. Concerning FSH, we do not know – we have a slight decrease with high amounts of FSH, but at the same concentration as for LH, if you can compare hormones in that way, we get no effect with FSH.

Graham: I would like to ask if you have any preliminary data on the RNA content of your cells following various treatments, and in particular, if you know anything about the RNA content of the oocytes.

Hamberger: I think you are referring to my statement in the concluding remarks in my paper. I have some preliminary data, but it would be premature to discuss them now. In the whole ovary, on the other hand, we have results on the RNA pattern. We have been fractionating RNA on agarose polyacrylamide gel, and in these experiments we get certain acute effects by gonadotrophic hormones – but that is on the whole organ.

Kohler: How long do cells remain viable in the diver? Also, have you measured the gonadotrophin effect on oxygen uptake for periods longer than two hours?

Hamberger: It depends upon what you mean by survival. If you take respiration as a criterion, if you say that the cells survive as long as they show a linear respiratory rate, then we know that in these systems they will survive at least 6–10 hours. It is hard to tell why they will not survive any longer.

Lunenfeld: Although in absolute quantities you use very small amounts of gonadotrophins, in relation to the number of cells these doses may by far exceed physiological levels. Secondly, how do you exclude contamination of FSH with LH or LH with FSH in experiments dealing with carbohydrate metabolism, because in the preparations you use, the hormones are contaminated with each other. And last, how do you explain the stimulatory effect of 3′,5′-AMP on protein synthesis and amino acid uptake, whereas gonadotrophins had no stimulatory effect? If 3′,5′-AMP is increased under the influence of gonadotrophins, how would you explain the different effects?

Hamberger: To your first question, of course you never know what corresponds to a physiological level *in vitro*. As you said, it is probably a very high concentration of hormone even if you go down to around 1 μg/ml.

Concerning contamination of LH with FSH, I think we have that problem together with quite a lot of other people. We have tried, however, to treat our preparations with urea and we have used various types of preparations. We have used chorionic gonadotrophin with very high purity from the Leo Company (Hälsingborg, Sweden), but, of course, you can never exclude the possibility that you have a small contamination by another hormone. Anyway, if you deliberately contaminate your LH preparation with high amounts of FSH, you don't get any dramatic changes in the response of the cells.

Concerning the effects of cyclic AMP, we get it in certain steps in the glucose metabolism, for instance, on glucose uptake and on amino acid uptake, on uptake of amino acid analogues, as AIB or cycloleucine, and on the incorporation of amino acids into protein. There we experienced certain difficulties, because the effect we get with cyclic AMP is very much dependent on the concentration of the nucleotide. In low concentrations we get a stimulatory effect and we reach a maximum. With further increase, we get again an inhibition, even under the control level. I cannot explain why we get effects by cyclic AMP on certain steps in the protein metabolism *in vitro* which we cannot get with FSH, but if you inject FSH very shortly (5 min) before you remove the ovaries, you get a stimulatory effect on the protein metabolism. *In vitro* we get no effect.

Ryan: Have you tried to correlate the response that you obtain to your gonadotrophin with the size of the follicle from which you derive the cells? The pertinence of the question, of course, is whether you are dealing with follicles that are becoming atretic? And what about the prior effect of gonadotrophins *in vivo* on the response that you obtain *in vitro*?

Hamberger: I am afraid that so far we haven't looked into that problem very carefully. We have realized it rather late, so in our first studies we just chose follicles varying in size from 100 µm up to 500 µm, and in the granulosa cells we have no dramatic changes in respiratory rates between these types of follicles. These are pre-pubertal follicles; you don't have very big follicles in that type of ovary. For the isolated oocytes, however, I think we have data indicating that oocytes taken from the smaller follicles are less active metabolically. Also, we cannot obtain any decrease in respiration by luteinizing hormone when we add it to oocytes taken from small follicles.

Diczfalusy: Dr. Hamberger, do you think that the micro-diver method in the way you use it would be a suitable method for the study of pituitary or adrenal cells, isolated by the method of Dr. Sayers?

Hamberger: When I started with this technique in 1962, I started with cells from the adenohypophysis, but I did not succeed in separating the various cell types in un-stained material. When I stained it afterwards, I found a mixture of cell types in my cell samples. For the adrenals we have shown that it is possible to isolate the cells and to have them respiring in the system. We have not tested any hormonal effects in that area. For isolated cells from the testis, we have made some experiments on isolated Leydig cells, where we get acute effects with LH, but no effects with FSH (*Hamberger & Steward* 1968). For the moment we also work with isolated para-thyroid cells from rat parathyroid, where we have excellent possibilities to study the respiration under various experimental conditions.

Reference:

Hamberger L. A. & Steward V. W.: Endocrinology *83* (1968) 855.

Department of Pharmacology, Cambridge University, England,
and the Department of Anatomy, Harvard Medical School,
Boston, Massachusetts, U. S. A.

ULTRASTRUCTURAL CRITERIA
FOR ASSESSING THE FUNCTIONAL INTEGRITY OF
ENDOCRINE CELLS IN VITRO

By

A. Josephine Milner[1] *and David W. Hamilton*[2]

ABSTRACT

The morphological and biochemical evidence supporting a relationship
between structure and function has been examined for those endocrine
cells involved in steroid biosynthesis. Recent evidence indicating that
this relationship may not be a simple one has been presented and the usefulness of a morphological approach in assessing the functional activity
of cells is discussed.

In recent years there has been a rapid expansion in the application of techniques for studying the physiology of cells *in vitro*. However, few attempts
have been made to examine the morphology of these cells to assess whether
normal structural relationships are maintained during experimental periods
in vitro. The usefulness of an ultrastructural approach for assessing the functional integrity of endocrine cells, whether *in vivo* or *in vitro*, depends upon
the basic premise that structural features and biochemical phenomena are
related. Whilst it is reasonable to assume that any unique morphological
characteristic of a cell may be correlated with a specialised function, many
biochemical reactions of fundamental importance occur that involve changes

---

[1] Beit Memorial Research Fellow.
[2] Recipient of a Research Career Development Award, USPHS. Research supported
by The Population Council and by USPHS grant HD-04290.

below the resolution of the electron microscope. It is nonetheless true that specific ultrastructural features can often be directly correlated with the physiological state of a cell. Such correlations further our understanding of the functioning of cells, especially of those processes involved in the synthesis, storage and release of product. For a general consideration of this topic with relation to endocrine cells the reader is referred to the review by *Fawcett et al.* (1969). In this chapter we shall restrict our discussion to the ultrastructural features of steroid synthesising cells from a variety of tissues, of which only adrenal cortical cells have been extensively studied *in vitro*. The criteria for interpreting ultrastructural data are the same, however, whether the cells are from *in vitro* systems or from intact animals.

Evidence for the localisation of steroid biosynthetic enzymes in cells

a) *Histochemical.* The localisation of steroid dehydrogenases has been studied using histochemical techniques and a thorough analysis of their distribution is given in the review of *Baillie et al.* (1966). Unfortunately, the techniques available to date only allow the identification of cells exhibiting dehydrogenase activity without providing any information on its intracellular distribution. A histochemical procedure allowing the subcellular localisation of enzymes involved in steroid biosynthesis would be of great value.

b) *Biochemical.* The first direct evidence for the intracellular localisation of steroid biosynthetic enzymes was obtained from biosynthetic studies of subcellular fractions. Work in this field has recently been reviewed by *Christensen & Gillim* (1969) and will not be covered here. In general, cell fractionation studies indicate that cholesterol side-chain cleavage, steroid 11β-hydroxylation, 18-hydroxylation and 18-hydroxysteroid dehydrogenase are catalysed by mitochondrial enzyme systems. The conversion of acetate to cholesterol, in addition to the following enzymes, appears localised in the microsomal fraction: 3β-hydroxysteroid dehydrogenase, $\Delta^5 - \Delta^4$ isomerase, 17α-hydroxylase, 17-20 desmolase, 21-hydroxylase, 17β-hydroxysteroid dehydrogenase and the steroid aromatisation system. As the microsomal fraction is heterogeneous, being composed of membranes of the smooth and rough endoplasmic reticulum, the Golgi complex and probably some plasma membrane, further fractionation is necessary to establish more precisely the localisation of associated enzymes. Subfractionation of microsomes obtained from some cells have recently been carried out. *Chesterton* (1968) reported that the rough and the smooth endoplasmic reticulum were able to synthesise cholesterol from mevalonate. However, the morphological purity of these fractions was not checked to assess the extent of cross contamination of the fractions. Using preparations of porcine and rat adrenals *Inano et al.* (1969a) subfractionated microsomes and checked the purity of the subfractions by electron microscopy. They found that the

63

activities of 3β-hydroxysteroid dehydrogenase plus Δ^5 - Δ^4 isomerase, 17α-hydroxylase and 21-hydroxylase were predominantly associated with the smooth surfaced membranes.

Subfractionation of mitochondrial preparations to separate the inner and outer membranes is also possible (*Parsons et al.* 1966). *Yago & Ichii* (1969) osmotically lysed a mitochondrial preparation from hog adrenal and partitioned the resulting membranes by centrifugation on a discontinuous Ficoll gradient. They inferred from subsequent biochemical results that the enzyme systems involved in cholesterol side-chain cleavage and 11β-hydroxylation are associated with the inner mitochondrial membrane. More recently *Dodge et al.* (1970) have presented both morphological and biochemical confirmation for the localisation of steroid 11β-hydroxylase on the inner mitochondrial membrane.

As with all experimental procedures interpretation of results is governed by the limitations of the techniques adopted. We shall now mention some of the problems associated with sub-cellular fractionation studies as a note of caution in the interpretation of the observations discussed above.

When a cell homogenate is centrifuged to equilibrium conditions in a density gradient components of the cell of differing densities are grouped into different fractions. Although it has been assumed in many cases that a given fraction represents a given organelle it is considered that electron microscopic examination of an isolated fraction is required as minimal evidence of content and purity. Even when a fraction has been rigorously identified there is no assurance that its biochemical properties will be the same as those of the organelle(s) *in vivo*. Biochemical activity may be modified by factors imposed upon the cell during homogenisation, such as local heating (see *Avis* (1969)) and on alteration of ionic environment which is inevitable once the cell membrane is ruptured. During centrifugation there is evidence that the nature of the gradient may affect subsequent biochemical activity. It has been shown, for example, that the rate of steroid hydroxylation is lowered in membranes which have been subjected to centrifugation in caesium chloride (*Inano et al.* 1969a). In an homogenate it is also possible that some of the enzyme proteins may become redistributed in the cell fractions due to partitioning between the membrane and cytosol phases. The conditions of incubation, such as availability of co-factors, ionic variations and other variables, will directly affect the biochemical activity of any cell fraction (*Peron & McCarthy* 1968; *Cammer et al.* 1968; *Harding et al.* 1968; and others). Finally, when biosynthetic activity involves a series of sequential conversions, as in steroid biosynthesis, it is possible that normal metabolic activity may depend upon the maintenance of a defined set of spatial relationships within the whole cell. Only within these limitations can we allocate specific biochemical functions to specific cellular organelles on the basis of data obtained from subcellular fractions.

c) *Ultrastructural.* Cells involved in steroid biosynthesis characteristically exhibit the following features: an extensive smooth endoplasmic reticulum, a relatively small amount of rough endoplasmic reticulum, numerous mitochondria of variable size and shape, a prominent Golgi complex and varying numbers of lipid droplets and other inclusions (Figs. 1 to 8). Of these the most striking feature is the large amount of smooth endoplasmic reticulum and it is not surprising that early studies devoted much attention to this organelle (*Fawcett & Burgos* 1960; *Christensen & Fawcett* 1961, 1966; *Christensen* 1965; *Bjersing* 1967). In these cells the smooth endoplasmic reticulum is predominant of those organelles known to constitute the microsomal fraction, and a correlation can be drawn between the ability of a cell to synthesise cholesterol and its content of smooth endoplasmic reticulum (see *Christensen & Gillim* 1969). There is also strong evidence for a correlation between the amount of smooth endoplasmic reticulum and adrenal steroid 21- and 17α-hydroxylation, as we shall discuss later.

Recent experimental observations on steroid synthesising cells

We shall now examine in some detail recent data obtained from a variety of cell types involved in steroid biosynthesis, beginning with those of the adrenal gland. The adrenal cortex is composed of three concentric zones: the outer zona glomerulosa, a middle zona fasciculata and the inner zona reticularis. The zona glomerulosa secretes the steroid aldosterone and is partially dependent upon the renin-angiotensin feed-back system: morphologically it appears to be independent of the pituitary hormone ACTH. The cells of the inner two zones, however, are functionally dependent upon ACTH and show obvious morphological changes following ACTH administration or deprivation. Cells from all three zones have been studied in numerous species and details of the variation in their fine structure can be found in *Fawcett et al.* (1969) and *Long & Jones* (1967a,b, 1970). In the cells from the fasciculata and reticularis the most striking organelle in terms of volume is the smooth endoplasmic reticulum. There are also numerous mitochondria, a well developed Golgi complex and areas of rough endoplasmic reticulum which appear as discrete »basophilic bodies« in the light microscope. In the species studied the amount of smooth endoplasmic reticulum in the cells of the zona glomerulosa is significantly less than in the cells of the other two zones.

Observations on these cells have been obtained from both *in vivo* and *in vitro* experiments and thus allow us to draw comparisons between the two approaches. After hypophysectomy there is a decrease both in the amount of smooth endoplasmic reticulum in cells of the fasciculata and reticularis and in the number of mitochondria; at the same time there is a decrease in the output of adrenal steroids (for references see *Deane* 1962; *Fawcett et al.* 1969;

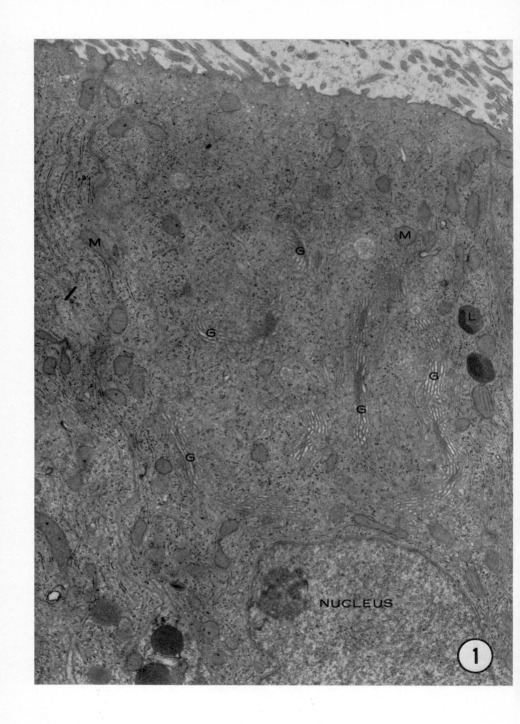

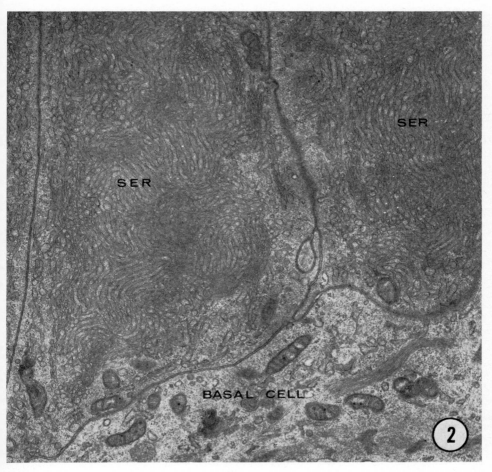

Fig. 2.

Principal cells from the rabbit epididymis contain large amounts of smooth endoplasmic reticulum (SER), a feature characteristic of steroid synthesizing cells. ×10 600.

Fig. 1.

The importance of proper fixation of cells to the interpretation of ultrastructural data is illustrated in this electron micrograph and in those following. This cell, a principal cell from the epithelium of the rat epididymis, is considered to be well-fixed in that no obvious artefacts can be seen, such as exploded mitochondria (M), dilated endoplasmic reticulum, empty cytoplasm or broken membranes. The Golgi apparatus (G) is uniformly fixed with little, if any, dilation of the lamellae (contrast this with the picture in Fig. 6) and the intercellular space is not swollen. Of particular importance to ultrastructural studies of the epididymis is the fact that the luminal surface of the cell is not ballooned out, rather it presents a flat surface studded with elongate microvilli. L = Lysosome. × 7000.

Nussdorfer 1970). Conversely, when ACTH is administered to an intact animal there is a proliferation of the membranes of the smooth endoplasmic reticulum, an increase in the number of mitochondria and an increase in steroid biosynthetic activity. Moreover, in some species the morphology of the mitochondria is also dependent upon ACTH. In the rat adrenal the mitochondria from fasciculata and reticularis cells are highly characteristic in that the inner membrane forms vesicular cristae (*Sabatini & de Robertis* 1965; *Giacomelli et al.* 1965; *Kahri* 1966). These vesicular cristae contrast strikingly with the lamellate cristae found in mitochondria from many other cell types. *Idelman* (1966) observed that the cristae became tubular following hypophysectomy but reverted to the vesicular form when ACTH was administered.

The morphology of adrenal cortical cells grown in tissue cultures of foetal rat adrenals has been studied in detail by *Kahri* (1966). Kahri observed that the cells resemble those of the zona fasciculata only when ACTH is added to the tissue culture medium. When cultured in the absence of ACTH the cortical cells lack many features of the differentiated cell type *in vivo*, in particular the smooth endoplasmic reticulum is not well developed and the mitochondria are small with lamellate cristae. ACTH induces both proliferation of the smooth endoplasmic reticulum and transformation of the mitochondria into the form with vesicular cristae. Further studies on tissue cultures of human foetal adrenals have demonstrated that during the ACTH-induced morphological transformation of the cortical cells there is a concomitant rise in their steroid biosynthetic activity (*Milner et al.* 1969; *Milner & Villee* 1970). This increase in biosynthetic activity would be expected if there is a direct correlation between biosynthetic activity and both the amount of smooth endoplasmic reticulum and the form of mitochondria. Both cholesterol side-chain cleavage and steroid 11β-hydroxylation are catalysed by mitochondrial enzyme systems whilst 17α- and 21-hydroxylation are catalysed by enzymes assumed to be associated with the smooth endoplasmic reticulum (*Inano et al.* 1969b). The activity of all these enzyme systems increases in the ACTH-transformed cells (*Milner & Villee* 1970). This provides an experimental system in which ultrastructural transformation can be induced whilst at the same time any related changes in the functional activity of the cells may be monitored.

In further studies the transformation and biochemical activity of the mitochondria in tissue cultures of foetal rat adrenals has been investigated (*Kahri & Milner* 1969; *Kahri* 1970; *Milner* 1971). The ACTH-induced mitochondrial transformation is inhibited by chloramphenicol, an antibiotic which specifically inhibits protein synthesis on mitochondral ribosomes in eukaryotic cells. The cytoplasmic ribosomes are not affected and chloramphenicol does not affect the ACTH-induced proliferation of the smooth endoplasmic reticulum. When ACTH is administered in the presence of chloramphenicol the 21-hydroxylating activity of the cells increases but the increase in mitochondrial 11β-hydroxylation is blocked. This results in a decrease in corticosterone production and a corresponding increase in the yield of 11-deoxycorticosterone from progesterone. The inhibitory effect of chloramphenicol is reversible and, when mitochondrial transformation is allowed to proceed on withdrawal of chloramphenicol there is an increase in 11β-hydroxylation similar to that observed in normal ACTH-treated cells.

As they stand these results indicate a close correlation between mitochondrial form and function in the rat adrenal. However, it was noted that in those cells which had been treated with chloramphenicol alone and then with ACTH the mitochondria transformed and developed vesicular cristae (*Kahri*, personal communication), but their 11β-hydroxylating activity had been irreversibly impaired and did not increase above the untreated control levels (*Milner* 1971). These are mitochondria which, although appearing normal at the ultrastructural level, have impaired biosynthetic capacity.

As we have indicated the morphology of the mitochondria in cells of the zona fasciculata and reticularis in the rat adrenal provides some indication of their functional state (under normal conditions). Such a clear morphological indication of mitochondrial activity is unusual and probably fortuitous, owing to the highly characteristic appearance of these mitochondria *in vivo*. In contrast, the mitochondria of the cells in the zona glomerulosa have the more typical lamellate cristae and do not appear to reflect synthetic activity at the ultrastructural level. In the opossum the effects of sodium deprivation on the morphology of the cells of the zona glomerulosa have been studied by *Long & Jones* (1970). Sodium deficiency results in increased production of aldosterone by the zona glomerulosa; the biosynthesis of aldosterone from cholesterol involves enzymes localised in the smooth endoplasmic reticulum and the mitochondria. It is interesting to note that, although sodium deprivation results in an increase in the amount of smooth endoplasmic reticulum, no changes in the structure of the mitochondria were noted by *Long & Jones* (1969) although these organelles are the site of the rate limiting step in the conversion of cholesterol to aldosterone.

In addition to the adrenal cortex, cells of the ovary and testis are actively involved in steroid biosynthesis. Recently it has been suggested that the epididymis is also a steroid synthesising organ (*Hamilton et al.* 1969, in prep.; *Hamilton & Fawcett* 1970; *Hamilton* 1971). There is abundant evidence supporting the existence of a direct relationship between the steroid synthesising activity and the amount of smooth endoplasmic reticulum in cells (see, for instance, *Belt et al.* 1970; in addition to the evidence cited above). It was this evidence which led to the suspicion that the large amount of smooth endoplasmic reticulum present in epididymal epithelial cells from many species (Fig. 2) might be associated with steroid biosynthetic activity (*Hamilton et al.* 1969). It was of some surprise, therefore, when cells from the rat epididymis and vas deferens were shown to synthesise testosterone from acetate because

69

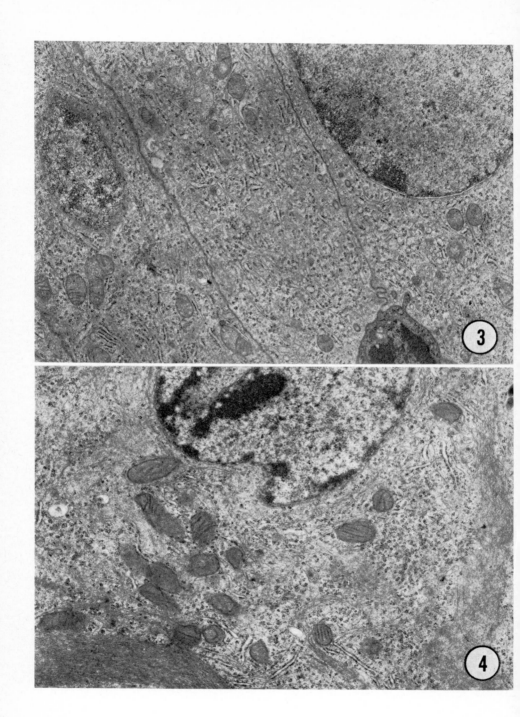

in this species the cells contain relatively little smooth endoplasmic reticulum (*Hamilton* 1971). Indeed, the uptake of [1-^{14}C] acetate into testosterone per unit weight of epididymal tissue was the same in the rat as in the mouse, although the epididymal cells in the mouse are packed with membranes of the smooth endoplasmic reticulum (*Hamilton* 1971). In a further series of experiments *Hamilton et al.* (in prep.) developed a technique for isolating the epithelium from the vas deferens in the rat. They were thus able to demonstrate that the synthesis of dehydro*epi*androsterone from acetate occurs only in the epithelial fraction, poor in smooth membrane content (Fig. 4). They also made the interesting observation that the smooth muscle surrounding the vas deferens is capable of synthesising significant amounts of cholesterol.

In general steroid biosynthetic cells contain characteristically large amounts of smooth endoplasmic reticulum. However, it is clear from the above data that one cannot predict the steroid synthetic capacity of a cell on the basis of morphological evidence alone.

GENERAL DISCUSSION

When a cell has been subjected to experimental conditions, either *in vivo* or *in vitro*, some indication of its morphological state may modify the interpretation of any biochemical observations. For example, mitochondria which appear obviously abnormal in the electron microscope might be expected not only to exhibit impaired synthetic activity but also to result in more general, secondary effects upon the biochemistry of the cell as a whole. This situation is encountered when cells of the adrenal cortex are cultured for prolonged

---

Figs. 3 and 4.

Fig. 3: In this well-fixed principal cell from the rat vas deferens, the basal cytoplasm of the cell is filled with profiles of rough endoplasmic reticulum, scattered mitochondria and free ribosomes. The cells illustrated here are from an intact animal and were fixed by vascular perfusion. × 20 000.

Fig. 4: This electron micrograph illustrates a region comparable to that in Fig. 3, but is from an *in vitro* epithelial preparation from the rat vas deferens. The vas deferens was removed from the animal and placed in ice-cold, oxygenated bicarbonate buffered Krebs-Ringer solution (KRB) and, over a period of 5 to 10 minutes, the epithelium was removed and placed in a separate vial of KRB. Following dissection of 5 animals (60 minutes) this epithelium was randomly chosen from the pooled samples and fixed for electron microscopy. The remainder of the samples were incubated in KRB (37°C) and were shown to be able to synthesize cholesterol and dehydro*epi*androsterone from acetate. Comparison of Figs. 3 and 4 shows that this type of *in vitro* treatment has not greatly altered the morphology of the cells or their organelles. × 20 000 (micrograph after *Hamilton et al.,* in preparation).

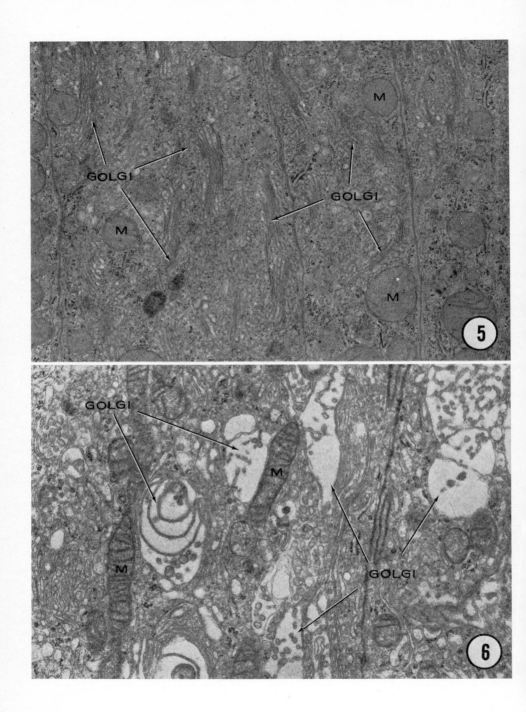

periods in the presence of chloramphenicol, the mitochondria appear abnormal (*Kahri,* personal communication) and the overall utilisation of progesterone as a precursor for steroid biosynthesis is diminished (*Milner* 1971). Alternatively some experimental procedures may have adverse effects on other cellular organelles, such as the membranes of the smooth endoplasmic reticulum.

More specifically we have used three examples to illustrate the possible pitfalls in the interpretation of ultrastructural data from a functional point of view. First, the morphology of mitochondria in rat adrenal cortical cells is not necessarily related to their functional activity. Secondly, no differences in the mitochondria are observed in glomerulosa cells presumed to be synthesising aldosterone at different rates even though the rate limiting biosynthetic step is localised within the mitochondria. Finally, steroid biosynthesis has been shown to occur in cells containing comparatively little smooth endoplasmic reticulum, although the bulk of the evidence supports the hypothesis that there is a correlation between steroid synthesis and the volume of smooth endoplasmic reticulum. Whilst these examples represent exceptions to a simple, unifying hypothesis relating structure and function, they nevertheless pose interesting problems by the very nature of their exceptions and may offer clues to the more precise nature of intracellular relationships.

A direct correlation between the observable ultrastructure and the functional activity of cells involved in steroid biosynthesis cannot be generally assumed. For example, the smooth endoplasmic reticulum is found to varying degrees in all cells. The prominence of this organelle in steroid synthesising cells from different tissues does not necessarily mean that it has the same function in all. Indeed, in cell types from non-steroid synthesising organs it has been implicated in a variety of functions, including drug detoxification in hepatocytes (*Jones & Fawcett* 1966) and excitation-contraction coupling in muscle (see *Fawcett* 1965). It seems clear from observations on cultured cells that the volume of the smooth endoplasmic reticulum is directly related to steroid synthesis in the adrenal cortex. However, it is not yet known whether the proliferation of the reticulum which is induced by ACTH is associated

---

Figs. 5 and 6.
These electron micrographs illustrate the hazards of variable fixation on cell structure. Both illustrations are derived from rat vas deferens fixed by immersion in similar aldehyde fixatives. In Fig. 5, the overall fixation of the cells is uniform and comparable to that illustrated in Fig. 1. The Golgi apparatus is composed of membrane lamellae with no obvious vesiculation or gross distortion. In Fig. 6, on the other hand, Golgi lamellae are grossly distorted and other features of the cell not illustrated here show that in general this fixation was not good. Variability such as this may represent real functional differences, but often it can be produced by the preparative methods employed. M = Mitochondria. Fig. 5, × 20 000. Fig. 6, × 26 700.

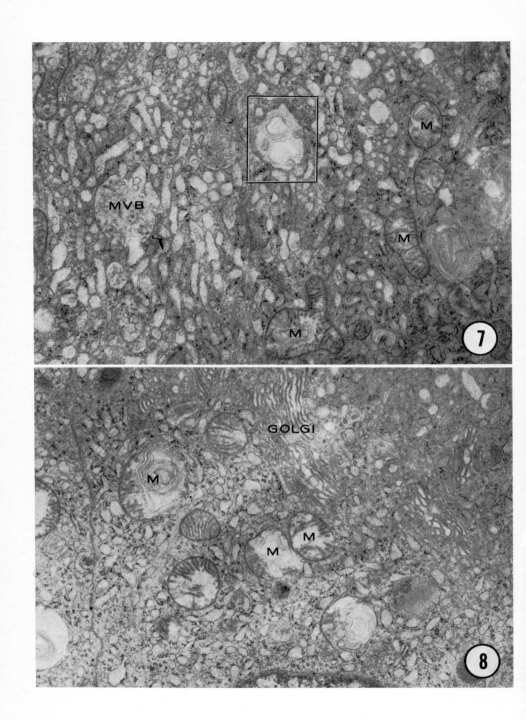

with increasing enzyme concentration, substrate concentration or product concentration. It has been suggested by *Fawcett* (1965) and *Christensen & Fawcett* (1966) that the membranes of the smooth endoplasmic reticulum may act as a site for precursor (cholesterol) storage in some cells. A further possible function of the smooth membrane system might be to increase the polar:nonpolar interface within the cell for the accommodation of intermediate steroid substrates prior to and during enzymic conversion.

REFERENCES

Avis P. J. G. In: Birnie G. D. and Fox S. M., Eds. Subcellular Components. Butterworth and Co. Ltd., London (1969) 1.

Baillie A. H., Ferguson M. M. & Hart D. McK.: Developments in Steroid Histochemistry. Academic Press, London and New York (1966).

Belt W. D., Cavazos L. F., Anderson L. L. & Kraeling R. R.: Biol. Reprod. 2 (1970) 98.

Bjersing L.: Z. Zellforsch. 82 (1967) 187.

Cammer W., Cooper D. Y. & Estabrook R. W. In: McKerns K. W., Ed. Functions of the Adrenal Cortex, Vol. II. Appleton-Century-Crofts, New York (1968) 897.

Chesterton C. J.: J. biol. Chem. 243 (1968) 1147.

Christensen A. K.: J. Cell Biol. 26 (1965) 911.

Christensen A. K. & Fawcett D. W.: J. biophys. biochem. Cytol. 9 (1961) 653.

Christensen A. K. & Fawcett D. W.: Amer. J. Anat. 118 (1966) 551.

Christensen A. K. & Gillim S. W. In: McKerns K. W., Ed. The Gonads. Appleton-Century-Crofts, New York (1969) 415.

Deane H. W. In: Deane H. W., Ed. Handbuch der experimentellen Pharmakologie, Vol. XIV/1. The adrenocortical Hormones. Springer-Verlag, Berlin (1962) 77.

Dodge A. H., Christensen A. K. & Clayton R. B.: Endocrinology 87 (1970) 254.

Fawcett D. W. In: Seno S. and Cowdry E., Eds. Intracellular Membraneous Structure. Chugoku Press Ltd., Okayama (1965) 15.

Figs. 7 and 8.

The problem of fixation and its effect on interpretation of experimental data is highlighted in these electron micrographs. Fig. 8 illustrates principal cells from the mouse caput epididymis from an animal given AY9944 (a Δ^7-reductase inhibitor). The cells were fixed by vascular perfusion. In fixing the tissue, however, vascular occlusion occurred at the start of the perfusion and before free flow of fixing fluid was achieved some 20 to 30 seconds had elapsed. This period of anoxia must have had deleterious effects on the tissue, but it is difficult to separate the effects of anoxia and poor fixation from effects of the experimental treatment. It is clear from Fig. 7, however. that poor fixation must have resulted in the mitochondrial artefacts seen in Fig. 8, since Fig. 7 is from an untreated normal animal in which the same problems in perfusion occurred as with the animal of Fig. 8. Contrasting Fig. 1 with Figs. 7 and 8 illustrates how the assessment of experimental effects on cell structure is dependent upon the quality of fixation. Fig. 7, $\times$ 26 700. Fig. 8, $\times$ 26 700.

Fawcett D. W. & Burgos M. H.: Amer. J. Anat. *107* (1960) 245.

Fawcett D. W., Long J. A. & Jones A. L.: Recent Progr. Hormone Res. *25* (1969) 315.

Giacomelli F., Weiner J. & Spiro D.: J. Cell Biol. *26* (1965) 499.

Hamilton D. W. In: Balin H. and Glasser S., Eds. Reproductive Biology. Excerpta Medica Foundation, New York (1971).

Hamilton D. W. & Fawcett D. W.: Proc. Soc. exp. Biol. Med. *133* (1970) 693.

Hamilton D. W., Jones A. L. & Fawcett D. W.: Biol. Reprod. *1* (1969) 167.

Hamilton D. W., Schantz I. C. & Fawcett D. W.: (in preparation).

Harding B. W., Bell J. J., Oldham S. B. & Wilson L. D. In: McKerns K. W., Ed. Functions of the Adrenal Cortex, Vol. II. Appleton-Century-Crofts, New York (1968) 897.

Idelman S.: Ann. Sci. Nat. Zool. Biol. Animale *8* (1966) 205.

Inano H., Inano A. & Tamaoki B-I.: Biochim. biophys. Acta (Amst.) *191* (1969*a*) 257.

Inano H., Machino A. & Tamaoki B-I.: Steroids *13* (1969*b*) 357.

Jones A. L. & Fawcett D. W.: J. Histochem. Cytochem. *14* (1966) 215.

Kahri A. I.: Acta endocr. (Kbh.) Suppl. *108*, 52 (1966).

Kahri A. I.: Amer. J. Anat. *127* (1970) 103.

Kahri A. I. & Milner A. J.: J. Cell Biol. *43* (1969) 62a.

Long J. A. & Jones A. L.: Amer. J. Anat. *120* (1967*a*) 463.

Long J. A. & Jones A. L.: Lab. Invest. *17* (1967*b*) 355.

Long J. A. & Jones A. L.: Anat. Rec. *166* (1970) 1.

Milner A. J.: Endocrinology *88* (1971) 64.

Milner A. J. & Villee D. B.: Endocrinology *87* (1970) 596.

Milner A. J., Kahri A. I. & Villee D. B. In: The Endocrine Society Program of the Fifty-First Meeting (1969).

Nussdorfer G. G.: Z. Zellforsch. *106* (1970) 143.

Parsons D. F., Williams G. R. & Chance B.: Ann. N. Y. Acad. Sci. *137* (1966) 643.

Péron F. G. & McCarthy J. L. In: McKerns K. W., Ed. Functions of the Adrenal Cortex, Vol. 1. Appleton-Century-Crofts, New York (1968) 897.

Sabatini D. D. & de Robertis E.: J. Cell Biol. *26* (1965) 499.

Yago N. & Ichii S.: J. Biochem. (Tokyo) *65* (1969) 215.

DISCUSSION

Nakane: On some of your electron micrographs, some mitochondria tend to have an extremely high electron density, whereas some have a very slight electron density. Is this a reflexion of your fixation or is it a reflexion of some of the functions?

Milner: The cultured cortical cells all go through the same fixation procedure, so this may be a reflexion of function.

Nakane: Are these mitochondrial changes which you have observed an effect of the precursor? In other words, if you expose the cells to 11-deoxycorticosterone, does the mitochondrial structure change?

Milner: I don't know. This is a good point which might be investigated further, although I know of no evidence suggesting an accumulation of 11-deoxycorticosterone within adrenal cortical cells.

Johannisson: In 1968 I studied the functional morphology of the human foetal adrenal glands (*Johannisson* 1968). In some of the cases investigated, 60 IU of ACTH was given intraamniotically to foetuses at midgestation and then, immediately after interruption of pregnancy, the foetal adrenals were removed. In these cases, stimulated for 7 hours, there was an obvious increase in free ribosomes when compared to the control cases. In the adrenal cortex of the stimulated foetuses there were many dark cells, as well as light cells. In the dark cells found, there was a dilatation of the endoplasmic reticulum following ACTH stimulation. The mitochondria were sometimes enormously increased in size, revealing a tubular formation of the internal structure.

In other experiments, 30 000 IU of HCG was injected intraamniotically into foetuses at midgestation. In these cases, the dark cells did not show any dilatation of the endoplasmic reticulum similar to that found after ACTH stimulation. The mitochondria were enormously increased, and there was also a depletion of the lipid osmiophilic droplets. When midgestation foetuses were perfused with an anti-HCG serum, there was a significant increase in the dark cells of the adrenals. When these pictures were compared with the control cases, perfused only with blood, we could not find any increase in dark cells. Hence the increase appears to be due to the administration of anti-HCG. I would like to ask you, Dr. Milner, if you have observed any increase of the free ribosomes in the *in vitro* system you have investigated?

Milner: It is difficult to give a direct answer to this, since you also get an increase in the cytoplasmic volume following ACTH administration.

Johannisson: Did you observe any change in the osmiophilic droplets in the cytoplasm? Was there any depletion?

Milner: There was an increase.

Ryan: I think all of us were rather intrigued and sort of amazed by Hamilton's observations on the ability of non-gonadal tissue to, supposedly, make gonadal hormones. This would imply, from the physiological point of view, that if you castrated a male mouse it should not show any signs of testosterone deficiency, unless the capacity to synthesize hormones in this tissue were very low. I wonder if anyone has confirmed these data. I am not surprised that acetate would be converted to cholesterol, since practically any cell in the body can do this, but the conversion of acetate to testosterone in the non-gonadal tissue does surprise me.

Milner: I can only say that the morphology of the smooth endoplasmic reticulum in these epididymal cells and in the vas deferens is dependent upon the presence of testosterone (*Hamilton et al.* 1969).

Ryan: Are you aware of anyone having confirmed this or having tested their observations? These are not your observations?

Milner: No, these are from studies of *Hamilton* and his coworkers.

Eshkol: How did you determine 11-deoxycorticosterone and corticosterone? Secondly, the results in your oral presentation were expressed as cpm $\times 10^{-3}$, which is very low. Could you give us any idea of how much this is in per cent of conversion of the carbon-labelled progesterone?

Milner: I identified corticosterone and 11-deoxycorticosterone by first running them in several different chromatography solvent systems and by derivative formation (see *Milner & Mills* 1970). Expressing the results as per cent conversion of precursor to product may be misleading. Binding of the precursor to proteins present in the culture medium will affect the amount of precursor available to the cultured cells (see *Milner & Villee* 1970 for discussion of this point).

Means: For those of us who are not experts in this area I have two basic questions. First of all, what kind of physiological significance would you possibly attach to the fact that epididymis and vas deferens might make testosterone *in vitro?* Secondly, what significance could be attached to a hormone increasing the number of free ribosomes? Does this mean a decrease in the bound versus an increase in the free, or an increase in the synthesis of ribosomes? I would like some clarification on these points.

Milner: Concerning the *in vitro* observation that these cells are capable of synthesizing steroids, I think that, if this occurs *in vivo,* then the interpretation is that this might be involved in sperm capacitation.

Diczfalusy: There was some information presented at the Bethesda meeting last October suggesting that the extraordinarily high concentration of testosterone in the epididymis is of significant importance for the frequency of successful implantation following the removal of sperm from different parts of the epididymis (*Orgebin-Christ,* data presented at the Conference organized by the Population Centre, NIH (October 1970, Bethesda). Sperm removed from the caput epididymis did not fertilize. Sperm removed from the cauda epididymis did fertilize in more than 90 % of the cases. If the rabbits were castrated, the fertilizing ability of the sperm decreased, but could be restored by the administration of testosterone.

Johannisson: About the significance of the increase in number of free ribosomes: In immature undifferentiated cells there are numerous free ribosomes. In the adrenals of very young foetuses (1.5 cm) the cells are totally undifferentiated. They are immature, containing numerous free ribosomes, and they do not have any developed endoplasmic reticulum. These cells are undifferentiated from a morphological point of view. However, with increased differentiation of the cells and increased protein synthesis, there is a decrease in the free ribosomes. In the mature cells you will find very few free ribosomes, and the ribosomes are attached to some part of the endoplasmic reticulum forming the granulated endoplasmic reticulum. The increase of free ribosomes following the ACTH stimulation would therefore suggest a possible stimulation of the cell growth induced by ACTH.

Lerner: I think that *Berliner et al.* (1958) and *Pearlman et al.* (1960) presented some evidence that progesterone and testosterone are converted to various steroid metabolites not only by uterine fibroblasts, but also by fibroblasts from subcutaneous adipose tissue. The same was reported for other tissues, such as submaxillary glands (*Rosner et al.* 1969).

Another question to Dr. Milner: We know that some tissues have the capability to utilize or synthesize different sorts of steroids, but what happens with tissues (such as the human placenta) in which we have evidence that acetate cannot be converted to cholesterol, while the tissue has the ability to carry out 17α-hydroxylation (*e. g. Telegdy et al.* 1970)? All of us know that we have smooth endoplasmic reticulum there; I wonder if it is just a compartmentalization of enzymes, or is it because one part, or one pair of enzymes are absent from the same organelle?

Milner: The smooth endoplasmic reticulum appears to serve different functions in different tissues. I know of no direct evidence for compartmentalization of enzymes associated with the smooth endoplasmic reticulum in steroid synthetic tissues.

Baulieu: Is there any work dealing with the transformation of cholesterol to pregnenolone which could be studied in terms of morphology and, also, in which you would have used chloramphenicol? A connected question would be, since you have different steps of steroid biosynthesis located in different structures, to know the effects of cyclic AMP.

Milner: I am at present investigating the effects of chloramphenicol on the utilization of cholesterol as a precursor for steroid biosynthesis, including the acute response, which develops in the ACTH-treated cells but is absent in the control cells (*Milner* 1971). Preliminary results indicate that cyclic AMP does induce a general increase in steroid biosynthesis, although I have not yet observed mitochondrial transformation in AMP-treated cells in culture.

Baulieu: Referring to your comment concerning the rat epididymis cell structure, is there any morphological evidence that there is some continuity between mitochondria and endoplasmic reticulum?

Milner: Despite a close association, a continuity between the outer membrane and the mitochondria of the smooth endoplasmic reticulum has not been observed.

Lunenfeld: During your beautiful studies, did you find any clues as to the regulation of transport of steroid precursors or intermediate products into mitochondria and from the mitochondria to the smooth endoplasmic reticulum?

Milner: No.

Ryan: Dr. Milner, do you know if there is any information on whether the vesicular mitochondria sediment any differently in cell fractionation preparations? The reason I bring this up is that all of us who have studied steroid biosynthesis *in vitro* and prepared subcellular fractions have, at one time or another, been hopelessly misguided. I wonder if you could shed any light on this point?

Milner: No, but I hope to develop a procedure for isolating these vesicular mitochondria and then isolate the actual vesicles and study their properties.

Nakane: Some technical questions: The series of photographs you presented on the adrenal and the series you presented on the epididymis obviously went through different fixations and processes. The preservation of the epididymis was much superior to that of the adrenal. In your experience, are these tissues affected differently during the fixation?

Milner: That is the best we have obtained so far. Ultrastructural preservation is particularly difficult in adrenal cortical cells; indeed, in this culture system, the other cell types present often show much better preservation than the cortical cells in the same culture.

References:

Berliner D. L., Swim H. E. & Dougherty T. F.: Proc. Soc. exptl. Biol. Med. *99* (1958) 51.

Hamilton D. W., Jones A. & Fawcett D. W.: Biol. Reprod. *1* (1969) 167.

Johannisson E.: Acta endocr. (Kbh.) Suppl. *130* (1968).

Milner A. J.: Endocrinology *88* (1971) 64.

Milner A. J. & Mills J. H.: J. Endocr. *47* (1970) 369.

Milner A. J. & Villee D. B.: Endocrinology *87* (1970) 596.

Pearlman D., Jackson P. W., Giuffre N. & Fried J.: Canad. J. Biochem. Physiol. *38* (1960) 393.

Rosner J., Macome J. C. & Cardinali O. P.: Endocrinology *85* (1969) 1000.

Telegdy G., Weeks J. W., Lerner U., Stakemann G. & Diczfalusy E.: Acta endocr. (Kbh.) *63* (1970) 91.

Swedish Medical Research Council, Reproductive Endocrinology Research Unit,
Karolinska sjukhuset, Stockholm

ISOLATION AND CYTOCHEMICAL PROPERTIES
OF HUMAN ENDOMETRIAL CELLS

By

Elisabeth Johannisson and Kerstin Hagenfeldt

ABSTRACT

Quantitative cytochemical methods were employed for the determination of some cellular properties of isolated endometrial cells. Two different methods have been used: an absorption microspectrophotometric method for the estimation of Feulgen-DNA and a microfluorometric technique for the assessment of glycogen. The two methods have been evaluated with respect to their specificity when applied to isolated human endometrial cells.

The variation in endometrial DNA and glycogen during the menstrual cycle was studied in isolated cells taken from normally menstruating women. During the first part of the proliferative phase from cycle day (c. d.) 1 to c. d. 10–11 the Feulgen-DNA values in the endometrial cells remained at a constant level, corresponding to the pre-synthesizing phase (G_1). However, in the samples obtained from cycle days 14, 16–18, and 19–23 the cells were mainly in the DNA-synthesizing phase (S), revealing a higher amount of Feulgen-DNA per nucleus than in the early proliferative phase. By c. d. 27 a statistically significant drop in Feulgen-DNA per cell nucleus was found and the endometrial cells were again in G_1-phase.

The deposit of glycogen showed a gradual increase from c. d. 1 to c. d. 16–18, with a slope of 0.0079 ± 0.0022. This was followed by a significant decrease between c. d. 16–18 and c. d. 27 with a slope of -0.0139 ± 0.0042.

Stromal glycogen remained low and constant throughout the entire menstrual cycle.

81

The morphological changes of the human endometrium during the normal menstrual cycle reflect the ovarian secretion of sex hormones. Biochemical, histochemical and ultrastructural parameters have also contributed to the knowledge of the hormonal effects upon the uterine mucosa. Significant cyclic variations in the amount of nucleic acids, proteins and carbohydrates have been reported as well as changes in enzymatic activities. However, the mechanism of action of the principal ovarian hormones, 17β-oestradiol and progesterone, upon the endometrium is still incompletely understood.

In order to study the effect of ovarian hormones upon the human endometrium at the cellular level, the use of cytochemical methods appeared to be promising. Such methods have been employed by previous investigators for the quantitative estimation of intracellular substances in various types of cells such as the content of DNA in human leukocytes (*Hale & Wilson* 1959, 1963; *Hale* 1963; *Perugini et al.* 1957), in human uterine tumours (*Atkin & Richards* 1956; *Atkin et al.* 1959) and in cells obtained in various pathological conditions (*Leuchtenberger & Leuchtenberger* 1960). Newer techniques have also been developed to study the carbohydrate content of neutrophile leukocytes (*Gahrton* 1964, 1966; *Yataghanas et al.* 1969). In order to find out whether or not cytochemical methods are suitable for the study of isolated human endometrial cells two investigations were performed in a group of fertile women with normal menstrual periods. The amount of DNA was estimated per cell nucleus using a microspectrophotometric technique. The amount of glycogen per endometrial cell was also determined with a microfluorometric method.

By estimating the variation in DNA and glycogen content in isolated cells obtained from endometrial samples at various phases of the menstrual cycle a parameter of proliferative activity could be correlated with one of the differentiation of endometrial cells.

CLINICAL MATERIAL AND SAMPLING OF ENDOMETRIAL CELLS

In the present study a group of five volunteers of the age between 25 and 30 years with proven fertility and regular menstrual periods was investigated. Endometrial cells were obtained by a brush technique described by *Johannisson & Engström* (1971). The instrument used in this method was a 25 cm long polyethylene catheter with a diameter of 3.5 mm enclosing a thin nylon brush. The advantage of this technique is that the catheter can be introduced into the uterine cavity without any cervical dilatation and without anaesthesia and therefore endometrial samples can be taken on frequently repeated occasions without discomfort to the patient. In the present study, however, also a biopsy was taken after the collection of the endometrial cells, in order to get a histological dating of the uterine mucosa.

Specimens were taken on cycle days 1, 6, 10, 14, 17, 22 and 27, with a variation of 1 to 2 days. Only one sample was obtained per cycle in order to minimize a possible interference with the physiological development of the uterine mucosa during the menstrual cycle. The material was grouped in the following way:

Group I, endometrial cells obtained at cycle days 1– 4
Group II   ,,   ,,   ,,   ,,   ,,   ,,   6– 7
Group III   ,,   ,,   ,,   ,,   ,,   ,, 10–11
Group IV   ,,   ,,   ,,   ,,   ,,   ,, 14
Group V   ,,   ,,   ,,   ,,   ,,   ,, 16–18
Group VI   ,,   ,,   ,,   ,,   ,,   ,, 19–23
Group VII   ,,   ,,   ,,   ,,   ,,   ,, 25–27

By using the brush technique isolated cells were removed from the uterine mucosa. The thin nylon brush was enclosed in the catheter during the passage through the cervical canal in order to avoid any contamination of cervical and vaginal cells. The endometrial cells were spread out on glass slides and immediately fixed in absolute methanol for 30 min at +4°C. The smears were then allowed to dry. One of the slides was used for the DNA determination whereas the others were kept for comparative cytochemical assays of glycogen per cell and also for conventional light-microscopical examination after staining according to Papanicolaou.

The biopsies, taken for the histological dating of the endometrium were fixed in Bouin's solution, embedded in paraffin, sectioned and stained by haematoxylin-eosin.

DETERMINATION OF NUCLEAR DNA

The DNA-content of the isolated endometrial cells was determined by Feulgen microspectrophotometry, mainly in accordance with the technique described by *Deitch* (1966).

In connection with the estimation of the nuclear DNA-content of the endometrial cells methodological studies of the optimal hydrolysis time as well as the wavelength for the maximal absorption were also performed in a standard cell population. Peripheral blood lymphocytes, representing a mitotically inactive cell population and thus providing a diploid value of the Feulgen-DNA content per cell nucleus were smeared like the endometrial cells on glass and fixed in methanol for 30 min at +4°C. The lymphocytes also served as control for the Feulgen staining reaction.

Absorption curves were recorded for the standard cell population hydrolysed for different periods of time in 1-N HCl at 60°C. The optimal time of hydrolysis was estimated to be 10 min.

The procedure employed for the Feulgen reaction was as follows:

1. After hydrolysis the smears were rinsed briefly in cold 1-N HCl and distilled water.

2. The nuclei were then stained with freshly prepared Schiff's reagent for 1 h at room temperature; during the staining procedure the smears were kept in a closed and dark container.

3. The slices were then transferred into three changes of sulphurous acid bleach for a total of 30 min.

4. The smears were rinsed for 5 min in running tap water followed by distilled water. The material was then dehydrated through graded series of alcohols and mounted from xylene in Cargille oil with a refractive index at n_D 1.550 to 1.570.

Cytophotometry

The cytophotometrical measurements were carried out using a Leitz microspectrophotometer equipped with a Leitz monochromator and a photomultiplier, type MFLK,BN 5001 T (Knott Electronic, Munich, Germany). Cells and cell constituents are inhomogeneous in concentration of the chromophore. This heterogeneity of the chromophore with the measurement area leads to a distributional error (*Patau* 1952). Several methods have been developed to reduce this error. By using *integrating scanning cytophotometers* the cell is divided into a large number of small spaced homogeneous samples. The optical density of each sample is measured and summed to give the total optical density for the cell (*Caspersson & Lomakka* 1962). By using the *plug method* (*Swift & Rasch* 1956) or its variant, the *two-area one wavelength* method (*Garcia & Iorio* 1966), the average optical density of a relatively homogeneous part of the cell is estimated and extrapolated to the whole cell area. A third method, the *two-wavelengths method* (*Ornstein* 1952; *Patau* 1952), allows the integrated optical density of the cell to be measured without any major distributional error. The principle of this method is that the entire cell nucleus is contained within the field and the transmission is measured at two wavelengths chosen to give specific absorptivities at two-to-one for the chromophore.

In the present study the *two-wavelengths method* was used. The measurements were performed according to the principles described in detail by *Ornstein* (1952) and *Patau* (1952). The accuracy of the two-wavelengths method depends upon the proper choice of wavelengths. The first step in the two-wavelengths procedure is therefore the selection of wavelengths appropriate for the Feulgen reaction chromophore. Therefore in the present study the absorption versus wavelength was estimated using the standard preparation of lymphocytes.

In each cell an area of 1.5 μm in diameter was selected, where the chromophore was relatively homogeneously distributed. The extinction $(\log \frac{I_0}{I})$ was then estimated at different wavelengths from 475 nm to 610 nm. The mean extinction values were calculated out of 20 cell nuclei and an extinction curve was prepared as shown in Fig. 1.

The maximal absorption appeared between 565 nm and 575 nm. According to the two-wavelengths method the proper choice of the two wavelengths, a and b, is based upon measurements in uniformly absorbing areas where extinction a $(E_a) = \frac{1}{2}$ extinction b (E_b). Wavelength b was set at 567 nm. Wavelength a could either be the green zone between 505 nm and 510 nm or in the red zone beyond 600 nm. Since the photomultiplier in the present investigation was less sensitive in the red zone wavelength a was set at 510 nm. The coefficient of variation for the mean extinction values at 567 nm was 1.69 % and at 510 nm 0.77 %.

The endometrial smears were then processed according to the standardized Feulgen reaction and the amount of Feulgen-positive substance was determined

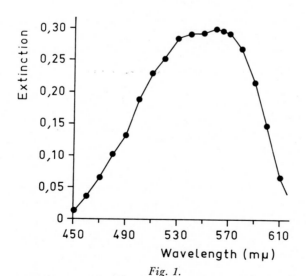

Fig. 1.
Extinction curve for the standard cell preparation of lymphocytes after hydrolysis for 10 min in 1-N HCl at 60°C and Feulgen reaction.

in a minimum of 50 cell nuclei per endometrial sample. The values obtained at the two-wavelengths were calculated according to the procedure described by *Patau* (1952) as modified by *Mendelsohn* (1966). The results were expressed in arbitrary units of DNA calculated for each nucleus measured. The measurement obtained with the standard lymphocytes served as the diploid DNA value. A histogram was prepared for each individual woman covering the complete cycle and the results were statistically analysed.

RESULTS

The minimal nuclear content of DNA corresponded to the diploid DNA values of the standard cell population of lymphocytes. As shown in Fig. 2 most of the cell nuclei obtained at cycle days 1–4 (Group I) were in this stage, *e. g.* phase G_1 (the pre-synthetic interval of the cell cycle).

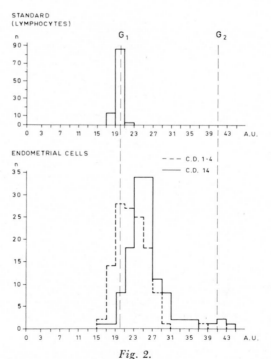

Fig. 2.

Comparison between two Feulgen-DNA histograms prepared from cycle days 1–4 and 14, respectively in the same patient (K. C.).

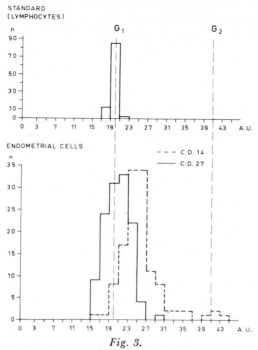

Fig. 3.

Comparison between Feulgen-DNA histograms prepared from cycle days 14 and 27, respectively, in the same patient as shown in Fig. 2.

An increased amount of absorbing material per cell nucleus was found at the time of ovulation on cycle day 14 (Group IV). In these samples a fewer number of cell nuclei were found in phase G_1 than in other phases of the cell cycle. Most of the cell nuclei were in the S-phase (the synthesizing phase) revealing a higher amount of Feulgen - reactive substance per nucleus than the diploid control value of the lymphocytes.

The findings of cycle day 14 were then compared with the results obtained at cycle days 25–27 (Group VII), as illustrated in Fig. 3.

At the premenstrual stage very few cell nuclei were found in the S-phase. The Feulgen - DNA content found in the majority of cell nuclei at cycle days 25–27 (Group VII) corresponded to the standard diploid value of DNA as well as to the content at cycle days 1–4 (Group I).

In order to estimate the variation of Feulgen - DNA per cell nucleus during the normal menstrual cycle, the mean of the values obtained from the cell nuclei in G_1-phase and S-phase was calculated in each endometrial sample and expressed in arbitrary units. These mean values are shown in Table 1.

87

Table 1.

Amount of Feulgen-DNA per nucleus (arbitrary units).

Pat.	I c. d. 1–4 Mean ± SE	II c. d. 6–7 Mean ± SE	III c. d. 10–11 Mean ± SE	IV c. d. 14 Mean ± SE	V c. d. 16–18 Mean ± SE	VI c. d. 19–23 Mean ± SE	VII c. d. 25–27 Mean ± SE
I. P.	20.43 ± 0.52	23.55 ± 0.49	19.62 ± 0.24	23.75 ± 0.46	24.97 ± 0.49	23.88 ± 0.29	21.69 ± 0.42
M. G.	23.62 ± 0.40	22.83 ± 0.50	23.21 ± 0.48	28.13 ± 0.47	25.97 ± 0.45	23.64 ± 0.42	23.51 ± 0.23
K. L.	(21.2*)	23.32 ± 0.48	22.56 ± 0.43	24.11 ± 0.40	21.20 ± 0.53	27.00 ± 0.26	18.90 ± 0.30
K. C.	20.68 ± 0.45	22.01 ± 0.36	23.79 ± 0.31	24.21 ± 0.55	23.59 ± 0.38	23.29 ± 0.35	18.38 ± 0.38
M. L. E.	22.40 ± 0.54	21.40 ± 0.37	22.24 ± 0.54	25.14 ± 0.28	26.88 ± 0.37	25.19 ± 0.39	21.90 ± 0.30
Mean	21.67	22.62	22.29	25.07	24.53	24.44	20.88

* Statistically calculated value (*Finney* 1964).

Table 2.

Factorial analysis between Feulgen-DNA values.

Cycle days (groups)	I	II	III	IV	V	VI	VII	Divisor	M.S.	F-value
(I, II, III, VII) (IV, V, VI)	−3	−3	−3	+4	+4	+4	−3	420	66.72	26.71***
(I, II, III) (IV)	−1	−1	−1	+3	0	0	0	60	30.99	12.41**
(I) (II)	−1	+1	0	0	0	0	0	10	2.26	0.90
(I) (IV)	−1	0	0	+1	0	0	0	10	28.83	11.54**
(IV, V, VI) (VII)	0	0	0	+1	+1	+1	−3	60	54.15	21.68***
(IV) (V, VI, VII)	0	0	0	+3	−1	−1	−1	60	11.93	4.78*
(IV) (V,VI)	0	0	0	+2	−1	−1	0	30	1.13	0.39
(V, VI) (VII)	0	0	0	0	+1	+1	−2	30	43.34	17.36***
(IV) (VII)	0	0	0	+1	0	0	−1	10	48.85	17.56***
(VI) (VII)	0	0	0	0	0	+1	−1	10	31.76	12.72**
Totals	108.36	113.11	111.43	125.34	122.64	122.22	104.40			

$M.S._{res}$: 2.4974.

No differential diagnosis was made between the nuclei of the glandular cells and those of the stromal cells.

An analysis of variance indicated that the variation between various phases of the cycle exceeded significantly the variation between patients ($P < 0.01$). Furthermore, a factorial analysis was performed according to the method described by *Snedecor* (1956). The results of this comparison are shown in Table 2.

As illustrated in Table 2 there is a significant statistical difference between the DNA-values obtained in groups IV, V and VI when compared with those obtained in groups I, II, III and VII ($P < 0.001$). During the proliferative phase there is a statistically significant difference between group IV and the preceding three groups I, II and III ($P < 0.01$) whereas there is no statistically significant difference between group I and II. During the secretory phase a statistically significant difference is found between group VII and groups IV, V and VI ($P < 0.001$), whereas there is no difference between groups V and VI when compared with group IV. Also between groups VI and VII there is a statistically significant difference ($P < 0.01$).

DISCUSSION

The present study indicates that there is a varying amount of Feulgen-measured DNA per cell nucleus in the human endometrium during the menstrual cycle with a statistically significant increase in Feulgen-DNA content at the late proliferative and early secretory phases.

The DNA-content of mammalian tissue has often been considered as a non-varying parameter of the cell number and therefore it has been used as a basis for the calculation of other cell constituents. The DNA content as a non-varying parameter of the cell number may be true provided the amount of DNA is estimated within a defined cell population with a statistically normal distribution of the cell division (*Davidson & Leslie* 1950; *Richterich et al.* 1961).

Histological observations of the human endometrium (*Noyes et al.* 1950) have indicated a variation of the mitotic frequency during the menstrual cycle. In the glandular cells there is an increase of the cell number during the proliferative phase and the frequency of mitoses reaches a peak at cycle day 14 of the normal 28-days cycle. A slight increase in the frequency of the mitoses of the endometrial stroma was also found at days 24 and 25 in addition to the peak at the time of ovulation (*Noyes et al.* 1950). An increased frequency of mitoses in the endometrium appears simultaneously with an increased production of oestrogens as reflected by their urinary excretion (*Brown et al.*

1959). There is therefore reason to believe that oestrogenic hormones are influencing the endometrial proliferative activity. Several animal experiments have also given support to this theory. Thus *Gorski* (1964), *Segal* (1967), *Hamilton* (1968) and *Mueller* (1968) among other investigators have demonstrated the stimulatory effect of oestrogens upon the RNA-protein synthesis. Furthermore *Leroy* (1969*a,b*) and *Leroy & Galand* (1970) reported an increased amount of Feulgen-DNA in the rat uterine mucosa between early and late oestrus. During di-oestrus the Feulgen-DNA content returned to the low values observed in pro-oestrus. However, concomitant studies by *Leroy & Galand* (1970) of the uptake of labelled thymidine in the rat endometrium showed some discrepancy when compared with the Feulgen-DNA content. These authors reported a significant decrease in the uptake of thymidine from the end of the oestrus to the first half of the di-oestrus.

The Feulgen reaction for DNA is the procedure that has been mostly used in cytophotometric studies. The reaction is considered as a reasonably specific and quantitative method for demonstrating DNA. The principle of the Feulgen reaction involves a prior acid hydrolysis of the DNA, which removes the purines and unmasks the aldehyde groups of the deoxyribofuranose sugars. The aldehydes formed react with a decolourized Schiff reagent, which is converted into its coloured form. By this reaction a specific binding to the nuclear DNA takes place *in situ* without diffusion (*Lessler* 1956; *Overend* 1949). In spite of several studies, however, there is as yet no adequate explanation of the exact mechanism by which the Schiff reagent reacts with aldehydes (*Wieland & Scheuing* 1921; *Barka & Ornstein* 1960).

Nevertheless the specificity of the Feulgen reaction for DNA is not in doubt, provided the method is rigorously standardized. The Feulgen reaction is negative after complete removal of DNA either enzymatically (*Brachet* 1946) or by extraction of the tissue with hot trichloroacetic acid (*Schneider* 1945). RNA does not give the Feulgen reaction and pretreatment with ribonuclease has no effect on the intensity of the reaction (*Barka & Dallner* 1959). Only the deoxysugars behave as true aldehydes after the removal of the purines by acid hydrolysis (*Vischer & Chargaff* 1948).

Previous reports of the DNA content in the human endometrium investigated by histochemical methods have been based upon determination of the Feulgen reactive substance in sections (*Vokaer et al.* 1953; *Wagner et al.* 1968). *Wagner et al.* (1968) studied the DNA content of human endometrial gland cells during the menstrual cycle and reported a broad distribution of DNA values between the diploid and tetraploid DNA levels in the proliferative endometrium, whereas in the late secretory endometrium a very restricted distribution of the DNA values was found. Their findings did not give any support to previous data which claimed the presence of a significant number of aneuploid cells in the human endometrium (*Timonen* 1950; *Therman &*

Timonen 1951; *Manna* 1954). However, *Wagner et al.* (1968) demonstrated a consistent difference in DNA modal values between lymphocytes and gland cells ranging up to 20 per cent. *Vokaer et al.* (1953) estimated the Feulgen DNA in sections of the human endometrium and reported variations in the content of DNA in the human uterine receptors during the menstrual cycle with an increase in late proliferative phase.

The statistically significant increase in number of endometrial cells in S-phase at the time of ovulation as found in the present study indicates a synchronization of the DNA synthesis during the menstrual cycle. Cell nuclei in G_1-phase corresponding to the standard diploid DNA value of the lymphocytes were found mainly in the premenstrual and menstrual phases. During the proliferative phase and early secretory phase an increased number of cell nuclei was found in the S-phase. These findings are to some extent in agreement with the data published by *Vokaer et al.* (1953). These investigators, however, could not make any conclusion with regard to the synchronization of the DNA synthesis.

The suggested synchronization of the DNA synthesis in the human endometrium during the menstrual cycle with an accumulation of the nuclei in S-phase between cycle days 14 and 22 could either be due to an accelerated proliferative rate or to a prolongation of the S-phase. A third possibility would be that the nuclei remained dormant in the premitotic phase (G_2). On the basis of the data presented in this study it can be excluded, however, that the main part of the nuclei should be in G_2-phase. The frequency of cell nuclei in G_2 at the time of ovulation and in the early secretory phase never exceeded 4 %.

The role of DNA-limited proteins (histones) may interfere with the picture of synchronized DNA synthesis as indicated by the present data. Recent studies have revealed the importance of an increased amount of nuclear proteins for the DNA replication (*Ringertz* 1969). The histones, rich in arginine and histidine, have been shown to increase in synchrony with DNA synthesis (*Ringertz* 1969). On the other hand it has been demonstrated by *Hamilton* (1968) that chromatin isolated from the uterine tissue of normal rats in oestrus had an increased DNA template capacity but contained significantly less histone than that in di-oestrus. Further studies of the deoxyribonucleo-protein complex in the human endometrial cells during the menstrual cycle are required therefore in order to clarify the influence of oestrogen and progesterone on the synchrony of synthetic nuclear processes.

Quantitative cytochemical methods for the estimation of glycogen in the human endometrium have not been reported as yet. However, there is a microspectrophotometric method for glycogen determination in isolated cells based upon the periodic acid-Schiff (PAS) reaction (*Gahrton* 1964, 1966). This absorption method has been applied to PAS stained neutrophil leukocytes. The glycogen in these cells is relatively homogeneously distributed, which allows a microspectrophotometric registration of the absorption using the scanning technique. To study cells with a more irregularly distributed glycogen in their cytoplasm other techniques have been developed. One of these methods is fluorescence cytophotometry which allows quantitative estimation of inhomogeneously distributed glycogen in cells (*Yataghanas et al.* 1969). The technique is based upon the reaction of glycogen with fluorescent Schiff-type reagents (*Kasten et al.* 1959; *Kasten* 1961; *Burns & Neame* 1936) and it has been successfully applied to certain types of blood and bone marrow cells. In the present study the microfluorometric method (F-PAS) described by *Yataghanas et al.* (1969) was used in order to estimate the glycogen deposit in the human endometrial cells during the menstrual cycle.

The same material as used for the DNA determination was studied. Simultaneously with the sampling of the endometrial cells a standard was prepared from normal neutrophil leukocytes separated from peripheral blood. The leukocytes were smeared and fixed in methanol for 30 min at +4°C, dried and stored until control for the staining reaction.

The staining procedure was performed according to the method described by *Yataghanas et al.* (1969). The fluorescent dye, 2,5 bis (4′aminophenyl - 1) 1,3,4 oxdiazol (BAO), Ciba, Basle, Switzerland was used (*Ruch* 1966). A 0.01 % (w/v) stock solution of BAO in distilled water was prepared. This was kept at +4°C for a maximum of one month. Immediately before staining 1 ml 1-N HCl and 0.5 ml of 10 % freshly prepared $Na_2S_2O_5$ were added to 10 ml of the BAO solution. After mixing, the resulting Schiff-type reagent was rapidly filtered.

1. The slides were immersed in a freshly prepared 0.5 % periodic acid solution for 60 min.

2. The slides were rinsed in three baths of distilled water, 1 min each.

3. The cells were then incubated in the BAO - Schiff reagent for 100 min.

4. The slides were transferred into two changes of sulphurous acid, 3 min each.

5. The material was rinsed for 5 min in running tap water.

During the staining procedure the smears were kept in a closed and dark container. After staining the smears were allowed to dry, after which they were stored in dark before measurement.

Microfluorometry

A Leitz microfluorometer was used, which was equipped with an Opak-illuminator Type Ploem, constructed for incident excitation light. A Xenon high-pressure lamp XBO 75 (Osram) fed from a stabilizer (Type Knott Electronic, Munich, Germany) served as the light source for the excitation. The wavelength suitable for the excitation light was estimated to be 365 nm and the emission was measured at 430 nm. The filter combination used in the present study was as follows:

Excitation filters, 4 mm BG 38 + 2 × 2 mm UG 1; barrier filters, K 400 + K 430. The following optics were used: Objective, Leitz achromat 54 × (Oil immersion) with the numerical aperture 0.95, combined with Opak-illuminator Type Ploem (Leitz GmBH, Wetzlar, Germany). The emitted light intensities were measured by a photomultiplier-amplifier, Type MFLK, BN 5001 T (Knott Electronic, Munich, Germany) fed from an ultrastabilized high-voltage supply (Knott Electronic, Munich, Germany). The background fluorescence from the microscopic field was suppressed by a diaphragm in a place where it could regulate the size of the measuring field.

Neutrophil leukocytes were used for the standardization of the micro-fluorometric method. They were stained with three different concentrations of BAO, 0.01 %, 0.001 % and 0.0001 %. Prior to the fluorescence measurements the smears were mounted under coverslips using a nonfluorescent immersion oil ($n_D = 1.516$) as the mounting medium. In order to investigate the variation in fluorescence intensity following the exposure to the excitation light the fluorescence yield was recorded at different times of illumination. As shown in Fig. 4 there was a rather rapid fading of the fluorescence during the first 3 min of illumination. However, after three to four min of illumination a certain degree of stability in the fluorescence yield of the leukocytes was found. The error due to fading was minimized by measuring the fluorescence exactly 4 min after excitation.

The data illustrated in Fig. 4 are based upon the mean values obtained from the measurements of 20 leukocytes for each BAO concentration. As also shown in Table 3 the fluorescence yield at different times of illumination depended upon the concentration of BAO.

The coefficient of variation of the mean values was less among the leukocytes stained by the highest concentration of BAO (0.01 %) at any time of illumination than among the leukocytes stained by the two lower BAO concentrations. Therefore, 0.01 % BAO was consistently used.

The influence on fluorescence intensity by storing the preparations in dark after staining was also investigated. As illustrated in Fig. 5 there was no significant difference between leukocytes stored for 48 h and those stored for 168 h.

In order to study the specificity of the reaction, the influence of diastase

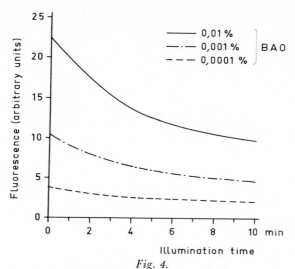

Fig. 4.

Fluorescence fading during illumination in standard preparations of leukocytes stained
with three different concentrations of BAO.

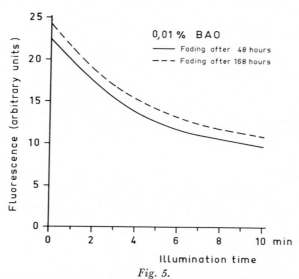

Fig. 5.

Fluorescence fading during illumination in standard preparations of leukocytes stored
in the dark for 48 and 168 h, respectively, after staining with BAO.

Table 3.

BAO-fluorescence intensity of the standard preparation of human leukocytes at different concentrations of BAO and at different times of illumination, expressed in arbitrary units.

Time min	0.01 % BAO			0.001 % BAO			0.0001 % BAO		
	Mean	S.D.	C.V.	Mean	S.D.	C.V.	Mean	S.D.	C.V.
–	22.43	2.42	10.8 %	10.41	1.17	11.2 %	3.75	0.39	10.4 %
1	19.73	2.02	10.2 %	9.10	1.16	12.7 %	3.28	0.44	13.4 %
2	16.97	1.54	9.1 %	7.78	0.96	12.3 %	2.97	0.36	12.1 %
3	15.15	1.35	8.9 %	7.06	1.00	14.2 %	2.75	0.37	13.5 %
4	13.74	1.24	9.0 %	6.35	0.81	12.8 %	2.63	0.39	14.8 %
5	12.60	1.25	9.9 %	5.91	0.83	14.0 %	2.47	0.42	17.0 %
6	11.78	0.96	8.1 %	5.56	0.83	14.9 %	2.38	0.44	18.5 %
7	11.12	1.08	9.7 %	5.28	0.76	14.4 %	2.25	0.38	16.9 %
8	10.58	1.13	10.7 %	5.00	0.74	14.8 %	2.22	0.45	20.3 %
9	10.13	1.12	11.1 %	4.78	0.77	16.1 %	2.16	0.43	19.9 %
10	9.68	1.09	11.3 %	4.60	0.76	16.5 %	2.06	0.38	18.4 %

was also assessed. A diastase concentration of 1 mg/ml and a digestion time of 16 h at room temperature was used. More than 50 % of the stainable material was thereby removed.

The endometrial cells were stained by the 0.01 % concentration of BAO together with a standard cell population of leukocytes, which served as control. During the time of illumination, which was estimated to be 4 min, each cell was photographed and its position on the slide was registered. After the micro-fluorometric measurements of the cells a planimetric study was performed on the photographed material and the area of each cell was calculated. Subsequently the cells were identified as either glandular cells or stromal cells.

RESULTS

As illustrated in Fig. 6 there was a certain variation in the amount of glycogen per cell during the menstrual cycle.

No variation was found among the stromal cells, whereas the glandular cells displayed a considerable increase of glycogen during the late proliferative

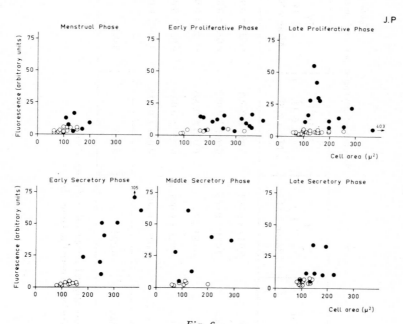

Fig. 6.

Distribution of glycogen per μm^2 in stromal and glandular cells during the menstrual cycle in a representative case.

97

Table 4.

Amount of glycogen per μm^2 in stromal cells (arbitrary units).

Pat.	I c. d. 1–4 Mean ± SE	II–III[1] c. d. 6–11 Mean ± SE	IV c. d. 14 Mean ± SE	V c. d. 16–18 Mean ± SE	VI c. d. 19–23 Mean ± SE	VII c. d. 25–27 Mean ± SE
I. P.	0.035 ± 0.003	0.022 ± 0.003	0.025 ± 0.002	0.024 ± 0.002	0.036 ± 0.005	0.047 ± 0.005
M. G.	0.024 ± 0.005	0.028 ± 0.002	0.033 ± 0.003	0.027 ± 0.005	0.029 ± 0.003	0.019 ± 0.003
K. L.	(0.022*)	0.025 ± 0.003	0.025 ± 0.003	0.028 ± 0.011	0.017 ± 0.001	0.020 ± 0.001
K. C.	0.021 ± 0.004	0.025 ± 0.005	0.027 ± 0.002	0.022 ± 0.005	0.027 ± 0.004	0.026 ± 0.005
M. L. E.	0.028 ± 0.008	0.025 ± 0.003	0.029 ± 0.003	0.032 ± 0.003	0.028 ± 0.003	0.020 ± 0.002
Mean	0.026	0.025	0.028	0.027	0.027	0.026

* Statistically calculated value (*Finney* 1964).

[1] Insufficient material in Group II.

Table 5.
Amount of glycogen per μm^2 in glandular cells (arbitrary units).

Pat.	I c. d. 1–4 Mean ± SE	II–III[1] c. d. 6–11 Mean ± SE	IV c. d. 14 Mean ± SE	V c. d. 16–18 Mean ± SE	VI c. d. 19–23 Mean ± SE	VII c. d. 25–27 Mean ± SE
I. P.	0.060 ± 0.015	0.042 ± 0.007	0.144 ± 0.035	0.154 ± 0.030	0.227 ± 0.075	0.101 ± 0.026
M. G.	0.104 ± 0.024	0.070 ± 0.012	0.248 ± 0.043	0.114 ± 0.044	0.075 ± 0.015	0.033 ± 0.006
K. C.	(0.050*)	0.079 ± 0.013	0.089 ± 0.018	0.255 ± 0.023	0.045 ± 0.008	0.044 ± 0.008
K. L.	0.047 ± 0.007	0.172 ± 0.084	0.135 ± 0.051	0.132 ± 0.013	0.056 ± 0.015	0.033 ± 0.007
M. L. E.	0.088 ± 0.013	0.098 ± 0.032	0.185 ± 0.040	0.318 ± 0.018	0.137 ± 0.036	0.066 ± 0.013
Mean	0.070	0.092	0.160	0.195	0.108	0.055

* Statistically calculated value (*Finney* 1964).
[1] Insufficient material in Group II.

99

7*

Table 6.

Factorial analysis between glycogen values in glandular cells.

Cycle days (groups)	I	II-III[1]	IV	V	VI	VII	Divisor	M.S.	F-value
(IV, V, VI) (I, II, III, VII)	−3	−3	+3	+3	+3	−3	270	0.0569	14.21 ***
(V) (I, II-III, IV, VI, VII)	−1	−1	−1	+5	−1	−1	150	0.0422	10.550***
(I, II-III) (IV)	−1	−1	+2	0	0	0	30	0.0253	6.322**
(II-III) (V, VI)	0	−2	0	+1	+1	0	30	0.0187	4.670**
(V) (VI, VII)	0	0	0	+2	−1	−1	30	0.0425	10.622***
(V, VI) (VII)	0	0	0	+1	+1	−2	30	0.0307	7.664***
(IV) (V)	0	0	−1	+1	0	0	10	0.0029	0.740
(V) (VI)	0	0	0	+1	−1	0	10	0.0185	4.687**
(VI) (VII)	0	0	0	0	+1	−1	10	0.0069	1.729
Totals	0.349	0.382	0.801	0.973	0.540	0.277			

M.S.$_{res.}$: 0.004.

[1] Insufficient material in Group II.

and early secretory phase. In two out of the five cases an increased deposit of glycogen in the glandular cells was found already in the early proliferative phase. During the middle secretory phase and in the premenstrual endometrium a decrease in glycogen content per cell area was found.

The amount of glycogen per μm^2, expressed in arbitrary units was estimated in the stromal cells as well as in the glandular cells. In Table 4 the mean values of the amount of glycogen per μm^2 in the stromal cells are given.

An analysis of variance of the amount of glycogen in the stromal cells verified the fact that there was no significant variation between the phases of the cycle.

In Table 5 the mean values of the amount of glycogen per μm^2 in the glandular cells are indicated.

A subsequent analysis of variance revealed a statistically significant variation between the phases of the menstrual cycle $(P = 0.01)$ which exceeded significantly the variation among the patients. A factorial analysis, as illustrated in Table 6, indicated that there was a statistically significant difference $(P < 0.001)$ between the amount of glycogen per μm^2 in the glandular cells in groups IV, V and VI compared with that in groups I, II, III and VII.

Furthermore, in the proliferative phase there was a significantly higher amount of glycogen per μm^2 at cycle day 14 (Group IV) than in earlier stages $(P < 0.01)$. No significant contrast was found between groups IV and V, representing late proliferative and early secretory phases, respectively. However, in the secretory phase the difference between group V and groups VI and VII was statistically highly significant $(P < 0.001)$. No difference was found between groups VI and VII.

A regression analysis revealed that the amount of glandular glycogen increased in the proliferative and early secretory phases from c. d. 1 to c. d. 17 with a slope of 0.0079 ± 0.0022. This was followed by a decrease in the secretory phase from c. d. 17 to c. d. 27 with a slope of -0.0139 ± 0.0042. No evidence of deviation from linearity was found.

DISCUSSION

In the present study significant increase of glycogen per μm^2 was found in the glandular cells of the human endometrium during late proliferative and early secretory phases as estimated by microfluorometry and expressed in arbitrary units. On the other hand no significant change in the amount of glycogen per μm^2 was found in the stromal cells.

Previous biochemical studies indicated a significant increase in endometrial glycogen between days 14 and 21 of the normal cycle with a peak at cycle day 17 (*Arronet & Latour* 1957; *Hagerman & Villee* 1953; *Payne & Latour* 1955). These findings are in agreement with the results of most (qualitative) histochemical studies (*McKay et al.* 1956; *Schmidt-Matthiesen* 1963; *Filipe* 1968; *Choi* 1966). Also electron microscopical studies have revealed an increased cytoplasmic deposit of glycogen in the glandular cells between c. d. 14 and c. d. 20 (*Nilsson* 1962*a,b*; *Themann & Schünke* 1963; *Wynn* 1967*a,b*; *Cavazos et al.* 1967; *Colville* 1968).

In the present study the glycogen content of the isolated endometrial glandular cells displayed a gradual increase from the first day of the cycle to the 16–18 days of the cycle. From this period the amount of glycogen per μm^2 decreased significantly. It is most likely that the deposit of glycogen in the cytoplasm starts at the time when there is an increasing ovarian production of oestrogens. The influence of progesterone upon the deposit of glycogen in the endometrium can not be clearly assessed on the basis of the present study. However, the interference of progesterone with the oestrogen action on the carbohydrate metabolism reported in rat endometrium by *Schmidt et al.* (1967) may also be reflected in the human endometrium by a decreasing deposit of glycogen in the glandular cells during middle and late secretory phase.

In contrast to the glandular cells the glycogen content of the stromal cells was constant throughout the cycle. This indicates that glycogen deposition in these cells is not appreciably influenced by the cyclic variation in the secretion of ovarian hormones.

CONCLUSIONS

As illustrated in Fig. 7 the Feulgen-DNA pattern of the human endometrial cells during the menstrual cycle differs from that of glycogen in the glandular cells.

The concomitant increase in Feulgen-DNA and glycogen during the proliferative phase from c. d. 11 to c. d. 14 may reflect the ability of oestrogens to stimulate the growth of the endometrial cells simultaneously with a gradual differentiation as estimated by registration of the deposit of glycogen in the cytoplasm of the glandular cells. From c. d. 14 to c. d. 23 most of the endometrial cells remain in the DNA-synthesizing phase, whereas the deposit of glycogen in the glandular cells reaches its maximum at cycle days 16–19. Thus the Feulgen-DNA values remain at a high level from c. d. 17 to 23 in spite of a significant drop in the glycogen deposit per individual glandular cell.

It should be emphasized, however, that the Feulgen-DNA was estimated in a mixture of stromal and glandular cells since no identification of the different types of cell nuclei could be performed with the methods used in the

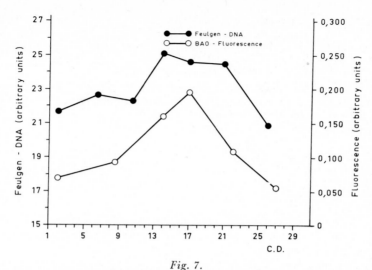

Fig. 7.

Feulgen-DNA in non-identified endometrial cells and glycogen deposit in glandular
cells during the normal menstrual cycle. Mean values of 5 women.

present study. Further investigations will be needed to find out whether or
not the variation in Feulgen-DNA per nucleus in stromal cells differs from
that in glandular cells.

From the present data no significant conclusion can be drawn about the
possible inhibiting effect of progesterone upon DNA synthesis and glycogen
deposit in the human endometrium. Further studies will be required to assess
the separate effects of 17β-oestradiol and progesterone, respectively, as well
as their influence when given sequentially. The effect of the increased secretion of 17α-hydroxyprogesterone at mid-cycle (*Lipsett* 1970) as well as the
influence of synthetic progestogens also deserve further investigation.

ACKNOWLEDGMENTS

The expert technical assistance of Miss Brit Östberg, Mrs. Ulla-Britta Edqvist and
Mrs. Pia Lagerhed is gratefully acknowledged. We are also indebted to Dr. P. Petrusz
for assistance with the statistical analysis.

The expenses of this investigation were defrayed by Research Grants from the Ford
Foundation, Swedish Medical Research Council (K69-12X-2712-01 and B70-12X-2712-
02) and from the Swedish International Development Authority.

REFERENCES

Arronet G. H. & Latour J. P. A.: J. clin. Endocr. *17* (1957) 261.

Atkin N. B., Richards B. M. & Ross A. J.: Brit. J. Cancer *13* (1959) 773.

Atkin N. B. & Richards B. M.: Brit. J. Cancer *10* (1956) 796.

Barka T. & Dallner G.: J. Histochem. Cytochem. *7* (1959) 409.

Barka T. & Ornstein L.: J. Histochem. Cytochem. *8* (1960) 208.

Brachet J.: Experientia (Basel) *2* (1946) 142.

Brown J. B.: Klopper A. & Loraine J. A.: J. Endocr. *17* (1958) 401.

Burns J. & Neame B. P.: Blood *28* (1936) 674.

Caspersson T. O. & Lomakka G. M.: Ann. N. Y. Acad. Sci. *97* (1962) 449.

Cavazos F., Green J. A., Hall D. G. & Lucas F. V.: Amer. J. Obstet. Gynec. *97* (1967) 833.

Choi H. Y.: Yonsei Med. J. *7* (1966) 7.

Colville E. A.: J. Obstet. Gynaec. Brit. Comm. *75* (1968) 342.

Davidson J. N. & Leslie I. A.: Nature (Lond.) *165* (1950) 49.

Deitch A. D. In: Wied G. L., Ed. Introduction to quantitative cytochemistry, Academic Press: New York (1966) 327.

Filipe M. I.: J. Path. Bact. *95* (1968) 243.

Finney D. J.: 2nd Ed. Statistical Methods in Biological Assay, Hafner Publishing Co., New York (1964).

Gahrton G.: Exp. Cell Res. *34* (1964) 488.

Gahrton G.: Quantitative cytochemical studies on normal and leukemic leukocytes with special reference to the PAS-reaction. Thesis, Balder: Stockholm (1966).

Garcia A. M. & Iorio R. In: Wied G. L., Ed. Introduction to quantitative cytochemistry. Academic Press: New York (1966) 239.

Gorski J.: J .biol. Chem. *239* (1964) 889.

Hagerman D. D. & Villee C. A.: Endocrinology *53* (1953) 667.

Hale A. J. & Wilson S. J.: J. Path. Bact. *77* (1959) 605.

Hale A. J. & Wilson S. J.: J. Path. Bact. *82* (1961) 483.

Hale A. J.: J. Path. Bact. *85* (1963) 311.

Hamilton T. H.: Science *161* (1968) 649.

Johannisson E. & Engström L.: Acta obstet. gynec. scand. In press.

Kasten F. H.: Histochemie *1* (1959) 466.

Kasten F. H., Burton V. & Glover P.: Nature (Lond.) *184* (1959) 1797.

Kasten F. H.: J. Histochem. Cytochem. *9* (1961) 599.

Leroy F.: Rev. Franc. Etud. Clin. Biol. *12* (1967a) 902.

Leroy F.: Ann. Endocr. (Paris) *28* (1967b) 699.

Leroy F. & Galand P.: J. Reprod. Fertil. *21* (1970) 203.

Lessler M. A.: J. Histochem. Cytochem. *4* (1956) 36.

Leuchtenberger C. & Leuchtenberger R.: Biochem. Pharmacol. *4* (1960) 128.

Lipsett M. B.: Acta endocr. (Kbh.) Suppl. *147* (1970) 155.

Manna G. K.: Nature (Lond.) *173* (1954) 271.

McKay H., Hertig A. T., Bardavil W. A. & Velardo J. T.: Obstet. and Gynec. *8* (1956) 140.

Mendelsohn M. L. In: Wied G. L., Ed. Introduction to quantitative cytochemistry. Academic Press: New York (1966) 201.

Mueller G. C. In: Karlsson P., Ed. Mechanism of Hormone action. Thieme Stuttgart (1965). Academic Press: New York (1965) 228.

Nilsson O.: J. Ultrastructure Res. *6* (1962a) 413.

Nilsson O.: J. Ultrastructure Res. 6 (1962b) 422.

Noyes R. W., Hertig A. T. & Rock J.: Fertil. and Steril. 1 (1950) 3.

Ornstein L.: Lab. Invest. 1 (1952) 250.

Overend W. G. & Stacey M.: Nature (Lond.) 163 (1949) 538.

Patau K.: Chromosoma 5 (1952) 341.

Payne H. W. & Latour J. P.: J. clin. Endocr. 15 (1955) 1106.

Perugini S., Torelli V. & Soldati M.: Experientia (Basel) 13 (1957) 441.

Richterich R., Schafroth P., Colombo J. P. & Temperli F.: Klin. Schr. 39 (1961) 987.

Ringertz N. R. In: Lima -de-Faria A., Ed. Handbook of Molecular Cytology, North Holland Publish. Comp.; Amsterdam (1969) 656.

Ruch F. In: Wied G. L. and Bahr G. F., Eds. Introduction to quantitative cytochemistry II. Academic Press: New York and London (1970) 431.

Schmidt H., Berle P. & Voigt K. D.: Acta endocr. (Kbh.) 61 (1969) 729.

Schmidt-Matthiesen H. In: Schmidt-Matthiesen H., Ed. Das normale menschliche Endometrium. Thieme: Stuttgart (1963) 149.

Schneider W. C.: J. biol. Chem. 161 (1945) 293.

Segal S. & Scher W. In: Wynn R. M., Ed. Cellular Biology of the Uterus. North Holland Publish. Comp.: Amsterdam (1967) 114.

Snedecor G. W.: Statistical methods, The Iowa State University Press: Ames (1956).

Swift H. & Rasch E. In: Oster G. and Pollister A. W., Eds. Physical Techniques in Biological Research Vol. 3, Academic Press: New York (1956) 353.

Therman E. & Timonen S.: Hereditas 37 (1951) 266.

Themann H. & Schünke W. In: Schmidt-Matthiesen H., Ed. Das normale menschliche Endometrium, Thieme: Stuttgart (1963) 111.

Timonen S.: Acta obstet. gynec. scand. Suppl. 81 (1950).

Wagner D., Richart R. M. & Terner J. Y.: Amer. J. Obstet. Gynec. 100 (1968) 90.

Vischer E .& Chargaff E.: J. biol. Chem. 176 (1948) 715.

Wieland H. & Scheuing G.: Ber. 54 (1921) 2527.

Vokaer R., Gompel C. & Ghilain A.: Nature (Lond.) 172 (1953) 31.

Wynn R. M. & Harris J. A.: Fertil. and Steril. 18 (1967a) 632.

Wynn R. M. & Wolley R. S.: Fertil. and Steril. 18 (1967b) 721.

Yataghanas X., Gahrton G. & Thorell B.: Exp. Cell Res. 56 (1969) 59.

DISCUSSION

Ferin: Can you distinguish between surface epithelial cells and glandular cells? Indeed, they do not have the same cycle.

Johannisson: The point is well taken. The preparation technique used in this study does not allow us to distinguish between surface epithelial cells and glandular cells. However, we have identified columnal cells and non-columnal cells, and the stromal cells do not have any columnal appearance. Studies are now in progress in order to isolate different types of cells of the human endometrium. We hope that these studies will provide possibility to study the cellular metabolism in different types of endometrial cells during the menstrual cycle.

Graham: On cycle day 14, roughly 60 per cent of your Feulgen-DNA values seem to fall within the S phase values. Do you have any other evidence, such as thymidine labelling, to confirm that figure?

Johannisson: So far we have not been able to do any studies with labelled thymidine, but it would be interesting, of course, to see in cell cultures how the incorporation of labelled thymidine would appear in this case.

Graham: It would be one of the highest figures reported for an adult tissue.

Lerner: Dr. Johannisson, I wonder if you have any data on IUD's on those parameters?

Johannisson: We are right now investigating the effect of IUD's on the DNA synthesis and on the deposit of glycogen in human endometrial cells, but so far we have no definite results.

Stumpf: Your clinical data regarding the oestrogen effect agree well with those obtained in the rat by *Epifanova* (1966), who obtained a 4-fold increase of the labelling index in the rat endometrium after oestradiol application. Regarding the opposing effect of progesterone to oestradiol, I may mention the studies of Dr. *C. Tachi* (personal communication), who found that [³H] uridine incorporation into uterine epithelium cells is stimulated by oestradiol but counteracted by progesterone.

Hamberger: You seem to interpret your results when you have demonstrated a variation in glycogen content during various phases of the cycle as due to changes in the steroid levels. Couldn't it be so that the variations in the gonadotrophic levels could influence the glycogen content of your cells?

Johannisson: In the present study, unfortunately, we did not measure the output of gonadotrophins. If, however, we compare our data with the findings in an atrophic endometrium in the menopause, where you have high levels of gonadotrophins, you will not find any similar changes in the endometrium. So it is hard to believe that the gonadotrophins would be responsible for this increased amount of glycogen.

Lunenfeld: I am concerned about your values on day 14, because day 14 could be preovulatory, ovulatory, or postovulatory. I wonder whether, in these cases, you have any idea from other parameters as to when ovulation presumably occurred?

Johannisson: As I said, unfortunately, we did not follow the output of LH in these patients, but according to histological and clinical data, ovulation had taken place in all the cases investigated.

Lunenfeld: That means that for you day 14 was postovulatory?

Johannisson: Using conventional histological methods, if you take a specimen on cycle day 14, even if you have had an ovulation, you will find a proliferative, or highly proliferative endometrium, and the morphological signs of a secretory activity in the endometrium will not appear until cycle day 16 or 17.

Wira: Have you studied DNA and glycogen content in women using oral contraceptives?

Johannisson: Such studies are in progress.

Lerner: Fig. 7 (p. 103) of this paper demonstrates an increase in endometrial glycogen and DNA during the first part of the cycle. This part of the cycle is believed to be under oestrogenic dominance, indeed oestrogens have a stimulatory effect on glycogen deposition.

After day 17 of the cycle, the glycolytic pathway is increased; at the same time your figure shows a plateau in DNA content. This suggests that perhaps another pathway, the pentose phosphate shunt, might be activated because of the increasing needs of ribose for DNA synthesis. A conclusion might be that glycogen is degraded through different pathways.

Since studies have not yet been done on the glucose-glycogen turnover in human endometrium, it is difficult to know whether glycogen is decreasing because of a diminished deposition in the early secretory phase, or because of an increased degradation through other pathways. Is this due to progesterone or to progesterone plus other factors?

I believe that this reflects an increased utilization of glycogen.

Dr. Hamberger, your data are based on the action of gonadotrophins upon lactic acid production; it is difficult to conclude that progesterone alone is acting at this point, producing a drop in glycogen, since other factors may be involved.

Schmidt-Matthiesen (1963), *Fuhrmann* (1963) and *Luh & Brandau* (1967) suggested that during prenidation, the glycogen content in the endometrium remains high because of the energy requirement of the egg, and it remains high in spite of the progesterone present.

The factor(s) or the regulatory mechanisms which maintain glycogen at a constant level and which are eventually responsible for its reduction are not well understood.

Ferin: I have a great experience with artificial cycles in ovariectomized women. Giving progesterone, or a progestational drug to an oestrogen-primed castrated woman regularly produces a dramatic increase in glycogen deposition. This increase begins to be obvious 14 hours after the start of a progesterone perfusion (*Ferin et al.* 1955). In cycling women, a significant increase in glycogen deposition occurs on day $+1$ (day 0 corresponds to the plasma LH peak) thus before ovulation, when progesterone is already increasing in plasma (*Delforge et al.* 1970).

Lunenfeld: In trying to relate the glycogen and DNA data to steroids, I have some difficulties.

If one assumes that there is no significant difference in glycogen content between days one and nine (Fig. 7) and the increase in glycogen content was first found on day 14 (*i. e.* postovulatory), then one could attribute this to the action of progesterone. This is first substantiated by the fact that the glycogen content continues to rise till day 17.

As to the DNA, I feel that here also the data do not permit any definite correlation.

Johannisson: In the early secretory phase, we have a peak between cycle days 16 and 18 in the deposit of glycogen in the glandular cells. Whether or not the progesterone is responsible for this peak, we do not know. However, when the progesterone has reached a certain level in the blood, there is a drop in the deposit of glycogen per cell. It is difficult to say if it is really an effect of progesterone.

Ferin: This drop could be due to the excretion of glycogen in the lumen of the glands.

Nakane: It is commonly known that glycogen depletes rapidly within the cells when they start to undergo mitosis. Isn't that glycogen depletion just a simple indication of mitotic activity?

Johannisson: From cycle day 14 to the mid-secretory phase, the majority of the endo metrial cell nuclei remained in S phase. However, some of these cells were in G_2 phase. The G_2 phase is much shorter – probably more difficult to get in the sample. The number of cells in G_2 phase was never exceeding 4 per cent from cycle day 14 to cycle day 23, but we had quite a lot of cells in S phase. According to these data, most cells were going to divide between cycle day 14 and cycle days 16–17, and there was no difference in the amounts of cells in G_2 phase in this period compared to the following period (cycle days 16–17 to cycle day 23).

Eshkol: Have you tried to do any similar study in patients receiving oestrogens and progesterone as a sequential contraceptive? I think that the correlation in such a planned experiment would be much easier.

Johannisson: We have studies in progress to investigate the specific effect of oestrogens and progesterone as well as that of synthetic steroids on the human endometrium.

References:

Delforge J. P., Thomas K. & Ferin J.: Acta Europaea Fertilitatis 2 (1970) 141.
Epifanova O. I.: Exptl. Cell Res. 42 (1966) 562.
Ferin J., Bonte J. & Vassilopoulos J.: Boll. Soc. roy. belge Gynéc. Obstét. 25 (1955) 265.
Fuhrmann K. In: Schmidt-Matthiesen H., Ed. Das normale menschliche Endometrium. Thieme Verlag, Stuttgart (1963) 269.
Luh W. & Brandau H.: Geburtsh. Gynäk. 168 (1967) 14.
Schmidt-Matthiesen H. In: Schmidt-Matthiesen H., Ed. Das normale menschliche Endometrium. Thieme Verlag, Stuttgart (1963) 149.

Carcinogenesis Program, Biology Division, Oak Ridge National Laboratory, Oak Ridge, Tennessee 37830, U. S. A.

ASSESSMENT OF HORMONE ACTION IN CULTURED CELLS*

By

Kai-Lin Lee and Francis T. Kenney

ABSTRACT

Corticosteroids effect a rapid and marked increase in the enzyme tyrosine transaminase in cultured cells of the Reuber or H-35 hepatoma. This change is comparable in all essential aspects to changes in the livers of rats treated with the same hormones. Methods of cell culture and of biochemical analysis designed to determine the mechanism of steroid action on cultured cells are described.

In 1964, *Pitot et al.* reported success in adapting cells of the Reuber or H-35 minimal deviation hepatoma to tissue culture, and they found that induction of the enzyme tyrosine transaminase by adrenal steroids could be observed in such cultures (*Pitot et al.* 1964). The same aspect of the action of steroid hormones has been studied intensively in rats, beginning with the demonstration by *Lin & Knox* (1957) that tyrosine transaminase is selectively and quickly increased in liver after glucocorticoid treatment. A brief review of this *in vivo* work has been given recently by *Kenney* (1970). Assessment of hormone action at the molecular level in animals suffers from many difficulties, including the obvious one that effects observed may be several steps removed from the primary event triggered by an administered hormone. This and other complexities are largely obviated by experimentation with the steroid-responsive,

---

* Research jointly sponsored by the National Cancer Institute, National Institutes of Health, and the United States Atomic Energy Commission under contract with the Union Carbide Corporation.

permanent cell line developed by *Pitot et al.* Accordingly, we have turned to cultured H-35 cells in our continuing study of the mechanisms involved in induction of enzyme synthesis by steroid hormones. This report describes some of the methods we have developed in our work which should be of value in the assessment of similar aspects of hormone action in other experimental systems, and presents our interpretation of the results we have obtained.

Cell culture

Unlike cells of the similar HTC cell line (*Tomkins et al.* 1966) H-35 cells do not grow in suspension culture but must maintain contact with suitable surfaces of culture flasks in order to grow. H-35 cells can be maintained in suspension culture, and hydrocortisone will induce tyrosine transaminase under these conditions (*Reel et al.* 1970). We have used »monolayer« cultures (*i. e.*, cells growing on surfaces of culture flasks) in most of our experimentation so we shall describe them here.

To initiate a growth cycle, cells from stationary phase cultures are scraped into their growth medium and packed by a brief centrifugation. After suspension in fresh growth medium, aliquots containing $1 - 3 \times 10^5$ cells (determined by Coulter or hemocytometer counting) are transferred to fresh flasks (Falcon, 75 cm²) together with 10 ml of growth medium, made up of Eagle's Basal Medium (BME) enriched by addition of the constitutive amino acids and vitamins to 4 times their concentration in the basal medium, and supplemented with 20 % foetal calf serum and 5 % calf serum. Although not essential, a mixture of penicillin and streptomycin (1000 units and 1000 μg per flask, respectively) is usually added as well. The medium is replaced by fresh medium every 4 days. Under these conditions H-35 cells grow as »monolayers« with a doubling time of about 24 hours; stationary phase is reached after 9 days of growth (Fig. 1).

The response to hydrocortisone does not differ significantly in log phase or stationary phase cells. For most experiments we have used cells in the 8th day of growth. At that time the enriched medium is replaced by BME without addition of sera or additional vitamins and amino acids. H-35 cells do not grow in serum-free BME but will resume growth on readdition of serum after as long as 6 days in its absence. The cells are left on unenriched BME for 24 hours before experiments are initiated; this ensures that all cells are in interphase and also reduces intracellular amino acid pools to levels which permit introduction of labelled amino acids without excessive dilution.

Kinetics of enzyme induction

The basic technique in all our experiments is an assay of tyrosine trans-

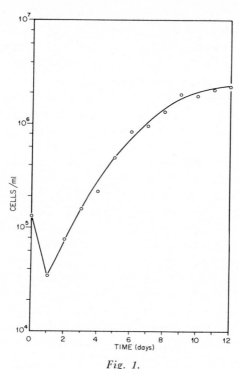

Fig. 1.
Growth curve of H-35 hepatoma cells in monolayer culture (from *Reel et al.* 1970).

aminase content of cells as a function of time after addition of inducing hormone to the medium, or after some other treatment. For example, Fig. 2 shows kinetic measurements of transaminase activity after addition and withdrawal of hydrocortisone. Hydrocortisone (10^{-6} M) is added at zero time (Fig. 2A) to a group of flasks prepared as described above. Prior to and at intervals after this addition, flasks are removed from the incubator, and the cells are scraped into the medium, centrifuged, and washed with 0.15 M NaCl. Cells are suspended in 0.15 M KCl-0.001 M EDTA-0.005 M α-ketoglutarate (1 ml per flask) and then lysed by freezing and thawing 3 times, alternating between liquid N_2 and a 37°C bath. Homogenates are centrifuged at $100\,000 \times g$ for 35 minutes, and the clear supernatant solutions, containing more than 90 % of the transaminase, are used for transaminase assay by the procedure of *Diamondstone* (1966) and protein determination by the method of *Lowry et al.* (1951). In Fig. 2B are presented similar measurements made after hormone withdrawal. This is accomplished by pipetting off the hormone-containing

111

medium, washing the cell »monolayer« 3 times with Hank's balanced salt solution (5 ml per flask), and restoring 10 ml of BME.

The points and broken lines of Fig. 2 represent experimental data obtained after these manipulations. We have compared the curves with theoretical curves derived from mathematical treatment of the model shown in Fig. 3 (*Hoel* 1970). Since the degradation rates λ_1 and λ_2 are known for this system (see below) it is possible to predict the kinetics of changes in E after increasing or decreasing either C_1, the rate of transcription, or C_2, the rate of translation. The solid line of Fig. 2A is the theoretical curve obtained when C_1 is increased at zero time by a factor equivalent to the increase in enzyme content obtained under these conditions. It can be seen that the model predicts the pronounced lag observed and also the nearly linear approach to the new induced steady-state level of enzyme. The solid lines of Fig. 2B represent theoretical curves obtained when the rate C_1 is returned to the basal rate at zero time. Line 1 was obtained using the experimentally derived value of λ_1 and λ_2 and line 2 by reducing the degradation rates by about 30 %. The latter gives a better fit to experimental data, but both theoretical curves show the observed pattern of a slow decay accelerating after several hours, until the basal steady-state is approached. We interpret the kinetic patterns as indicating the necessity of increasing the mRNA component before enzyme synthesis assumes its maximal rate after hormone addition (Fig. 2A) and of maintaining induced mRNA for several hours before enzyme degradation reached its maximal rate after hor-

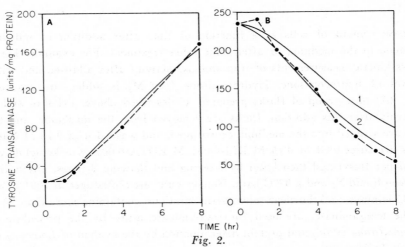

Fig. 2.

Kinetics of enzyme change following hydrocortisone addition (A) and withdrawal (B); theoretical curves for transcriptional induction (from *Lee et al.* 1970).

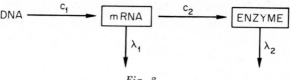

Fig. 3.

Model of cellular processes determining enzyme level (from *Lee et al.* 1970).

mone withdrawal (Fig. 2B). The model predicts quite different kinetics of change in E after addition or withdrawal of a translational inducer – the kind of change we observe with insulin as inducer (*Lee et al.* 1970).

Immunochemical measurements

The assays described above actually tell us only that the *activity* of tyrosine transaminase in H-35 cells is changed by hydrocortisone. They do not indicate whether enzyme *concentration* is changed, or, if it is, whether a change in concentration is brought about by changes in the rate of synthesis or of degradation of the enzyme. It must be remembered that there is a plethora of known mechanisms for changing the activity of a given amount of enzyme, as well as several well established instances of altering enzyme concentration by adjustment in degradative rate rather than synthetic rate (*e. g., Schimke et al.* 1965; *Reel & Kenney* 1968). The matter can be resolved in several ways, but we prefer the immunochemical approach since it demands (in principle) only one complete purification of the enzyme. Tyrosine transaminase is a minor component of the proteins of liver or H-35 cells (about 0.01 %) and its purification is therefore not undertaken lightly. Fortunately, the liver enzyme is immunologically identical to that in H-35 cells, so we can prepare antiserum in rabbits against enzyme purified from rat livers. Methods of enzyme purification and preparation of antiserum were published some time ago (*Kenney* 1962). Treatment of a single rabbit with 2–3 mg of pure enzyme yields 50 ml or more of antiserum which reacts with liver or H-35 extracts to form a single antigen-antibody band on double diffusion analysis. Antiserum is usually used without further treatment.

The question whether enzyme concentration changes along with enzyme activity after hormone treatment can be answered by a simple titration experiment (Fig. 4). A constant amount of antiserum (10 μl of 1:10 dilution, capable of quantitatively precipitating 160 units of transaminase from a freshly prepared soluble fraction of liver) is reacted with various amounts of crude enzyme from untreated cells and from both hydrocortisone- and insulin-treated cells. The mixtures are brought to a constant volume by addition of buffer

113

and incubated at 4°C overnight. After enzyme-antibody complexes are centrifuged off, the supernatant solutions are assayed for unreacted enzyme. It can be seen that enzyme from all three cell preparations reacts with the same amount of antibody, despite the differences in enzyme content of the cells. (Specific transaminase activities in units per mg protein were 21, 125, and 224 for control, insulin-treated, and hydrocortisone-treated cells, respectively). Thus the differences in enzyme activity are mirrored by differences in antibody-reactive enzyme, a measure of number of enzyme molecules rather than their catalytic activity. The constant point of equivalence seen in Fig. 4 also indicates that both of the hormone-induced enzymes are immunologically identical to the basal enzyme; *i. e.*, the hormones induce production of more of the same enzyme rather than formation of a different enzyme. For assays of this kind a completely specific antiserum is not required, as observations are limited to the transaminase-antitransaminase interaction, which is not altered by the presence in the serum of antibodies to other cellular proteins.

Such impurities cannot be tolerated, however, if the antiserum is to be used to measure rates of enzyme synthesis or degradation. In these analyses the antiserum is used as a reagent capable of selectively precipitating tyrosine

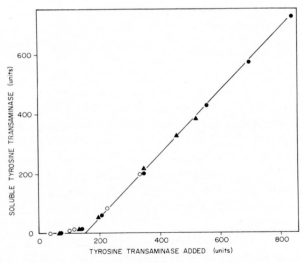

Fig. 4.

Immunological titration of transaminase preparations. Crude enzyme preparations (105 000 × g soluble fractions) from hydrocortisone-treated (●), insulin-treated (▲), or control (o) H-35 cells were titrated against antitransaminase serum sufficient to precipitate 160 units of transaminase from a fresh rat liver soluble fraction (from *Reel et al.* 1970).

114

transaminase from cell extracts containing a large number of proteins. This permits measurement of the extent of radioactive labelling of the enzyme, and thereby, with appropriate labelling techniques, an estimate of the rate of synthesis or degradation of the enzyme. Relative rates of enzyme synthesis are determined by exposure of cells to radioactive amino acids for a period of time (usually 15 minutes) which is brief compared to the half-life of the enzyme (about 2 hours). In these circumstances loss of enzyme radioactivity due to degradation can be ignored, and the extent of incorporation of labelled amino acid into the enzyme is a direct (although only relative) measure of the rate at which it is being synthesized during the »pulse« exposure to isotope. To measure enzyme degradation a »chase« labelling procedure is employed. The cells are exposed to isotopic amino acid for a period of time sufficient to label the enzyme highly: we usually use a 2-hour labelling period. Then they are washed and placed on »cold« medium containing unlabelled amino acid, and at intervals measurements are made of the residual isotope in the isolated enzyme. These yield a typical first-order degradation curve, of which the slope is λ_2, the rate of enzyme degradation.

It is also possible to use two isotopes and discriminatory liquid scintillation counting to measure both synthesis and degradation in the same experiment, as in Fig. 5, where we wished to determine the effect of high and low concentrations of actinomycin on both processes. Flasks of cells (7 per measurement) are treated with hydrocortisone for 22 hours before measurements are begun, to ensure that the content of enzyme is at the induced steady-state level and that the rate of enzyme synthesis is high (*i. e.*, induced). For the last 2 hours of the interval the cells are exposed to [14C] leucine and thus the transaminase is highly labelled as well. At zero time the cells are washed twice with medium containing hydrocortisone, and then incubated in medium containing: (1) hydrocortisone; (2) hydrocortisone plus 5 μg per ml actinomycin; (3) hydrocortisone plus 0.2 μg per ml actinomycin. The [14C] leucine is also removed at this time, so that subsequent measurements of the 14C content of the enzyme will yield the rate of degradation. To measure rates of synthesis the cells are pulse-labelled with [3H] leucine for 15 minutes before they are collected at zero time and at 3- and 6-hour intervals after the start of experiment.

Suspensions of cells from similarly treated flasks are pooled, and soluble fractions are prepared as described above. These are assayed directly for transaminase activity and protein content, yielding the data presented in the top portion of Fig. 5.

The problem that remains is to precipitate selectively the transaminase containing at most a few thousand cpm from a mixture containing about 5×10^5 cpm in protein. We have found that this is not possible, despite the apparent specificity of our antitransaminase serum, unless the enzyme is purified to a considerable extent from the soluble fractions, and the unstable, labelled pro-

115

8*

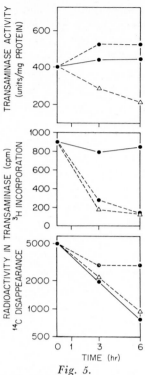

Fig. 5.

Effects of high and low concentrations of actinomycin on transaminase synthesis and degradation in H-35 cells. Hydrocortisone alone, ●——●; hydrocortisone plus 5 μg/ml actinomycin, ●– – –●; hydrocortisone plus 0.2 μg/ml actinomycin △– – –△.

teins which tend to coprecipitate, are removed. Accordingly each extract is subjected to a preliminary purification. Pyridoxal phosphate (30 μg/ml) is added to stabilize the enzyme, and the preparations are then heated to 62°C and quickly cooled. They are then centrifuged to remove denatured protein. To the clear supernatant solutions, which contain the labelled transaminase, aliquots of partially purified (unlabelled) enzyme containing 25 000 transaminase units are added. This addition brings the transaminase content of all preparations to the same level, high enough to ensure precipitation with antibody, and also facilitates recovery in the subsequent purification step. The preparations are then added to small columns of DEAE-cellulose equilibrated with 0.1 M K-phosphate (pH 7.9) with EDTA and α-ketoglutarate added (10⁻³ M and 5 × 10⁻³ M, respectively). For this purpose we employ a battery of 5-ml syringes, filled to the 2-ml mark with packed resin. After the preparation is absorbed the columns are washed 5 times with the phosphate buffer, removing much non-transaminase protein. The transaminase is then eluted with the same buffer solution (adjusted to pH 7.0) and supplemented with 0.4 M KCl. The enzyme is completely eluted in 3 column volumes (about 6 ml). Recovery at this point varies between 85 % and 95 % of the initial transaminase activity, but in a given experiment there is very little variation, indicating that different batches of DEAE are responsible.

The preparations are dialyzed overnight in 0.05 M K-phosphate (pH 7.4) and centrifuged to remove traces of insoluble (and labelled) protein. Then they are treated with a slight excess (30 000 units) of antitransaminase serum. After standing overnight at 4°C, the antigen-antibody complex is centrifuged off, and the supernatant solutions are put aside. The complexes are washed 3 times by suspension in 6 ml of 0.15 M NaCl and recentrifugation. They are then dissolved in 0.1 ml of 0.5 N NH$_4$OH and quantitatively transferred to filter-paper disks (Whatman, 3 mm). The tubes are rinsed with another 0.1 ml of 0.5 N NH$_4$OH, and this is also added to the paper disks. After thorough drying to remove NH$_4$OH the disks are added to 5 ml of scintillation fluid (scintillators dissolved in 100 % toluene) and counted in a liquid scintillation spectrometer adjusted to discriminate between ^{3}H and ^{14}C in two channels. The data are corrected for »spillover« and yield the total ^{3}H and ^{14}C radioactivity of the enzyme, together with a small amount of coprecipitated, radioactive, non-transaminase protein.

To evaluate the extent of error introduced by coprecipitation we routinely carry out a second transaminase-antibody precipitation from the supernatant solutions of the first precipitation. To these solutions, which are devoid of transaminase activity, we again add 25 000 units of unlabelled, partially purified transaminase, and follow this with 30 000 units of antibody. Transaminase-antibody complexes are collected and counted as described above, yielding a measure of the coprecipitated, non-transaminase radioactivity. This value is subtracted from the value obtained in the first precipitation to yield the true transaminase radioactivity. If all the steps described are carried out correctly the radioactivity of the second precipitate is both small and constant. For example, in an experiment where the ^{14}C radioactivity of 10 samples of the first precipitate varies from 1000 to 200 cpm, depending on experimental treatment, the radioactivity of the second precipitate is 30–40 cpm in all samples. If it is appreciably higher than this, or if it varies with experimental treatment, an error in preparation is indicated and the experiment is discarded.

The middle portion of Fig. 5 shows the data for [^{3}H] leucine incorporation into the enzyme. Each point is a measure of the rate of transaminase synthesis at that point in time. In cells treated only with hydrocortisone the rate of enzyme synthesis remains at the high induced level throughout the experiment. The induced rate is some 10–12 times higher than in cells not treated with hormone (not shown), which establishes that hydrocortisone does accelerate

117

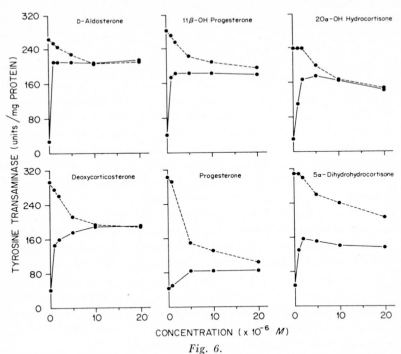

Fig. 6.

Effect of various inducing steroids on tyrosine transaminase levels and on its induction by hydrocortisone in H-35 cells. Steroids were added at the concentration indicated with (●---●) or without (●——●) hydrocortisone (10^{-6} M)
(from *Kenney & Lee* 1970).

are recorded in Table 1. Cells are treated with [³H] hydrocortisone alone or in combination with unlabelled steroids, some of which are competitive by the criteria described above, while others are not. After 3–5 hours cells are lysed and separated by differential centrifugation into supernatant (soluble at $105\,000 \times g$, 30 minutes) and nuclear (insoluble at $600 \times g$, 5 minutes) fractions. Radioactivity bound to the washed nuclear fraction is determined directly. In the supernatant fraction the determination is made after passage over Sephadex G-100 (20 ml packed resin per ml extract) separates radioactive steroid bound to macromolecules, which is of interest here, from free steroid, which is not.

[³H] Hydrocortisone by itself elevates the transaminase content from the basal level of about 40 (units per mg protein) to a level of 209 and produces appreciable labelling of both supernatant and nuclear receptors. Supplementation with either oestradiol or tetrahydrohydrocortisone, which neither induce nor

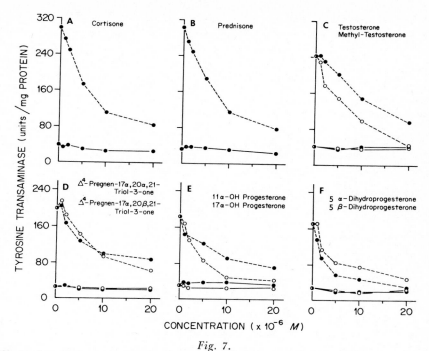

Fig. 7.

Effect of various noninducing steroids on tyrosine transaminase levels and on its induction by hydrocortisone in H-35 cells. The steroids were added with 10^{-6} M hydrocortisone (broken lines) or without it (solid lines). (C) testosterone, solid circles; methyl testosterone, open circles. (D) 20β-derivative, solid circles; 20α-derivative, open circles. (E) 11α-derivative, solid circles 17α-derivative, open circles. (F) α-derivative, solid circles; β-derivative, open circles (from *Kenney & Lee* 1970).

compete, has no effect on the enzyme level or on the extent of hydrocortisone binding in either cellular fraction. The 17α- and 11α-hydroxy derivatives of progesterone, which compete but do not induce (Fig. 7), lower the extent of hydrocortisone binding appreciably, especially in the nuclear fraction. Of the two, the 17α-derivative is more effective, both in reducing the extent of induction by hydrocortisone and in displacing the labelled steroid from receptor sites. Corticosterone and 11β-hydroxyprogesterone, both of which are effective inducers (Fig. 6) similarly compete with labelled hydrocortisone for receptor sites in both soluble and nuclear fractions, as, of course, does unlabelled hydrocortisone.

We conclude that the observed competition in enzyme induction does, indeed, reflect competition for intracellular receptor sites. These can be distinguished in both soluble and nuclear fractions of H-35 cells. The limited

Table 1.

Correlation between the effects of various steroids on the induction of tyrosine transaminase by hydrocortisone and the uptake of [³H] hydrocortisone to receptors in H-35 cells.

Nonradioactive steroid added	Transaminase Units/mg protein	Radioactivity, cpm/mg protein	
		Supernatant fraction	Nuclear fraction
None	209	3,586	9,810
17β-Oestradiol	215	3,167	8,558
Tetrahydrohydrocortisone	205	3,758	9,859
17α-Hydroxyprogesterone	73	1,528	2,939
11α-Hydroxyprogesterone	125	2,261	5,790
11β-Hydroxyprogesterone	171	1.012	2,478
Corticosterone	221	1,583	3,468
Hydrocortisone	207	1,170	2,459

data available suggest that the nuclear receptors may be more directly involved in the induction process, insofar as steroids which compete have a greater effect on the binding of labelled hydrocortisone to nuclear than to soluble receptors. This is in accord with our conclusion that the steroid accelerates enzyme synthesis by an action on nuclear transcriptional processes.

ACKNOWLEDGMENTS

This research was jointly sponsored by the National Cancer Institute, National Institutes of Health, and the United States Atomic Energy Commission under contract with the Union Carbide Corporation.

REFERENCES

Diamondstone T. I.: Anal. Biochem. *16* (1966) 395.
Hoel D. G.: J. biol. Chem. *245* (1970) 5811.
Kenney F. T.: J. biol. Chem. *237* (1962) 1605.
Kenney F. T. In: Munro H. N., Ed. Mammalian Protein Metabolism, IV, New York (1970) 131.
Kenney F. T. & Lee K. L.: Proc. 3rd Int. Congr. Hormonal Steroids, in press.
Lee K. L., Reel J. R. & Kenney F. T.: J. biol. Chem. *245* (1970) 5806.

Lin E. C. C. & Knox W. E.: Biochim. biophys. Acta (Amst.) *26* (1957) 85.

Lowry O. H., Rosebrough N. J., Farr A. L. & Randall R. J.: J. biol. Chem. *193* (1951) 265.

Pitot H. C., Peraino C., Morse P. A. Jr. & Potter V. R.: Natn. Cancer Inst. Mongr. *13* (1964) 229.

Reel J. R. & Kenney F. T.: Proc. Nat. Acad. Sci. (USA) *61* (1968) 200.

Reel J. R., Lee K. L. & Kenney F. T.: J. biol. Chem. *245* (1970) 5800.

Schimke R. T., Sweeney E. W. & Berlin C. M.: J. biol. Chem. *240* (1965) 322.

Tomkins G. M., Thompson E. B., Hayashi S., Gelehrter T., Granner D. & Peterkof-sky B.: Cold Spring Harb. Symp. quant. Biol. *31* (1966) 349.

Tomkins G. M., Gelehrter T. D., Granner D., Martin D. W., Jr., Samuels H. H. & Thompson E. B.: Science (N. Y.) *166* (1969) 1474.

DISCUSSION

Sato: Doesn't Gordon Tomkins have different data?

Lee: Yes.

Sato: As I remember it, actinomycin D does not affect the turnover of protein in his experiments.

Lee: In their experiments actinomycin D did not affect the turnover. In our experiments it did. Unfortunately, they did not measure the rate of enzyme synthesis when they showed that the rate of transaminase degradation was not inhibited by actinomycin D (*Auricchio et al.* 1969). In their recent publication (*Thompson et al.* 1970), they measured the rate of the transaminase synthesis in the presence of 5 μg/ml of actinomycin D. The rate of enzyme synthesis did increase, but they did not perform the experiment under the conditions we would like them to do. As I pointed out in my presentation, when the rate of enzyme synthesis is measured, the time for labelling should be brief enough compared to the degradation rate of the enzyme. To measure the rate of synthesis, they used two hour labelling time, which is about one generation of enzyme turnover. We routinely use 15 minutes labelling time for this measurement. So, I think that what they observed, the increase in the rate of transaminase synthesis by high concentration of actinomycin D, is not very clearcut because the labelling time is too long.

Sato: How do you recognize the difference in turnover?

Lee: I really do not know. We consistently found the inhibition of the transaminase degradation by high concentration of actinomycin D.

Lunenfeld: Your first slide showed that these cells respond also to dibutyryl 3′,5′-AMP as reflected by an increase in tyrosine transaminase. You did not, however, discuss these findings in your paper. Please elaborate.

Lee: The degree of the induction by dibutyryl cyclic AMP varies from one experiment to another. I would like to point out that cyclic AMP does not induce the enzyme, but the dibutyryl analogue does. The kinetic change of the enzyme activity by dibutyryl cyclic AMP is very similar to that of insulin.

Lunenfeld: Which of them evokes a more rapid response?

Lee: It varies. In general, this is an immediate increase in enzyme activity after the addition of dibutyryl cyclic APM or insulin. But these two inducers are not acting through the same mediator, because we have seen additive effect on the enzyme activity when both are added together.

Rodbell: Does your insulin contain glucagon?

Lee: About three years ago, we showed that glucagon induced the enzyme. We found out later, however, that the apparent induction by glucagon is due to the contamination of insulin in the glucagon preparations. The vice versa is not true, because the amount of insulin we used was 1 mIU/ml, and we had to use 1 mg/ml of glucagon to observe the induction.

Rodbell: The strain of cells you use, is that the same as Tomkins used?

Lee: No. Routinely we use Reuber H-35 cells. As far as »superinduction« is concerned, we found identical results with either HTC cells or H-35 cells.

Rodbell: Does your strain contain or not adenyl cyclase?

Lee: I think cyclase is there but cannot be stimulated by glucagon. We did observe the cyclase activity in the presence of fluoride. So I think that the cyclase is present in the H-35 cells, maybe just the receptor for glucagon is not.

Wira: Have you had any opportunity to test cortexolone, a steroid that is an anti-glucocorticoid in that it competes for binding sites and at the same time blocks biological effects of glucocorticoids?

Lee: Yes. The results are shown in Fig. 6.

Baulieu: You wash your cells and you incubate them further without hydrocortisone. You have a lag time before seeing the decrease. On your graphs I didn't see enough data to see if you have also a lag time for the effect of actinomycin. Could you comment on the respective significance of these lag periods?

Lee: The delayed decay of induced enzyme activity after the removal of hydrocortisone is roughly from one to one-half hour. Addition of actinomycin D or competitive steroids, such as cortisone, progesterone, after removal of hydrocortisone will not change the kinetics of delayed decay.

If hydrocortisone increases the amount of the transaminase mRNA we will expect that after removal of hydrocortisone the increased mRNA decreases to basal level before we observe the first order of decay in enzyme activity.

What we consider to be the delayed decay of the induced enzyme activity after removal of hydrocortisone represents the time required for degradation of mRNA.

Robyn: Dr. Lee, I would like to come back to the immunological titration of transaminase preparations. It appears from your Fig. 4 (p. 114) taken from *Reel et al.* (1970) that in the presence of antigen excess a fixed amount of antiserum neutralizes the same amount of transaminase activity whatever the excess of enzymatic activity may be. Thus, the transaminase neutralizing potency of the antiserum is not influenced by the fraction of enzymatic activity to be neutralized. These data confirm experimental evidence derived from biological studies of antigonadotrophic sera that antigen and antibody are additive in the presence of antigen excess (*Petrusz et al.* 1970). This principle of additivity forms the basis of bioassay methods for the estimation of anti-human chorionic gonadotrophin (anti-HCG), anti-follicle stimulating hormone (anti-FSH) and anti-luteinizing hormone (anti-LH) potencies of antisera, expressed in terms of the neutralized biological activity (*Robyn & Diczfalusy* 1968a,b). The proposed unitage is the Anti-Unit (AU). One AU is defined as the amount of antiserum which neutralizes the specific activity of 1.0 IU of hormone.

Means: Going back to the superinduction business, we all know that actinomycin is indeed a very potent antibiotic and has all sorts of systemic effects. It is also relatively reversible and probably, at least in low concentrations, preferentially an inhibitor of ribosomal RNA synthesis. We have available to us a very nice reversible inhibitor of nucleic acid synthesis, abbreviated as MPB. Have you tried this inhibitor in your system?

Lee: No, we have not tried this inhibitor. Dr. W. D. Wicks tried another inhibitor, α-amanitin, which is supposed to be more specific than actinomycin D. The induction of tyrosine transaminase by hydrocortisone in his foetal liver organ culture system is inhibited by α-amanitin (personal communication). Dr. *Sekeris* (*Sekeris et al.* 1970) also observed the inhibitory action of α-amanitin on the induction of the transaminase by hydrocortisone in rat liver.

Nakane: Dr. Lee, if I understood correctly, you isolated transaminase for the immuno-logic reactions from soluble fractions of liver. There is a possibility that there may be some structural change. When the transaminase is no longer needed it changes its solubility and will precipitate with the sediment and may not be detected since you are isolating only the soluble fraction.

Lee: I think this is unlikely, because the change of enzyme activity is parallel to the change of its rate of synthesis when the measurements are made at the time when the new steady state is reached.

References:

Auricchio F., Martin D. (Jr.) & Tomkins G.: Nature *224* (1969) 806.
Petrusz P., Robyn C., Diczfalusy E. & Finney D. J.: Acta endocr. (Kbh.) *63* (1970) 160.
Reel J. R., Lee K. L. & Kenney F. T.: J. biol. Chem. *245* (1970) 5800.
Robyn C. & Diczfalusy E.: Acta endocr. (Kbh.) *59* (1968a) 261.
Robyn C. & Diczfalusy E.: Acta endocr. (Kbh.) *59* (1968b) 277.
Sekeris C. E., Wiessing J. & Seifert K. H.: FEBS Letters *9* (1970) 103.
Thompson B., Granner D. K. & Tomkins G. M.: J. Mol. Biol. *54* (1970) 195.

Department of Biology,
University of California, San Diego, La Jolla,
California, U. S. A.

ENRICHMENT CULTURE TECHNIQUES FOR SELECTION OF CELL CULTURE STRAINS WITH DESIRABLE PHYSIOLOGICAL AND GENETIC PROPERTIES

By

Gordon Sato, Jeffrey Clark, Martin Posner[1],
Hyam Leffert, Dieter Paul[2], *Michael Morgan*[3]
and Clarence Colby[3]

ABSTRACT

Experimental approaches for selecting hormone-dependent cells, hybrid cells, and haploid cells are discussed. Experiments are described for isolating mammary tumour cells which are dependent on the presence of prolactin and insulin for growth.

Tissue culture techniques are being applied with increasing frequency and success to problems of physiology and genetics of higher organisms. The growing realization that virtually any kind of cell type can be maintained in culture is largely responsible for this recent surge of activity. We would like to discuss how the scope of problems amenable to tissue culture techniques can

---

[1] Department of Physics, University of Massachusetts, Boston, 100 Arlington Street, Boston, Massachusetts, U. S. A.

[2] Salk Institute for Biological Studies, La Jolla, California, U. S. A.

[3] Biology Division, Microbiology Section, University of Connecticut, Storrs, Connecticut, U. S. A.

be further increased by the judicious selection of biological material and application of currently available technology. We are going to cite examples from our own laboratory to show how tissue culture techniques can be applied to such diverse problems as regulation of cell growth and function by trophic hormones, liver regeneration, and mammalian cell genetics.

MATERIAL AND METHODS

TSH producing thyroxin-inhibited tumours were obtained from Dr. Jacob Furth (*Dent et al.* 1956). Steroid dependent leiomyosarcomas and kidney tumours were obtained from Dr. Hadley Kirkman (*Kirkman & Algard* 1965). Ovarian and testicular tumours were developed by the method of intersplenic transplantation (*Biskind & Biskind* 1944; *Furth* 1968). Tissue culture techniques have been described previously (*Buonassisi et al.* 1962).

RESULTS

Prolactin Dependent Mammary Tumour Cells

A large number of cell types in the body are dependent on the presence of trophic hormones for maintenance and growth. However, tissue culture strains dependent on trophic hormones have not been found as yet. We are attempting to select for such strains using transplantable hormone-dependent tumours as starting material. These tumours are enriched for hardy cells by the method of alternate culture and animal passage (*Buonassisi et al.* 1962). When in culture, cells are kept in the continuous presence of trophic hormones. Cultures maintained in this way consist of three cell types: the original hormone-dependent cell, variants of this cell which have become autonomous, and cells of the supporting tissue which always were autonomous. To eliminate these hormone-independent cells, cultures are first placed in media devoid of hormone. Under these conditions the dependent cells cease to grow while the autonomous cells continue to grow oblivious to the absence of hormone. Drugs, such as BUdR, which selectively kill proliferating cells are then added (*Puck & Kao* 1967), resulting in enrichment of the cultures for the dependent cells. These methods were applied to a mammary tumour developed in our laboratory by feeding female Wistar-Furth rats 3-methylcholanthrene. In this way pure epithelial cultures were obtained which depend on prolactin and insulin for growth (Table 1).

Table 1.

Medium		No. of Cells/flask
DME + 10 %		3.0×10^4
hypophysectomized		
dog serum		
DME + 10 %		6.0×10^5
hypophysectomized		
dog serum		
+ rat prolactin	1 gamma/ml	
+ rat growth hormone	1 gamma/ml	
+ bovine insulin	1 gamma/ml	

Falcon plastic culture flasks containing 10 ml of Dulbeccos Modified Eagle Medium + 10 % serum from a hypophysectomized dog were inoculated with 4.0×10^4 cells of a clonal strain of mammary tumour cells. To one set of flasks the indicated hormones were added. After twenty days of incubation at 37°C in a humidified atmosphere of 95 % air and 5 % CO_2, the cells were harvested and counted. Without hormone supplementation there is a slight decrease in cell number, while there is a 15 fold increase in cell number in the hormone supplemented flasks. Other experiments show that no growth occurs under these conditions if either insulin or prolactin is omitted.

Development of a Culture System for Studying Liver Regeneration

To our knowledge it has not yet been possible to establish conditions suitable for culturing euploid hepatocytes which still maintain responsiveness to normal growth controls. Therefore we are studying the regulation of DNA synthesis in primary foetal rat liver cultures for the purpose of developing an assay for the study of serum factors which initiate DNA synthesis in liver cells. Single cells are plated in arginine deficient medium containing dialyzed foetal calf serum. This medium is supposed to select against cells whose survival depends on the presence of arginine in the medium, for example, cells of non-parenchymal origin. Surviving cells are able to transform [14C] ornithine into [14C] arginine. Cultures of non-parenchymal origin tested to date are unable to effect this transformation. In preliminary experiments [3H] thymidine (specific activity 20 C/mM; final concentration 1×10^{-7} Molar) incorporation over 24 hours into trichloracetic acid (TCA) precipitable material was studied as a function of the concentration of serum (dialyzed normal rat serum) in the liver cell cultures. The results of such experiments are shown in Fig. 1. Pulse labelling studies, in which [3H] thymidine incorporation into TCA precipitable material is followed over a period of 24 hours, show that cultures in 10 % serum from partially hepatectomized rats (Fig. 2) incorporate more [3H] thymidine than cultures in 10 % normal rat serum. Recent studies with an im-

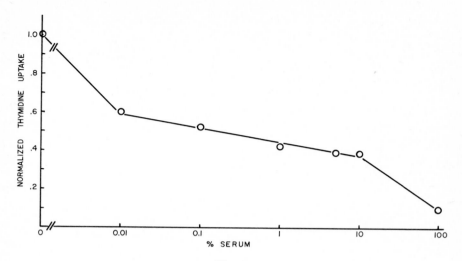

Fig. 1.

[³H] Thymidine incorporation into TCA precipitable material in primary foetal rat
liver cultures at different concentrations of normal rat serum.

The label is added for 24 hours to dishes containing varying concentrations of dialyzed
normal rat serum. The 5 day old cultures are then washed and trypsinized. The cell
suspension is divided into two equal volumes: one is used for the determination of cell
number; the second is filtered on a millpore filter, washed, extracted with TCA, dried
and radioactivity determined in a scintillation counter. The points represent data
pooled from these experiments. Ordinate: Normalized thymidine uptake (specific
activity – cpm/10^5 cells – is normalized such that maximum thymidine uptake is equal
to 1.0). Abscissa: % Serum concentration in medium.

proved assay system, using higher thymidine concentration, show different
patterns of both curves. Therefore we refrain from interpretation at this time.
However, such a system might be suitable to gain insight into the mechanisms
which regulate liver regeneration and organ size.

The Selection of Hybrid Cells with Lytic Viruses and Interferon

Several techniques have been developed for selecting hybrid cells from a
mixture of hybrid and parental cell types. The most notable example is the
HAT method of *Littlefield* (1966). This method requires the prior selection of
mutants to be used as parent cells, and for this reason is unsuitable in certain
cases where mutagenesis may be detrimental to the objectives of the experiment. We are attempting to select for hybrid cells using normal parental
cells from different species, the lytic animal virus Vesicular Stomatitis Virus

129

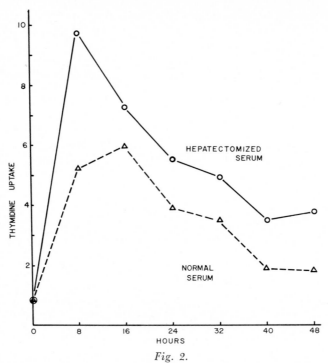

Fig. 2.

[³H] Thymidine incorporation into TCA precipitable material in primary foetal rat liver cultures in the presence of 10 % normal rat serum and 10 % serum of partially hepatectomized rats as a function of time.

Eight hour pulse labelling of the cultures is followed at different times after medium change (Hours = 0) in 5 day old cultures. Specific activity is determined as outlined in the legend to Fig. 1. Ordinate: Thymidine uptake (cpm/10^5 cells $\times$ 10^{-3}). Abscissa: time after medium change (hours).

(VSV), and interferons induced by Newcastle disease virus. This method is based on the observation that the protection of cells from virus infection by interferon is species specific, *e. g.*, mouse cells can only be protected by mouse interferon. Mouse L cells and human fibroblasts are fused with inactivated Sendai virus. The resulting mixed population is then exposed to human interferon and VSV virus. This treatment eliminates parental mouse L cells while human parental fibroblasts and hybrids survive. The cultures are then incubated in normal media for about two weeks to allow recovery. Cultures are then exposed to VSV and mouse interferon. The second treatment kills the remaining parental line, human fibroblasts, leaving only the hybrids in culture. In preliminary experiments, 4 out of 6 clonal isolates from such a selected population were found to be hybrid in that they could be protected from VSV virus by either human or mouse interferon. Preliminary evidence also indicates that at least some of these clonal strains are capable of producing both mouse and human interferon.

DISCUSSION

Our preliminary results indicate that it is possible to apply selection techniques for the development of culture strains which are dependent for growth on the presence of trophic hormones. It should be possible to apply these techniques to a wide variety of established transplantable tumours, freshly induced tumours, and normal tissues. It should be noted that many hormone-dependent tumours become autonomous upon serial passage and it is often necessary to undergo the time-consuming process of developing fresh tumours. We would like to cite additional examples from our laboratory to give an idea of the variety of cell types which lend themselves to selection procedures.

We have established tissue cultures from a TSH producing, thyroxine-inhibited pituitary tumour developed by Dr. *Jacob Furth*. These tumours produce TSH and will only grow in animals that have been thyroidectomized. In this instance culture studies are very useful because animal studies do not indicate whether the growth of these cells is inhibited by thyroxin or prevented or retarded by the lack of the hypothalamic hormone, TSH releasing factor (TRF). Preliminary results indicate that the cultures respond to TRF.

We are also trying to develop cell strains from androgen and/or oestrogen-dependent hamster tumours developed by Dr. *Hadley Kirkham*. These tumours were induced by subcutaneously implanting steroid pellets in hamsters, and the tumours are carried in steroid implanted animals. These tumours are remarkable because of their complete dependence on steroid hormones. The tumours inevitably regress when the pellets are removed.

We are presently trying to develop cell cultures which are dependent on gonadotrophins. We employ a classical technique for the induction of ovarian and testicular tumours. Foetal ovaries and testes of the rat are implanted in the spleen of castrated animals. Ordinarily a transplant of gonadal tissue would produce steroid hormones which would inhibit the secretion of gonadotrophins by the pituitary, and in this way limit its own growth. However, as the spleen is drained by the hepatic portal system, steroids produced by the splenic transplant are immediately destroyed in the liver before they can reach the general circulation. The pituitary, sensing a deficiency of the sex steroids, secretes gonadotrophins at an elevated rate, thus stimulating the growth of the splenic transplant.

These splenic transplants can be used like transplantable tumours in initiating cell cultures. The splenic transplants also eventually progress to neoplasias. Whether benign or malignant, these tumours are useful for initiating cell cultures. We are also using long established tumour lines of gonadal origin established in this way by Dr. *Rigoberto Iglesias* of Santiago, Chile (*Iglesias* 1964).

We are presently developing TSH-dependent thyroid tumours by maintaining rats for a year or more on agents which block iodination such as propyl-thiouracil or tapazole (*Wollman* 1961). When initially induced, these tumors are TSH dependent and will only grow in animals maintained on thyroid blocking agents. These tumours present an interesting challenge because of the readiness with which they become autonomous.

The liver experiments are cited as an example of how selection techniques can be applied to a specific physiological problem. In this case selection was achieved by arginine deficiency. It is conceivable that the selection procedures can be made more stringent so as to select for cells which can only synthesize DNA in the presence of serum from hepatectomized animals. It is of course impossible at the present time to say whether or not the culture results are related in any way to liver regeneration.

The selection of hybrids using interferon and VSV has the advantage that prior mutagenesis is not necessary. Another hybrid selection technique with a similar advantage is being developed in our laboratory by Mr. *Steven Carlin*. This approach employs temporary nutritional deficiencies as selective markers for hybrid cells. The principle is based upon the observation by Dr. *David Gardner* that when cells are made deficient in nicotinamide they become extremely sensitive to acetylpyridine, an analogue of nicotinamide. We are presently searching for another vitamin-analogue combination. The procedure envisaged is as follows: Cell type A is starved for one vitamin and cell type B is starved for another vitamin. The two cells are then fused and placed in culture in the absence of both vitamins but in the presence of both analogues. Each parental cell should be killed by its corresponding analogue while the hybrid or heterokaryon should be resistant to both analogues.

Genetic studies of animal cells in culture would be greatly facilitated by the availability of haploid cell lines. A recent paper by the *Freeds* (1970) described haploid cell lines, apparently permanently established, which maintain the haploid karyotype. Their method consists of removing the maternal nucleus from *Rana pipiens* eggs immediately after fertilization. These eggs develop to the swimming larva stage which were used to initiate cell cultures. They reported that they were successful in only a few instances out of hundreds of attempts over a period of ten years, and conjectured that few of the haploids were free of lethals, which are not expressed in diploids. They had previously reported short term haploid cell cultures. In these cases the haploid karyotype could not be maintained in culture because of the high frequency of nuclear fusion and formation of homozygous diploids. We are presently trying to over-come both difficulties – the selection of viable haploid karyotypes and the reversion to diploidy. To increase the probability of finding suitable haploid karyotypes, we are producing haploid animals on a large scale by the UV irradiation of frog eggs immediately after fertilization. In this manner a larger number of animals can be produced than by the removal of the maternal nucleus by micromanipulation. We are also trying to seek methods to select for haploid cells in the mixed population of haploids and diploids formed by nuclear fusion. One possibility is to select for cell size because of the well known disparity in size of haploid and diploid cells. It is conceivable that these techniques can be applied to mammalian cells (*Tarkowski et al.* 1970).

ACKNOWLEDGMENTS

This work was supported in part by grants GM 17019 from the National Institutes of Health, USPHS, and grant NSF GB 15788 from the National Science Foundation. JC is a postdoctoral fellow of the NIH. HL is a candidate for the degree, Doctor of Medicine, Albert Einstein College of Medicine, Bronx, New York. DP is a postdoctoral fellow of the American Cancer Society, California Division, Grant J-147. MH is a Harkness fellow. The authors also wish to thank the National Institute of Metabolic Diseases and Arthritis and Dr. Albert Parlow, Harbor General Hospital, San Pedro, California, for supplying us with rat prolactin and rat growth hormone. We thank Mrs. Madge Whitehead for her devoted secretarial assistance.

REFERENCES

Biskind M. S. & Biskind G. R.: Proc. Soc. exp. Biol. & Med. *55* (1944) 176.
Buonassisi V., Sato G. & Cohen A. I.: Proc. Nat. Acad. Sci. (U.S.A.) *48* (1962) 1184.
Dent J. N., Gadsden E. L. & Furth J.: Cancer Res. *16* (1956) 171.
Freed J. J. & Mezger-Freed L.: Proc. Nat. Acad. Sci. (U.S.A.) *65* (1970) 337.
Furth J. In: Engel A. and Larsson T., Eds. Thule International Symposia, vol. 2, Cancer and Aging. Nordiska Bokhandelns Förlag: Stockholm (1968) 131.
Iglesias R. In: Proceedings of the 2nd International Congress of Endocrinology, London (1964). Excerpta Med. Found. Int. Congr. Ser. *83* (1965) 1072.
Kirkman H. & Algard F. T.: Cancer Res. *25* (1965) 141.
Littlefield J. W.: Exp. Cell Res. *41* (1966) 190.
Puck T. T. & Kao F. T.: Proc. Nat. Acad. Sci. (U.S.A.) *58* (1967) 1227.
Tarkowski A. K., Witkowska A. & Nowicka J.: Nature (Lond.) *226* (1970) 162.
Wollman S. H.: J. Nat. Cancer Inst. *26* (1961) 473.

DISCUSSION

Kohler: Dr. Sato, what sort of parameter were you following with the TSH-secreting tumour that appeared dependent on TRF? Was it growth or TSH secretion?

Sato: Only growth. We have not looked for hormone secretion because we don't have an assay yet. Antisera to rodent TSH are just becoming available.

Kohler: Has any hypothalamic-lesion work been done with animals bearing these tumours to see if removing as much TRF as possible has any effect on the tumours *in vivo?*

Sato: With these tumours? No.

Graham: Do the TRF dependent cells transform to hormone independence at the same frequency as the prolactin dependent mammary tumour cells?

Sato: We are not sure yet. There is a difference. Mammary tumours *in vivo* readily transform to autonomy, but this particular tumour very rarely does. We hope that if we select properly we shall be able to maintain hormone dependency.

Martini: Did you use a synthetic preparation of TSH-RF?

Sato: Yes.

Graham: What is the lowest chromosome number of the smallest L cells which you obtain by cell separation?

Sato: We don't trust our chromosome counts that well yet. We have many metaphase plates with about the haploid number of chromosomes.

Robel: I am a little puzzled by your Fig. 1, which shows that thymidine incorporation is inhibited by normal rat serum. Why do you think that hepatectomized rat serum contains a stimulatory factor; it may well be that it lacks an inhibitory factor present in normal rat serum?

Sato: Yes, that would be the simplest hypothesis, and that is one we are testing now. Our feeling is that the system is probably going to be very complicated, and probably both inhibitory and stimulatory factors are operating.

Stumpf: From your experiments, Dr. Sato, do you have indications that pituitary cell types can undergo transformation from one cell to another?

Sato: We have worked on pituitary tumours and have developed culture strains which make ACTH and MSH. We have developed another strain which produces growth hormone and prolactin. I think that Dr. Kohler can perhaps speak as to whether this strain produces hormones other than prolactin or growth hormone. Because these are tumour cells, probably frozen in their state of differentiation, they are probably useless for studying the differentiation of stem cells.

Kohler: As far as I am aware, there are only two reports of two similar pituitary hormones produced by clonal lines of cells in culture. These are the rat GH_{1-3} cells of Drs. *Sato, Yasumura & Tashjian (Tashjian et al.* 1970), which produce both growth hormone and prolactin, and cells isolated by *Orth et al.* (1970), which produce both MSH and ACTH, which he distinguishes immunologically. This does not mean that cells actually transform from one type to another, but that one clonal line makes both hormones.

Hansel: Dr. Sato, you stated in your paper that one can culture practically any cell, yet no one has been able to culture the corpus luteum, and I would like to know why.

Sato: I think that is a good one to attack *in vitro*. They die *in vivo*. Luteal cultures may be very useful for studying luteolysis.

Ryan: Dr. Hansel, the only response to that is that those cells don't grow *in vivo* either. They stop multiplying after a certain point, and the question is why. Perhaps when you have that answer, you can go to the *in vitro* situation.

Rodbell: Is it possible to use the phenomenon of contact inhibition to alter the fusion of cells so that they don't multiply rapidly? I understand that substances on the cell surface allow specific cell types to interact in a manner that will retard growth. Is there a way of using this phenomenon to select out specific cells, such as hormone-responding cells?

Sato: I don't see how we can use this phenomenon to select for hormone dependency.

Rodbell: I have heard that cyclic AMP controls contact inhibition in certain types of cells. If glucagon, for example, should increase the production of substances on the cell surface that are involved in contact inhibition, it seems possible that cells responding to this hormone would show retarded growth. On the other hand, cells not responding to the hormone in the same tissue may not exhibit contact inhibition and may grow more rapidly under tissue culture conditions. In other words, is it possible to use selective induction of contact inhibition in hormone-sensitive cells as a means of selecting these cells from a mixture of tissue cells?

Sato: The possibility you raise is that maybe these trophic hormones release contact inhibition. That is an interesting possibility.

Rodesch: Another tool for selecting cells would be the use of trypsin in any small amounts in the medium, which has exactly the opposite effect to cyclic AMP. It releases the cells from contact inhibition (*Burger* 1970). I think that experimental results obtained until now concerning the action of 3′,5′-AMP on contact inhibition are unconclusive.

Another question: There is a factor in the serum which stimulates the synthesis of DNA (*Todaro et al.* 1966). There is a paper by *Holley & Kierman* (1968) which indicates that this factor could be FSH or HCG, for example. So maybe the difficulty to find a cell line which is highly dependent on a hormone like FSH could be due to the fact that all cells are dependent on FSH, as an example, *in vitro*.

Sato: It is hard to believe that every cell in tissue culture needs FSH for growth.

Diczfalusy: Dr. Sato, when a tumour develops into steroid dependent tumour, are there any data on whether or not this tumour metabolizes the steroid upon which it depends, and in that case, how? Does it differ from the metabolism of normal tissue?

Sato: Such investigations have not been done. We are doing them now because it is very important for us to know whether or not these cells will specifically take up steroids and whether or not this dependency is direct or indirect.

Wira: Do you know if the oestrogen dependent tumours are as sensitive to oestrone as to oestradiol, and also, if one needs oestrogens to transplant these tumours *in vitro*? What levels of hormone are required for their continued growth?

Sato: Oestrone is less effective than oestradiol in inducing tumours. We implant pellets of about 20 mg of oestradiol, and that lasts for about six months.

References:

Burger M. M.: Nature (Lond.) *227* (1970) 170.
Holley W. R. & Kierman Y. A.: Proc. Nat. Acad. Sci. (U. S. A.) *60* (1968) 300.
Orth D. N., Nicholson B. S., Shapiro M. & Byymy R. In: Program of the Endocrine Society (1970) Abstract No. 200.
Tashjian A. H., Bancroft F. C. & Lewis L.: J. Cell Biol. *47* (1970) 61.
Todaro G. J., Lazar G. K. & Green H. J.: J. Cell Comp. Physiol. *66* (1966) 325.

KAROLINSKA SYMPOSIA ON RESEARCH METHODS IN REPRODUCTIVE ENDOCRINOLOGY
3rd Symposium . In Vitro Methods in Reproductive Cell Biology
January 25–27, 1971

Reproduction Research Branch, National Institute of Child,
Health and Human Development, Bethesda, Maryland 20014, U. S. A.

CLONAL LINES OF HUMAN CHORIOCARCINOMA CELLS IN CULTURE

By

P. O. Kohler, W. E. Bridson, J. M. Hammond, B. Weintraub, M. A. Kirschner and D. H. Van Thiel

ABSTRACT

Six clonal lines of human choriocarcinoma cells, isolated by the single cell plating technique, have been maintained in culture for over two years. These clones have been examined for expression of tissue-specific function. Individual clonal lines have retained the capacity to synthesize human chorionic gonadotrophin (HCG), human chorionic somatomammotrophin (HCS), and progesterone, and also to transform steroid precursors to oestrone and oestradiol. The HCG species produced by different clones have different biologic to immunologic potency ratios ranging from 0.5 to 2.0 which are constant within any particular clone. HCG synthesized in culture has been examined by polyacrylamide gel electrophoresis and isoelectric focusing and had approximately the same molecular size as a highly purified urinary HCG preparation, but a different net charge at an acid pH.

INTRODUCTION

Human trophoblast is a unique tissue which performs many varied endocrine functions in support of foetal survival and development. The complexity related to studying placental tissue, both normal and malignant, *in vivo* suggested the advantages of investigating trophoblast in a long-term homogeneous culture system. For this reason, we have developed and studied six clonal lines of human choriocarcinoma cells which have been in continuous culture for over two years.

Historically, *Gey* and coworkers (*Gey et al.* 1938; *Jones et al.* 1942) first proved that the placenta definitely secreted a gonadotrophin by the use of fragments of placental tissue and hydatidiform mole in short-term culture. *Waltz* and associates (1954) were able to measure gonadotrophin production by molar tissue in culture for over a year, although the molar cells did not continue to multiply.

Pattillo & Gey (1968) and *Pattillo et al.* (1968) using a reconstituted tropho-collagen matrix on which to grow cells and microsurgical techniques to remove fibroblasts, isolated a continuous line of malignant trophoblast from a tumour which had been adapted by *Hertz* (1959) to passage in the hamster cheek pouch. These BeWo cells were the first hormone-synthesizing human cell line in culture. To our knowledge, the JEG cells isolated in our laboratory (*Kohler et al.* 1969) are the first clonal human hormone-producing cell lines. The techniques we have employed are those used by Sato and colleagues (*Sato & Yasumura* 1966; *Yasumura et al.* 1966) to develop clonal hormone-producing lines from rat and mouse endocrine tumours.

MATERIALS AND METHODS

The human choriocarcinoma used to initiate the cell cultures was a tumour (Woods strain of Erwin-Turner tumour) which had been adapted to growth in the hamster cheek pouch by *Hertz* (1959). Tissue obtained after 387 transfers in the hamster was finely minced into explants and grown in F10 medium containing 13.5 % horse serum and 3.2 % foetal bovine serum. The medium also usually contained 50 U penicillin and 50 μg streptomycin per ml.

Plaque-like colonies of trophoblast which could easily be distinguished from fibroblasts appeared within several days. These plaques were mechanically removed and placed in the same medium in plastic dishes which contained a sparse layer of cloned human fibroblast-like cells previously treated with 10 000 rads of conventional irradiation. This X-ray dose prevents replication of the treated cells, but they continue to metabolize for several days thereby providing more favourable growth conditions for the transplanted trophoblast.

After a variable period of growth on the feeder layers, the choriocarcinoma cells were completely dispersed with 0.05 % trypsin, 0.02 % sodium versenate solution followed by vigorous pipetting. The dispersed cells were then diluted and placed in dishes containing fresh feeder layers of irradiated human fibroblasts. The colonies which developed were isolated with a stainless steel cylinder after the method of *Puck et al.* (1956). Cells which could not be completely dispersed were not used for cloning attempts. Two clones desig-nated JEG-1 and JEG-2 were isolated by this method. The remainder of the clones were isolated by reinjecting the hamster with uncloned cells, reisolating the new tumour tissue and following the same steps. To assure that each clone was derived from a single cell, all have been recloned by the same techniques. Six clones have been maintained in continuous culture in our laboratory.

Hormones produced by the choriocarcinoma cells were measured in the medium unless otherwise specified. HCG was measured by radioimmunoassay using the method of *Odell et al.* (1967). HCG was quantified by the radio-immunoassay method of *Weintraub & Rosen* (1971). Progesterone was measured by saturation assay employing corticosteroid-binding globulin (*Lipsett et al.* 1970).

The bioassay used for HCG was the mouse uterine weight response (*Kulin et al.* 1967).

Conversion of [^{3}H] labelled steroids to oestrogens was proved by the addition of one to ten μCi of either dehydro*epi*androsterone, dehydro*epi*androsterone sulphate, androstenedione, testosterone, progesterone, or pregnenolone to the regular culture medium and incubation with the cells for 24 hours. At the end of this period 4000 dpm of [^{14}C] oestradiol and [^{14}C] oestrone was added and the conversion of tritium-labelled precursors to oestrone and oestradiol determined by reverse isotope dilution after phenolic partition, thin layer chromatography, derivative formation, and crystallization to constant specific activity.

Polyacrylamide gel electrophoresis and pH gradient electrophoresis were performed in a variety of gel systems as described by *Chrambach & Rodbard* (1970). HCG eluted from gel slices was measured by radioimmunoassay. The R_F's of different HCG preparations at a variety of gel concentrations were compared by the »Ferguson plot« method of *Rodbard & Chrambach* (1971). Parallel lines on these plots theoretically indicate identical molecular size (*Rodbard & Chrambach* 1971). The intercept at the ordinate represents the mobility at a zero gel concentration which is a function of molecular net charge only.

Chromosome preparations were made as described by *Kohler et al.* (1971).

RESULTS

The appearance of the cells varied somewhat from clone to clone under identical culture conditions (Fig. 1). However, all of the clones grew as individual cells and true syncytia were not seen. By electron microscopy, the cells contained large amounts of glycogen, abundant tonofibrillae, and many desmosomes (*Vanha-Perttula et al.*, unpublished results).

The chromosomal distribution was examined in clone JEG-1. In 100 meta-

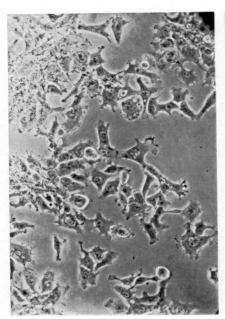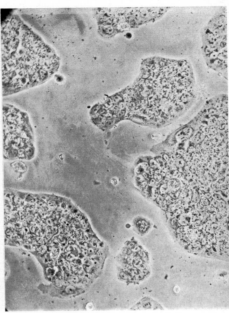

Fig. 1.

Appearance under phase contrast of two clonal lines of human choriocarcinoma cells in culture. Clone JEG-1 is on left and JEG-4 on right. Several of the clones show characteristic differences in gross morphology under identical culture conditions. (From *Kohler et al.*, in press).

phases counted, the modal number was 78 with moderate instability of chromosome number (*Kohler et al.* 1971).

All of the clones produced HCG although some invariably synthesized considerably more than others. HCG concentrations increased linearly over the 24-hour period between medium changes (Fig. 2). This effect was independent of cell mass.

The amount of HCG synthesized per cell was not constant, but increased with increasing cell density in culture (Fig. 3). After dispersion and replating of cells, replication showed a logarithmic increase while HCG production was in a relative lag phase. Only after cell multiplication began to reach a plateau, did HCG synthesis increase logarithmically.

Bioassay of HCG in the unextracted medium demonstrated that the cells in culture were synthesizing biologically active hormone rather than an immunologically active fragment. The linearized graded dose response curve using the mouse uterine weight assay showed parallelism between a standard reference preparation (Second International Standard HCG) and the hormone

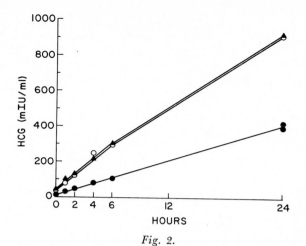

Fig. 2.

Comparison of HCG produced by cultures of different cell density from clone JEG-2.
The concentration of HCG in the medium increased approximately linearly over a
24-hour period.

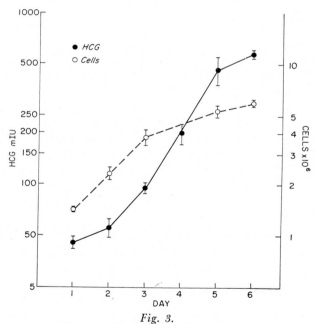

Fig. 3.

Relationship of hormone synthesis to cell count over a 7-day period after dispersion
and replating of JEG-4 cells. The number of cells initially increased logarithmically.
The HCG content in medium from a 24-hour period showed a lag phase before increasing logarithmically as the rate of cell replication began to reach a plateau.
(From *Kohler et al.*, in press).

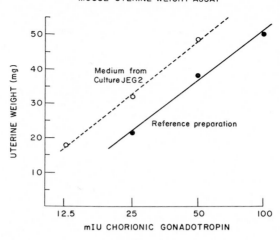

GRADED RESPONSE
MOUSE UTERINE WEIGHT ASSAY

Fig. 4.

Bioassay data showing graded responses of mouse uterine weight to doses of Second International Standard HCG and the gonadotrophin produced by clone JEG-2. Five animals were used per point. Statistical evaluation (*Bridson et al.*, in preparation) met criteria at 5 % level for homogeneity of variances and parallelism.

synthesized by the cells in culture (Fig. 4). Similar data have been obtained using the rat ventral prostate weight assay (*Bridson et al.* 1970).

As a test for the specificity of the bioassay and the similarity of the HCG preparations, several dilutions of antibody to HCG were incubated with the reference standard HCG and the hormone produced in culture. Neutralization of both preparations was essentially the same at the various antibody concentrations (Fig. 5).

A comparison of biological (B) to immunological (I) potency (B/I ratio) among the HCGs from the different clones grown in the standard medium showed that the B/I ratio varied from 0.54 for clone JEG-8 to about 2.0 for JEG-3 and JEG-7 (Fig. 6). The B/I ratio was essentially constant for each clone and was the same by either the mouse uterine weight or immature rat ventral prostate assay. The B/I ratio of the urinary reference preparations were unity.

Comparison of mobility of HCG synthesized in culture to two highly purified urinary HCG preparations (gifts of Dr. Jean Hickman and Dr. Robert Canfield) by polyacrylamide gel electrophoresis at pH 10.2 revealed identical mobilities at several gel concentrations indicating identity of molecular size and charge at this pH (Fig. 7). However, when electrophoresis was conducted

142

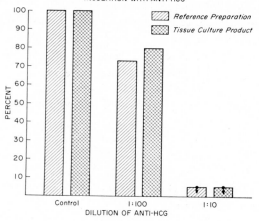

Fig. 5.

Neutralization with antibody to HCG of the mouse uterine weight response to Second International Standard HCG and the gonadotrophin produced by trophoblast cells in cultures. Neutralization at the various antibody concentrations were comparable, indicating immunological similarity of the two preparations and specificity of the assay.

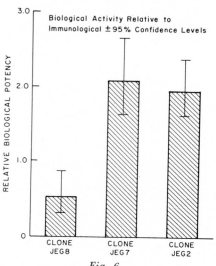

Fig. 6.

The biological to immunological (B/I) potency ratios of the HCG produced by three clonal lines. The bars indicate 95 % confidence limits. The B/I ratios appear to be relatively constant within a clonal line.

in a more acid system at pH 5.0, charge differences between the HCG synthesized by the clonal lines and the highly purified urinary HCG preparations were observed although on Ferguson plots the lines remained parallel (*Hammond et al.*, in preparation). The retardation coefficients of different HCG preparations from tissue cultures were similar to those of the highly purified HCG preparations (Fig. 8) indicating that molecular weights were similar. From retardation coefficients of proteins of known molecular size, the molecular weights of several HCG preparations have been estimated by the method of *Rodbard & Chrambach* (1970). Retardation coefficients for eight preparations from tissue culture and of the two highly purified HCG preparations were essentially identical with molecular weight estimates of 62 000 to 70 000. The 95 % confidence limits of these measurements, which incorporate the variability of the standard reference proteins, were 39 000 to 101 000.

The behaviour of the HCG produced by the JEG clones, was examined by pH gradient electrophoresis (isoelectric focusing) on polyacrylamide gel (Fig. 9). Two peaks of immunoreactive HCG were produced by each of the clones tested.

The B/I ratio of the two peaks from clone JEG-2 differed (Fig. 10). The

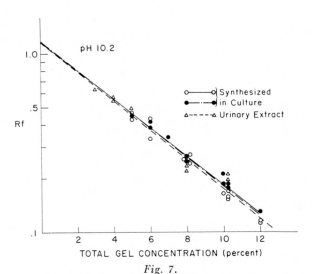

Fig. 7.

Comparison of mobility of highly purified HCG extracted from urine to two preparations of gonadotrophin from choriocarcinoma cells in polyacrylamide gel electrophoresis at pH 10.2. Illustration shows »Ferguson plot« of log R_F vs. total gel concentration. HCG was measured by radioimmunoassay. Parallel lines and indistinguishable ordinate intercepts indicate that no differences in molecular size or net change were detected under these conditions.

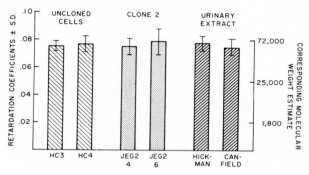

MOLECULAR SIZE MEASUREMENTS
OF TISSUE CULTURE AND URINARY HCG

Fig. 8.

Retardation coefficients for HCG synthesized by uncloned choriocarcinoma cells, clone
JEG-2, and for two highly-purified HCG preparations extracted from urine were
indistinguishable. Molecular weight estimates were made by comparison to a group
of proteins of known molecular weight.

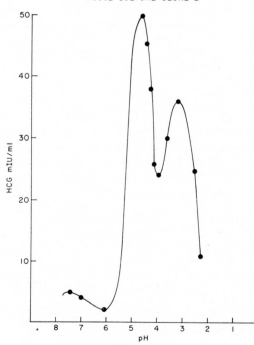

ISOELECTRIC FOCUSING HCG FROM
TISSUE CULTURE CLONE 2

Fig. 9.

pH gradient electrophoresis of HCG from JEG-2 showing two characteristic peaks.
HCG was measured by radioimmunoassay.

145

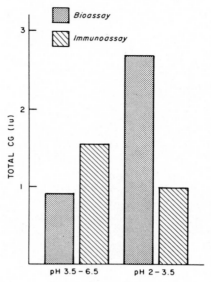

Fig. 10.

Immunological and biological (mouse uterine weight assay) potency estimates for the two species of HCG found by pH gradient electrophoresis. Hormone was eluted from the gel. The B/I ratio of the more acid peak was considerably higher than the material with an isoelectric point from pH 3.5 to 6.5.

HCG in more acidic peak (pH 2–3.5) had a high B/I ratio while the hormone in the less acid peak (pH 3.5–6.5) had a B/I ratio of less than one. The clones differed with regard to the relative amount of the two species of HCG. When grown on the standard F10 medium, clone JEG-7 produced a higher proportion of the more acid peak than JEG-8.

In addition to the production of HCG, three of the six clones produced detectable amounts of HCS, and JEG-3 had a particularly high synthesis and release of HCS into the medium (Table 1). However, when compared on the basis of mass, considerably more HCG than HCS was synthesized. Progesterone was also synthesized by all of the cell lines, although the rates varied among the clones (Table 1).

Aromatization of known precursors of oestrogens was initially tested in clone JEG-2. Dehydro*epi*androsterone, dehydro*epi*androsterone sulphate, androstenedione, and testosterone were converted to oestrone (1.1 to 5.0 %) and to oestradiol (5.4 to 7.7 %). Pregnenolone was not aromatized and conversion of progesterone to the oestrogens was barely detectable (oestrone,

146

Table 1.
Hormone synthesis by different clones of human choriocarcinoma in culture.

Clone	HCG $IU \cdot cell^{-1} \cdot day^{-1} \cdot 10^{-9}$	HCS $g \cdot cell^{-1} \cdot day^{-1} \cdot 10^{-15}$	Progesterone $g \cdot cell^{-1} \cdot day^{-1} \cdot 10^{-15}$
JEG-1	240	ND*	36.4
2	2710	.09	79.9
3	7290	3.5	21.9
4	–	ND	12.1
7	1850	0.2	13.1
8	180	ND	13.6

* Not detectable.

0.009 % and oestradiol, 0.053 %). Control culture of human fibroblasts showed no conversion of any of the precursors. A comparison of the conversion of dehydro*epi*androsterone sulphate to the oestrogens by the various clones is shown in Table 2.

DISCUSSION

The development of clonal lines of human choriocarcinoma has enabled us to create homogeneous populations of cells, each derived from a single tumour cell, and compare their tissue-specific functions. Studies with these clonal lines have indicated that single clones are capable of performing at least four complex endocrine functions simultaneously. This implies that for mammalian cells relatively large portions of the genome are being actively transcribed. The synthesis of more than one hormone by a clonal line of cells has been previously reported, but the hormones are usually structurally related such as growth hormone and prolactin (*Tashjian et al.* 1970) or ACTH and melano-cyte stimulating hormone (*Orth et al.* 1970). Trophoblast cells appear to be uniquely multipotent in that they are able to synthesize two structurally widely different protein hormones, HCG and HCS, as well as steroids.

The steroid synthesis found in the clonal trophoblast lines appears similar to that of the normal placenta in that large amounts of progesterone are synthesized, but a relative block occurs so that little or no progesterone is converted to oestrogen. However, steroids such as dehydro*epi*androsterone sulphate or testosterone are effectively converted to oestrogen, and particularly

Table 2.

Conversion of tritium-labelled dehydro*epi*androsterone sulphate to oestrone and oestradiol after 24 h incubation with clonal lines of human choriocarcinoma or fibroblasts.

Clone	Oestrone %	Oestradiol %
JEG-1	1.72	16
2	0.93	10
3	5.7	34
4	–	–
7	1.5	20
8	2.1	19
Fibroblasts	ND*	ND

* Conversion rates above 0.05 % could be measured.

to oestradiol. *Huang et al.* (1969) have also found progesterone synthesis in their choriocarcinoma cells in culture as well as conversion of androstenedione to oestrogen (personal communication from *Pattillo*).

The biologic to immunologic potency ratios of the JEG clonal lines were investigated because *Hobson & Wide* (1968) reported that the B/I potency of chorionic gonadotrophin synthesized by tumour cells was higher than that of the HCG found in normal pregnancy urine, where the B/I ratio may be less than unity. The clonal lines afforded an opportunity to determine whether the high B/I ratio, if present, were a characteristic of hormone produced by all the cells within a tumour; or alternatively, if the tumour were composed of a group of cells producing a family of HCG molecules with a spectrum of B/I ratios. Our studies indicate that B/I ratios of HCG produced by the clones vary from less than one to greater than two. Therefore, one might expect the B/I ratio of HCG produced to vary between tumours or perhaps within an individual tumour depending on the population of cells present at any particular time.

The tissue culture system also allowed us to investigate the physical properties of an HCG molecule which had not been subjected to degradation *in vivo* or the extraction procedures used in recovering HCG from the usual source, urine. The studies with various HCG preparations in polyacrylamide gel electrophoresis indicate that the molecular size of the gonadotrophin produced in culture is similar to that of HCG derived from urine. This is presumptive evidence that HCG retrieved from urine has not undergone gross changes in

148

molecular weight. The correlation of molecular size between the HCG produced by the cells in culture and the highly purified HCG preparation is relevant since crude urinary extracts contain HCG species with a wide variation in size (*Kaplan et al.*, in preparation).

Differences in net charge were noted among the purified reference preparation and the HCG produced in culture. These could be related to variations in the content of heavily electronegative sialic acid among the various preparations. However, whether these differences arise during or after synthesis is unknown. *Hammond et al.* (in preparation) have shown that no detectable degradation occurs when exogenous HCG is added to the choriocarcinoma cells. Thus, the dissimilarity observed between hormones from separate clonal lines presumably represent differences at the level of synthesis rather than degradation.

The isoelectric focusing data may more clearly demonstrate differences in net change of HCG synthesized by various clones. The three clones tested produced at least two species of immunoactive HCG with distinct isoelectric points. Therefore, each clone presumably produces differing ratios of these two species of HCG giving a characteristic net charge.

The above studies illustrate some of the advantages of looking at the properties of clonal lines of trophoblast. The JEG clonal lines have been utilized to synthesize HCG labelled with [14C] or [3H] labelled amino acids and carbohydrate precursors (*Bridson et al.*, unpublished results). Many other studies are in progress with choriocarcinoma cells in culture. *Hause et al.* (1970) have studied the highly negative surface potential of malignant trophoblast in comparison to normal and other tumour cells. Similar studies related to the possible masking of histocompatibility antigens by a surface coating with sialic acid are being carried out in our laboratory. Because of the remarkable retention of organ-specific function by clonal lines of choriocarcinoma in culture, these cells should provide a good mammalian system for attempts at manipulation of gene function.

REFERENCES

Bridson W. E., Ross G. T. & Kohler P.: Clin. Res. *18* (1970) 356.
Chrambach A. & Rodbard D.: Science (in press).
Gey G. O., Seegar G. E. & Hellman L. M.: Science *88* (1938) 306.
Hammond J. M., Bridson M. E. & Kohler P. O. In: Program of the Endocrine Society (1970) abstract No. 1.
Hause L. L., Pattillo R. A., Sances A. Jr. & Mattingly R. F.: Science *169* (1970) 601.
Hertz R.: Proc. Soc. exp. Biol. (N. Y.) *102* (1959) 77.
Huang W. Y., Pattillo R. A., Delfs E. & Mattingly R. F.: Steroids *14* (1969) 755.

Hobson B. & Wide L.: Acta endocr. (Kbh.) *58* (1968) 473.

Jones G. E. S., Gey G. O. & Gey M. K.: Bull. Johns Hopk. Hosp. *72* (1942) 26.

Kohler P. O. & Bridson W. E.: J. clin. Endocr. (in press).

Kohler P. O., Bridson W. E., Vanha-Perttula T. & Hammond J. M. In: Program of the Endocrine Society (1969) abstract No. 44.

Kulin H. E., Rifkind A. B., Ross G. T. & Odell W. D.: J. clin. Endocr. 27 (1967) 1123.

Lipsett M. B., Doerr P. & Bermudez J. A. In: Diczfalusy E. and Diczfalusy A., Eds. Steroid Assay by Protein Binding, Second Karolinska Symposium on Research Methods in Reproductive Endocrinology, Bogtrykkeriet Forum, Copenhagen (1970) 155.

Odell W. D., Rayford P. L. & Ross G. T.: J. Lab. clin. Med. *70* (1967) 973.

Orth D. N., Nicholson B. S., Shapiro M. & Byymy R. In: Program of the Endocrine Society (1970) abstract No. 207.

Pattillo R. A. & Gey G. O.: Cancer Res. *28* (1968) 1231.

Pattillo R. A., Gey G. O., Delfs E. & Mattingly R. F.: Science *159* (1968) 1467.

Pattillo R. A., Gey G. O., Mattingly R. F. & Woodruff J. D.: Obstet. and Gynec. *33* (1969) 153.

Puck T. T., Marcus P. I. & Ciecura S. J.: J. exp. Med. *103* (1956) 273.

Rodbard D. & Chrambach A.: Proc. nat. Acad. Sci. (USA) *65* (1970) 970.

Rodbard D. & Chrambach A.: Analyt. Biochem. *40* (1970) (in press).

Sato G. H. & Yasumura Y.: Trans. N. Y. Acad. Sci. *28* (1966) 1063.

Tashjian A. H., Bancroft F. C. & Lewis L.: J. Cell Biol. *47* (1970) 61.

Waltz H. K., Tullner W. W.. Evans V. J., Hertz R. & Earle W. R.: J. nat. Cancer Inst. *14* (1954) 1173.

Weintraub B. D. & Rosen S. W.: J. clin. Endocr. (in press).

Yasumura Y., Tashjian A. H. & Sato G. H.: Science *154* (1966) 1186.

DISCUSSION

Gurpide: We have considered using choriocarcinoma cells to study the uptake and metabolism of steroids by trophoblastic tissue. As you mentioned, such cells have an unusually high and variable DNA content and, although of human origin, may have suffered changes when transplanted into hamsters. I would like to hear your comments about the relevance of using this material if you have in mind problems related to the normal human placenta.

Kohler: Many people have attempted to grow normal placenta in culture. It has been a difficult problem. In general, with the exception of the lymphopoietic cells, any normal tissue tends to lose its specific function when placed in culture. For this reason tumours usually have been used, particularly by Dr. *Sato*, for endocrine studies. Hydatidiform mole was maintained in culture by *Waltz et al.* (1954). The problem was that the cells did not continue to divide, although they appeared to produce chorionic gonadotrophin for over a year. With normal placenta I think it is going to be a difficult task, as with any other normal tissue, to attempt to establish permanent differentiated cell lines. We plan to attempt this for comparative purposes, but we are going to begin with explant cultures. It may well be that normal tissue needs interaction with another type of cell, such as a stromal cell or fibroblast, in order to function, whereas a tumour does not. You may be familiar with the work done on the pancreas, for example. The pancreas in culture needs stromal cells in order to make zymogen granules.

Baulieu: I noticed that you find that dehydro*epi*androsterone sulphate was giving more oestrogen than free dehydro*epi*androsterone. That is what we found *in vivo* when we injected dehydro*epi*androsterone sulphate many years ago (*Baulieu & Dray* 1963), whereas, if I remember correctly, in Dr. Diczfalusy's laboratory, when they gave dehydro*epi*androsterone sulphate directly to the placenta, they found just the reverse, that the free compound was a better precursor. Do you have an explanation on that point?

Another question: Did you test any hormone preparation in connection with the yield of aromatization?

Kohler: I do not have any explanation for why dehydro*epi*androsterone sulphate works better, unless it may be more soluble in this particular system. We did not try adding anything to modify the aromatization.

Ryan: Dr. Kohler, you tried to relate cell number to hormone production. What are the interrelationships between cell division and growth and hormone production? Aren't they in a sense at odds with one another?

Kohler: The thinking has been that, as a cell slows down *in vivo*, for instance, the specialized function will frequently divide more slowly. However, this is not necessarily true in tissue culture. Some of the other hormone-producing lines seem to show a direct relationship between cell number and the amount of hormone produced. The situation here, where specialized function appears to increase as cell division decreases, is not unique among cell culture systems. In this particular case, it is difficult to say that this relates to cell differentiation. The fact remains that when we somehow inhibit cell growth, we have more gonadotrophin synthesis per cell.

Diczfalusy: A higher conversion of dehydro*epi*androsterone sulphate than of dehydro*epi*androsterone to oestrogen has also been reported by *Morato et al.* (1965). Using placental preparations *in vitro*, they got a higher conversion of the sulphate than of the free steroid. It might be a problem of entry of the tissue. I was interested in your finding progesterone production by these cells. In all perfusion studies we did so far, we consistently failed to show conversion of acetate to progesterone or to cholesterol, even to lanosterol. This raises the question whether these cells gain a capability which otherwise normal placental cells would not have. Another point: Did you find FSH-like activity in your HCG preparations produced by these cells? In some recent studies which we just submitted for publication, Drs. *Matthies, Petrusz* and myself (Acta endocr. (Kbh.) to be published), found that this activity is restricted to a certain molecular size, which can be separated on Sephadex G 100.

Finally, when HCG is chromatographed on Sephadex without any manipulation, it is a highly retarded fraction which possesses a very high immunological activity and relatively little biological activity (*Matthies & Diczfalusy*, Acta endocr. (Kbh.) to be published). If you take pregnancy plasma or serum and chromatograph it on your Sephadex columns, you get an HCG population with an entirely different molecular size. I was wondering therefore, why is your »fresh from the oven« HCG secreted by these cells similar to the urinary HCG?

Kohler: First of all, concerning the acetate question: our medium contains cholesterol. Therefore, to determine this, we are going to have to use a different medium or labelled acetate and measure labelled progesterone.

Regarding FSH-like activity, we have planned to look at this but have not done so yet.

The final question, about why our HCG is like urinary material, I don't know. We have not used columns such as yours, so I am not sure what we would find. We do find differences between crude urinary HCG and our tumour HCG with regard to isoelectric points. Crude urinary HCG also contains aggregates of HCG, which we did not find in culture. The hormone produced in culture does appear similar to highly purified HCG.

Gurpide: One comment concerning the entry of dehydro*epi*androsterone sulphate into choriocarcinoma cells. We have studied the permeability of Be-Wo cells, obtained from Dr. Pattillo, to oestrogen sulphates and found that the entry of sulphates is about one half the entry of the corresponding free oestrogens. Perhaps this will also be the case for free and sulphated dehydro*epi*androsterone. I would also like to mention the possibility that production of oestrogens is important for the normal function of the cells. It would be interesting to study the consequences of removing oestrogen precursors from the medium.

Lerner: What would happen if, in a cell culture system, you put together one normal placental sample with one choriocarcinoma sample and then treated this with VSV and interferon? It is possible to get a normal cell culture?

Sato: First of all, our selection system depends on the two parental cells being of different species, so that in itself would mean that it wouldn't work. I think the underlying question throughout many of these discussions is, what is the relevance of these strange *in vitro* systems, which grow for ever, to normal physiology? Obviously, in some cases, they can't be relevant to normal function *in vivo*. On the other hand, the mechanism whereby steroids cause liver cells to produce more tyrosine transaminases must be the same in the *in vitro* systems as in normal liver. If Dr. Kohler can work out the steps by which the protein moiety and carbohydrate moiety of HCG are assembled in cultured cells, I think that these will be the same as in normal placenta. Whether or not the relationship between cell growth and hormone secretion in these cultures is going to be relevant in any way to what goes on *in vivo* is not so obvious.

Rodbell: Concerning the behaviour of HCG on Sephadex, it should be pointed out that several peptide hormones bind to Sephadex and do not chromatograph in accordance with their molecular weight, particularly when »carrier« proteins are not present. In other words, I wonder whether the difference in behaviour of HCG in urine, which is undoubtedly low in protein concentration, and in serum might not reflect the protection by serum proteins against binding of the hormone to Sephadex.

Diczfalusy: It was tested by adding different amounts of urine to plasma from non-pregnant women.

Rodbell: Glucagon behaves as it should on Sephadex in the presence of 6M urea.

Robyn: Dr. Kohler, you could not detect immunological differences between HCG from cultured cells and HCG from urinary extracts, such as Pregnyl (Organon, Oss) preparations. This was concluded from animal experiments in which the two types of HCG activities were neutralized by anti-HCG sera. In these experiments, did you incubate the same amounts of HCG with different amounts of antiserum using serial dilutions (1/10, 1/100, etc.)?

Kohler: Yes, that is correct.

Robyn: In our experience, such biological techniques of semi-quantitative character are of very limited precision. Immunological differences between gonadotrophins of various origin are more accurately detected by methods based on partial neutralization of a given hormone and on subsequent specific and statistically valid bioassay of the fraction of hormone left unneutralized (*Robyn et al.* 1968; *Robyn* 1969). Using such a bioassay method, we have found that the HCG neutralizing potencies of anti-HCG sera were three times greater when tested against a semi-purified preparation (Pregnyl; 2160 IU/mg) than when tested against a highly purified preparation (Serono; 18 000 IU/mg). This indicates that the semi-purified preparation contained three times more immunologically active, biologically inert HCG than the highly purified preparation. Similarly, significant differences were also found in the antigenic properties of urinary HCG and placental HCG (*Petrusz*, personal communication).

The immunologically active, biologically inert material present in gonadotrophin preparations has been designated by *Petrusz & Diczfalusy* (1969) as antibody neutralizing factor (ANF). The anti-HCG and anti-FSH neutralizing factors can be estimated on a quantitative basis in bioimmunoassays as described by *Petrusz et al.* (1971).

Kohler: We initially compared the neutralizing effect of antibodies on the biological activity to make sure that the responses were not the effect of steroids in the medium. We have not detected immunologic differences between tumour and urinary HCG preparations by immunoassay or in our neutralizing experiments examined by parallel line statistical methods. We did not use your assay method for comparison, however, and immunologic differences may be present which we could not detect. We do know that there are other differences between the two types of HCG; the data regarding these have been presented.

References:

Baulieu E. E. & Dray J.: J. clin. Endocr. Metab. *23* (1963) 1298.
Morato T., Lemus A. E. & Gual C.: Steroids ,Suppl. *1* (1965) 59.
Petrusz P. & Diczfalusy E.: Acta endocr. (Kbh.) Suppl. *138* (1969) 23.
Petrusz P., Diczfalusy E. & Finney D. J.: Acta endocr. (Kbh.) *67* (1971) 40.
Robyn C.: Acta endocr. (Kbh.) Suppl. *142* (1969) 31.
Robyn C., Diczfalusy E. & Finney D. J.: Acta endocr. (Kbh.) *58* (1968) 593.
Waltz H. K., Tullner W. W., Evans V. J., Hartz R. & Earle W. R.: J. nat. Cancer Inst. *14* (1954) 1173.

KAROLINSKA SYMPOSIA ON RESEARCH METHODS IN REPRODUCTIVE ENDOCRINOLOGY

3rd Symposium . In Vitro Methods in Reproductive Cell Biology

January 25–27, 1971

Sir William Dunn School of Pathology,
South Parks Road, Oxford OXI 3RE, U. K.

VIRUS ASSISTED FUSION OF EMBRYONIC CELLS

By

Christopher F. Graham

ABSTRACT

A method is described for fusing mouse blastomeres together. These
fused combinations develop into tetraploid blastocysts. On subsequent
transfer to a foster mother they develop into large trophoblast masses.

This paper describes how the technique of virus assisted cell fusion must be
modified for use with the blastomeres of the mouse.

Many different cell types have been fused with the mouse ovum but the
heterokaryons failed to develop into normal blastocysts (*Graham* 1969; *Baranska & Koprowski* 1970). This was not surprising; the medium used to culture
the fused ova did not even support the development of normal fertilized
1-cell eggs.

Since these preliminary experiments, the techniques of mouse egg culture
have improved. A long series of meticulous studies has led to the development of a medium in which fertilized 1-cell mouse eggs will develop into
viable blastocysts (*Whitten & Biggers* 1968; *Whitten* 1970). For the first
time, it has become possible to manipulate the 1-cell mouse egg and follow
the consequences of the experiment in culture.

In addition to culture in *Whitten*'s medium (1970), it is also necessary to
take special precautions with the Sendai fusion technique (*Okada et al.* 1966;
Harris et al. 1966). The mouse egg is easily lysed, and to reduce this effect
various tricks must be employed. *Graham* (1969) fused eggs with the UV-
inactivated Sendai virus, and found that ovum lysis could be reduced by:

154

(a) Exposing the ovum to the virus for only one or two minutes;

(b) Sequestering the activity of the virus as soon as fusion has begun, by addition of serum;

(c) Exposing only one cell of the fusion partners to the virus suspension.

The UV-inactivated Sendai virus is known to have a cytopathic effect on several cell types, and this effect can be reduced by using beta propio-lactone (BPL) to inactivate the virus (*Neff & Enders* 1968). *Baranska & Koprowski* (1970) introduced the use of BPL inactivated Sendai virus into egg fusion work, and found that the survival of the fused ova was improved. This is also my experience.

This paper describes my current technique for fusing mouse blastomeres together. It incorporates the use of *Whitten*'s medium (1970) and the BPL inactivated Sendai virus. The effect of cell fusion on subsequent embryonic development was studied in detail. The fusion was conducted either between two fertilized 1-cell eggs or between two dissociated blastomeres obtained from a 2-cell embryo. In either situation tetraploid blastocysts developed; it will be argued that the manipulations involved in cell fusion do not necessarily impede embryonic development.

MATERIALS AND METHODS

1. *Supply of embryos*

Female mice were either from a randomly breeding closed colony of Swiss albino animals (Strain PO) or they were F_1C57BL/CBAT6T6 hybrids. Six to ten week old virgin females were superovulated (*Runner & Palm* 1953). Eight IU each of PMSG and HCG (Gestyl and Pregnyl: Organon Laboratories, U. K.) were injected ip 48 hours apart. After the injection of HCG, the females were each placed with one male of the PO strain.

Embryos were dissected only from females which mated (indicated by the presence of a copulation plug). One-cell fertilized embryos were obtained 19 hours after the HCG injection and 2-cell fertilized embryos were removed 44 hours after the HCG injection. A mouth pipette was used in all the subsequent manipulations of the embryo.

2. *Culture conditions*

Culture was always in *Whitten*'s medium (1970). The $NaHCO_3$ concentration of this medium was reduced to 1.4 g/l to maintain the pH at 7.2. It is important to make up this medium with pure water; Oxford water requires distillation at least four times, using a still in which the heating element is

covered with glass. The medium was warmed to 37°C and equilibrated with
90 % N_2, 5 % O_2, and 5 % CO_2, before embryos were placed into it.

During manipulation, the embryos were cultured in 1 ml of medium in a
37 mm diameter Falcon plastic petri dish. After manipulation, the embryos
were cultured in 0.05 ml microdrops of medium beneath liquid paraffin
(method of *Brinster* 1963; paraffin oil from Boots, U. K.). The glass culture
dishes were coated with silicon to prevent the naked embryos from adhering
to the surface (siliconised with 'Repelcote', BDH, U. K. and after drying soaked
twice in distilled water before final sterilization).

3. Removal of the zona pellucida
The technique of *Mintz* (1967) was followed exactly.

4. Cell dissociation
Two-cell embryos were dissociated into single blastomeres by sucking and
blowing them in and out of a mouth pipette.

5. Preparation of the virus
The virus was grown as described previously (*Harris et al.* 1966). It was
inactivated in BPL at a final concentration of 0.05 %, exactly as described
by *Neff & Enders* (1968). After this procedure, the solution was diluted to
1000 HAU/ml in ice cold phosphate buffered saline (solution A of *Dulbecco
& Vogt* 1954; abbreviated to PBS). It was spun at 250 rpm for 5 min to remove cell debris from the choriollantoic membrane of the chick egg, and the
supernatant was rapidly frozen to −70°C in 0.5 ml amounts. Immediately before use the virus suspension was quickly thawed and diluted to 200 HAU in
ice cold PBS.

6. Fusion
The virus suspension was placed in a Falcon dish with agar gel on its bottom
at 4°C (2 % agar dissolved in 0.6 % NaCl, UV-sterilized after gellation). The
eggs or blastomeres were placed beside each other in this medium for 1–4 min
and manipulated as described previously (*Graham* 1969). They were transferred to microdrops of *Whitten*'s medium at 37°C for subsequent fusion and
culture.

7. Observations of development
Fusion occurred during the first six hours culture in *Whitten*'s medium. At

this time the embryos were scored as either fused or unfused. If fused combinations divided during the following six hours they were discarded. On the fifth and the sixth day of pregnancy, the number of blastocysts which had developed was recorded.

8. Cell counting and microdensitometry

Air dried preparations were made of the fused and the unfused blastocysts (technique of *Tarkowski* 1966).

Liver nuclei were placed on each slide and all the nuclei were stained at the same time with the modified Feulgen technique of *Deitch et al.* (1968). The amount of Feulgen positive material in the embryonic and the liver nuclei was measured on a Barr and Stroud integrating microdensitometer (*Richards et al.* 1956). For each blastocyst it was only possible to measure the absorbance of some nuclei because many overlapped. In each blastocyst, at least four of the smallest nuclei and four of the largest nuclei were measured. At the same time cell counts and chromosome counts were made.

9. Embryo transfer

The blastocysts were transferred to pseudopregnant recipients by the technique of *McLaren & Michie* (1956). On the 10th day of pseudopregnancy the decidua were either fixed in Bouin's fluid and sectioned at 10 μm or they were dissected apart.

RESULTS

1. Success of fusion

The fusion observed in nine separate experiments is recorded in Table 1. There is considerable variation in the results. This appears to be due to variation in the time during which the blastomeres are exposed to the virus and also to variation in the temperature at which the fusion suspension is maintained.

In general, lysis occurs most frequently when the majority of the blastomeres fuse, and it occurs least often when the majority of the blastomeres fail to fuse. Lysis may occur before or after fusion. The fusion process is illustrated in Figs. 1 and 2.

2. Success of development

The effect of various manipulations on the development of 2-cell embryos

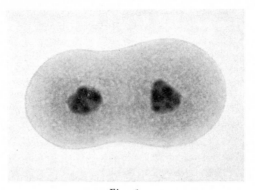

Fig. 1.

A pair of blastomeres from a 2-cell stage PO embryos at 10 min
after the start of fusion. Whole mount.

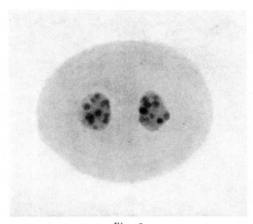

Fig. 2.

A pair of blastomeres from a 2-cell stage PO embryos at 20 min
after the start of fusion. Whole mount.

of strain PO was studied. Removal of the zona pellucida with pronase and the
manipulations involved in separating the two blastomeres reduced the success
of development to the blastocyst stage by 10 %. Exposure to the virus markedly
reduced the success of development to the blastocyst stage; it was surprising
that in all experiments, those blastomeres which fused developed more successfully than those which did not (Table 2).

158

Table 1.
The success of fusion.

Female	Male	Cell number	Unfused	Fused	Lysed
F$_1$C57BL/CBAT6T6	PO	1	10	21	1
PO	PO	2	20	5	3
PO	PO	2	3	19	6
PO	PO	2	18	6	0
PO	PO	2	25	7	4
PO	PO	2	13	5	1
F$_1$C57BL/CBAT6T6	PO	2	3	39	11
F$_1$C57BL/CBAT6T6	PO	2	16	3	0
F$_1$C57BL/CBAT6T6	PO	2	7	11	2

The number of unfused, fused, and lysed blastomere pairs was scored at six hours after they had been placed in virus suspension. The blastomere pairs were scored as lysed if one or both of the cells lysed.

Some of the deleterious effects of the virus can be overcome by using the tough embryos ovulated by F$_1$C57BL/CBAT6T6 hybrid females. Unlike the fertilized 1-cell eggs of PO females, fertilized eggs of these animals will develop into blastocysts in culture. And a few (19 %) fused 1-cell eggs will also develop into blastocysts. The superior development of these embryos is obvious when fusion is conducted at the 2-cell stage (Table 2). The success of development is increased by combining the fused cells into pairs by the technique of *Tarkowski* (1961); and in this case 100 % of the fusion products will develop into blastocysts.

3. Cell number of the blastocysts

An embryo may appear like a normal blastocyst when it only contains four cells. It is therefore important to perform cell counts on the blastocysts derived from fused blastomer; if fusion greatly reduced cell viability then they would be expected to contain an abnormally low cell number. In fact the blastocysts developing from fused blastomeres contain a similar number of cells to the blastocysts developing from normal 2-cell eggs contained inside the zona pellucida (Fig. 3). Both have a low cell number in comparison with blastocysts developing *in vivo*.

The cell number of blastocysts derived from fused blastomeres can be greatly increased by using the F$_1$ hybrid females and culturing the fused blastomeres in pairs (Fig. 4).

The blastocysts developing from eggs fused at the 1-cell stage contained the following number of cells: 34, 30, 28, 10, 8, 4.

4. DNA content of the nuclei of the blastocysts

On the fifth day of pregnancy, the trophoblast cells on the outside of the blastocyst growing *in vivo* begin to polyploidize (*Barlow & Graham* 1971). Polyploidization also occurs on the sixth day of pregnancy *in vitro* when blastocysts with the zona pellucida intact develop from the 2-cell stage. In both situations, the majority of nuclei contain 2C to 4C amounts of DNA, and of course the embryo precursor cells retain the diploid chromosome complement.

The nuclei of blastocysts which developed from fused blastomeres contained 4C to 16C amounts of DNA on the sixth day of pregnancy. This was the case

Table 2.
The development of manipulated blastomeres into blastocysts.

Female	Male	Embryonic stage	Treatment	Fraction developing into blastocysts	Percentage developing into blastocysts
PO	PO	2-cell	untreated	20/20	100
PO	PO	2-cell	– zona pellucida	19/20	95
PO	PO	2-cell	recombined	18/20	90
PO	PO	2-cell	unfused	15/33	46
PO	PO	2-cell	fused	21/31	68
F_1C57BL/CBAT6T6	PO	1-cell	– zona pellucida	9/10	90
F_1C57BL/CBAT6T6	PO	1-cell	fused	6/32	19
F_1C57BL/CBAT6T6	PO	2-cell	unfused (in pairs)	30/32	94
F_1C57BL/CBAT6T6	PO	2-cell	fused (in pairs)	10/10	100

This table contains the results from fusion experiments in which only the experimental manipulation applied to the embryo was varied. 'untreated' means that the embryos were placed in culture within 5 min of dissection from the mother. '– zona pellucida' means that the zona pellucida was removed with pronase. 'recombined' means that a 2-cell embryo was dissociated into single blastomeres and that these were next recombined in pairs without exposure to the virus suspension. 'unfused' means that the embryos were exposed to all the manipulations described above and, in addition, were placed in the virus suspension but failed to fuse during the next six hours. '(in pairs)' means that six hours after the blastomeres had been placed in the virus suspension and they were 'fused' or 'unfused', two groups of fusion partners were cultured beside each other in the same microdrop.

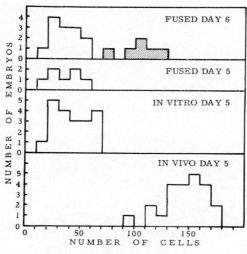

Fig. 3.

The cell number of blastocysts developing from 2-cell stage PO embryos which had either been left *in vivo*, or cultured *in vitro* with the zona pellucida intact, or fused. The cell numbers indicated with a hatched histogram are those of blastocysts obtained by fusing single blastomeres from 2-cell stage embryos (obtained from the cross F_1C57BL/CBAT6T6 X PO) and growing the fused cells in pairs.

in each of the 15 blastocysts which were studied in detail. The microdensitometry readings taken over the nuclei of three blastocysts are plotted in Fig. 5. In contrast, the nuclei of blastocysts which developed from unfused blastomeres which had been exposed to the virus contained 2C to 8C amounts of DNA (Fig. 6). It is concluded that the high DNA values are the consequence of fusion and are not due to the exposure of the blastomeres to the virus suspension.

Four of the 15 blastocysts developing from fused blastomeres contained one metaphase plate with 80 chromosomes. It is concluded that fusion initially produces tetraploid cells, and that some of the cells in the trophoblast layer of the blastocyst polyploidize further on the sixth day of pregnancy to give the observed 16C DNA amounts.

5. *Development of the blastocysts in vivo*

A total of 36 blastocysts which had developed from fused blastomeres were transferred into the uterus of recipient females in the early morning of the fourth day of pseudopregnancy. On the 10th day of pseudopregnancy, the recipient females were killed. Three out of four recipients were pregnant and

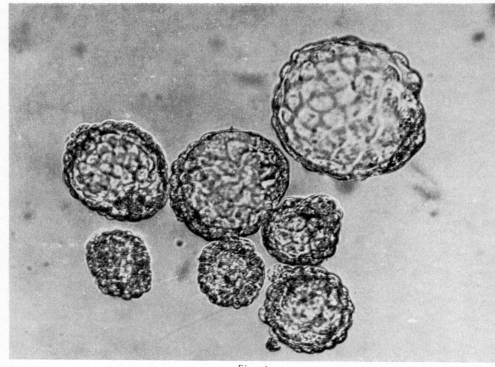

Fig. 4.

Seven tetraploid blastocysts on the sixth day of pregnancy. The cell counts of six of these blastocysts are shown in the hatched region of Fig. 3.

a total of 11 decidual swellings were found. Nine of these were dissected and no embryos could be found. The remaining two were fixed and sectioned. Each decidua contained a trophoblast growth (Fig. 7).

The failure of the tetraploid blastocysts to develop into live young could be due to two causes:

(a) The fusion technique
(b) Tetraploidy

To distinguish these two possibilities the following experiment was performed. Two-cell embryos were obtained from the cross CBAT6T6 × PO and cultured for about 24 hours when they had each formed a 4-cell embryo. The blastomeres were dissociated, and one was fused with one blastomere of a 2-cell stage PO embryo. The embryo now contained a diploid PO blastomere and a tetraploid (PO + F$_1$CBAT6T6/PO) blastomere. Seven of these com-

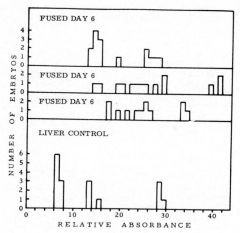

Fig. 5.

The relative absorbance of liver nuclei and the nuclei of three blastocysts which developed from fused blastomeres. The liver nuclei act as internal controls of the absorbance shown by 2C, 4C, and 8C nuclei. The nuclei of these blastocysts appear to contain 4C to 8C, and larger amounts of DNA.

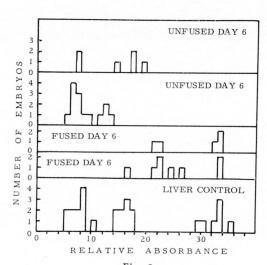

Fig. 6.

The relative absorbance of liver nuclei and the nuclei of blastocysts which developed from fused and unfused blastomeres which had both been exposed to the virus suspension. The nuclei of blastocysts derived from unfused blastomeres contain mainly 2C and 4C amounts of DNA; the nuclei of blastocysts derived from fused blastomeres mainly contain 4C to 8C amounts as do the blastocysts in Fig. 5.

163

11*

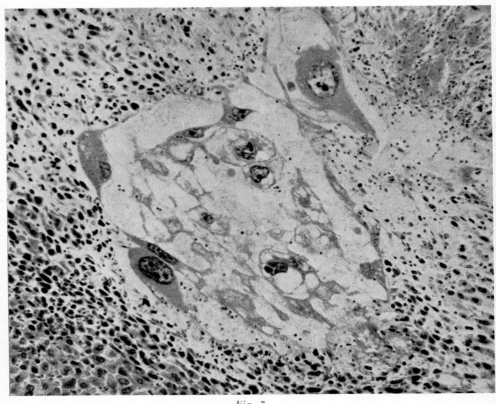

Fig. 7.

A trophoblast outgrowth of giant cells on the 10th day of pregnancy. This was obtained by transferring tetraploid blastocysts to the uterus during the early morning of the fourth day of pseudopregnancy.

binations were made and six developed into blastocysts. These were transferred to a pseudopregnant recipient and three white (PO) young were born.

This experiment demonstrates that exposure to the virus does not itself prevent the subsequent development of a blastomere into a live mouse. However, the tetraploid partner of such a blastomere appeared not to contribute to the formation of the embryo. The failure of the tetraploid blastocysts to develop into live young is therefore a consequence of tetraploidy rather than of the fusion technique.

DISCUSSION

It is clear that exposure of mouse blastomeres to the BPL inactivated Sendai virus reduces the success with which they normally develop into blastocysts. However, those blastomeres which do fuse develop rather better than those which do not. The blastocysts formed from fused blastomeres contain a similar number of cells to blastocysts developing from untreated blastomeres, and it therefore appears that fusion does not necessarily have a deleterious effect on development up to this stage.

Fusion may inhibit development after the blastocyst stage when the embryos are transferred back to a foster mother. It seems likely, however, that the failure of the tetraploid blastocysts to develop into live young is a consequence of tetraploidy itself rather than of the fusion technique.

ACKNOWLEDGMENTS

The technique described in this paper is the result of prolonged discussions with Dr. H. Koprowski, Dr. A. K. Tarkowski, and Dr. W. H. Whitten. I would like to thank them for their advice. Miss Z. A. White provided excellent technical assistance and the MRC supported the work.

REFERENCES

Baranska W. & Koprowski H.: J. exp. Zool. *174* (1970) 1.
Barlow P. B. & Graham C. F.: (1971) in preparation.
Brinster R. L.: Exp. Cell Res. *32* (1963) 205.
Deitch A., Wagner D. & Richart R. M.: J. Histochem. Cytochem. *16* (1968) 371.
Dulbecco R. & Vogt M.: J. exp. Med. *99* (1954) 167.
Graham C. F.: The Wistar Institute Symposium Monograph, Heterospecific genome interaction. Defendi V., Ed. (1969) 19.
Harris H., Watkins J. F., Ford C. E. & Schoefl G. I.: J. Cell. Sci. *1* (1966) 1.
McLaren A. & Michie D.: J. exp. Biol. *33* (1956) 394.
Mintz B. In: Wilt F. H. and Wessells N. K., Eds. Methods in developmental biology, New York, T. Y. Crowell (1967).
Neff J. M. & Enders J. F.: Proc. Soc. exp. Biol. Med. (N. Y.) *127* (1968) 260.
Okada Y., Murayama F. & Yamada K.: Virology *28* (1966) 115.
Richards B. M., Walker P. M. B. & Deeley E. M.: Ann. N. Y. Acad. Sci. *63* (1956) 831.
Runner M. N. & Palm J.: J. exp. Zool. *124* (1953) 303.
Tarkowski A. K.: Nature (Lond.) *190* (1961) 857.
Tarkowski A. K.: Cytogenetics *5* (1966) 394.
Whitten W. K.: Advances in Biosciences *5* (1970) in press.
Whitten W. K. & Biggers J. D.: J. Reprod. Fertil. *17* (1968) 399.

Johannisson: I wonder if these two blastomeres have to be in the same stage of the mitotic cycle? You told us that it is also possible to fuse a blastomere with an adult cell. In that case, what will happen to that heterokaryon?

Graham: There is an enormous body of literature (reviewed in *Harris* 1970), which suggests that if you wish both nuclei to contribute equally to the hybrid cell which develops from them, then those nuclei should be at similar stages of the cell cycle. Secondly, they probably should be from cells dividing at similar rates. In my experience, if you introduce a cell in the G_2 phase of the cell cycle into a blastomere which is in S phase, then they will divide in synchrony and you will end up with a tetraploid cell. On the other hand, if you introduce the nucleus from an adult cell in G_1 phase of the cell cycle into a blastomere which is in the G_2 phase of the cell cycle, in my experience, the adult cell nucleus normally becomes pyknotic as the recipient cell nucleus enters mitosis. This would be similar to the chromosome fragmentation phenomenon which has been described in other hybrid combinations.

Ryan: Have you tried to destroy the genetic material in one cell and then fuse, in essence, cytoplasm? What effect would this manipulation have?

Graham: I haven't tried very seriously. If one is thinking of moving towards the technique of nuclear transplantation in mammals, then it would obviously be necessary to have some means of enucleating the egg. It turns out that this is an extremely simple thing to do. When you place a mouse egg in culture, after exposing it to hyaluronidase to remove the cumulus oophorus, and also to pronase to remove the zona pellucida, then the egg is activated and a second polar body is given off. If during that time, you expose the egg to colcemid, then, in at least 40 per cent of the cases, the female pronucleus and the second polar body nucleus are both extruded into the second polar body. This provides you with a technique for enucleation, without exposure of the egg to X-rays or any other manipulation. The real problem is that any time you manipulate an egg, its development to the blastocyst stage is impaired. Most of the experiments I have discussed in this paper have been performed at the two cell stage, which is easy to culture to the blastocyst stage. Enucleation with colcemid must be performed at the one cell stage, and after manipulation this is more difficult to culture.

Rodbell: Is calcium ion required for the action of Sendai virus? Is low temperature incubation required for the fusion process to occur in the presence of the virus?

Graham: I do the fusion in phosphate buffered saline, and no doubt there are calcium contaminants. Five degrees centigrade increases the stickiness of the cells and the frequency with which they fuse at 37°C.

Nakane: Have you any idea of what happens to the Sendai virus after fusion? Do they continue to be amplified as they become a part of the plasma membrane, or are they being in some way discarded?

Graham: The Sendai virus is inactivated by β-propiolactone. I don't know the fate of the Sendai virus antigens in this situation.

Nakane: I have chased the Sendai virus with the antibody, and so far I can trace them at 4°C and perhaps one or two minutes later at 37°C, but somehow I have not been able to chase them beyond this. I wonder if you have any information?

Graham: I don't have any information, but I am encouraged, because, if the Sendai virus antigens remained on the cell surface for a long time, this might provide problems as far as the acceptance of the embryo by the mother is concerned.

Diczfalusy: Dr. Graham, you indicated that in the nine experiments you presented there was a considerable difference in the success rate of fusion. What, in your experience, are the optimal conditions?

Graham: The optimal conditions are described in my paper, and I now have to account for the enormous variations in the results.

First, the fusion potency of the virus is not directly correlated with the haemagglutinating ability of the virus, which is the titer which you measure when you are trying to compare similar virus suspensions. Secondly, during the manipulations, the blastomeres which are to be fused, are placed together at 5°C for a very short time, and then suddenly the temperature is raised to 37°C. This involves manipulating them, and there is a variation in the time it takes. The degree of clumsiness which one has on a particular day reflects one's physiological state, and that varies. I gave the success rate for different experiments in my paper because a lot of people, when they start this kind of work find it very hard, and a little bit later find it very easy. And so I thought I should be honest.

Johannisson: You were using the Feulgen technique in estimating the amount of DNA, and you were using spectrophotometrical methods. Did you develop any special technique for measuring the amount of DNA in the cells? I mean, it must have offered some difficulty when you have a blastocyst.

Graham: The microdensitometer readings were made on preparations of blastocysts obtained by the air dried technique. So one is dealing with what in effect is a monolayer of cells. For hydrolysis, I used 5 N HCl for 30 minutes of room temperature and this gave us the maximum absorbance following the Feulgen technique.

Reference:

Harris H.: Cell Fusion, Oxford University Press (1970).

KAROLINSKA SYMPOSIA ON RESEARCH METHODS IN REPRODUCTIVE ENDOCRINOLOGY
3rd Symposium . In Vitro Methods in Reproductive Cell Biology
January 25–27, 1971

Human Reproduction Research Unit,
Department of Gynaecology and Obstetrics, Hôpital Saint Pierre,
University of Brussels. Belgium

IMMUNOHISTOCHEMISTRY OF INDIVIDUAL ADENOHYPOPHYSIAL CELLS

By

P. Leleux and C. Robyn[1)]

ABSTRACT

Immunohistochemistry is the intracellular detection of antigens by the use of specific antibodies labelled with a tracer. The choice of the tracer is such that the sites of the antigen-antibody reactions can be visualized by microscopic examination. The present report refers to the human pituitary where most of the immunohistochemical identifications of adenohypophysial cells were conducted with antibodies specific of their hormonal content and labelled with fluorescein isothiocyanate as tracer. Such immunohistochemical identifications had to be correlated to the morphological nomenclatures of the glandular cells based on histochemical stainings. Confusion has been introduced in these nomenclatures by the definition of three to eight cell types using different criteria and different terminologies. In the present report, owing to this absence of standardization, the comparative evaluation of immunohistochemical data have been based on *Romeis* (1940) and *Pearse & van Noorden* (1963) nomenclatures.

There is strong experimental evidence supporting the localization of adrenocorticotrophic hormone (ACTH) in the basophils of Romeis β type (R-mucoids of Pearse). Somatotrophic hormone (STH) has been consistently found in the acidophils of Romeis α type. In the human, there is no direct evidence to support the localization of prolactin (LTH) in the acidophils of Romeis ε type. Luteinizing hormone (LH) and follicle stimulating hormone (FSH) have both been located in the basophils of Romeis δ type (S-mucoids of Pearse). Further investigations into the human and also into other mammalian species are required to determine

[1)] Chercheur Qualifié au Fonds National de la Recherche Scientifique (Belgium).

if the gonadotrophic hormones have different localizations on the cellular or on the subcellular level. The immunohistochemical localizations of thyroid stimulating hormone (TSH) and melanocyte stimulating hormone (MSH) have not been convincingly achieved.

The conclusions drawn from immunohistochemical studies of the adeno-hypophysis are essentially limited by the cross reactions existing between STH and prolactin, between ACTH and MSH and between LH, FSH and TSH.

More experimental data on these immunological cross reactions are still required before more accurate morphological discriminations can be achieved between the cell types secreting STH and prolactin, between those secreting ACTH and MSH and between those secreting LH, FSH and TSH. In addition, when hormones of the adenohypophysis are chemically and/or antigenically closely related, the cells responsible for their secretion are morphologically very similar too.

Finally, immunohistochemical studies revealed the lack of species speci-ficity of the pituitary hormones. Extensive cross reactions have been shown between human STH and STH of all mammalian species studied so far. Consistent cross reactions were also found between human gonado-trophins and those of several mammalian species.

When considering the characterization of the adenohypophysial cells, three steps can be recognized. First, morphological nomenclatures were elaborated on the basis of staining patterns obtained by histochemical methods. In the meantime, it appeared that the adenohypophysis was responsible for the secretion of protein hormones corresponding to seven biological activities: STH, prolactin (LTH), ACTH, TSH, FSH, LH and MSH. The next logical step was the assessment of a one to one relationship between the secretion of each of these hormones and a well defined cell type referring to a morphological nomenclature. The third step was the application of immunohistochemical procedures to the identification of adenohypophysial cells. Due to the in-creasing degree of specificity which can be reached in the preparation of antisera against isolated pituitary hormones, the secretory function of cells can be established with increasing reliability. A synthesis of all morphological, functional and immunohistochemical data is essential to attain the highest accuracy in the characterization of individual adenohypophysial cells.

1. *Histochemical techniques*. – Historically, the first histochemical techniques using acid and basic staining enabled establishment of distinctions between three cell types in the adenohypophysis. They were the *acidophils,* the *baso-phils* and the *chromophobes (Mallory* 1938). As the staining methods became more sophisticated, the described cell types became more numerous and the nomenclatures more confused. There are almost as many nomenclatures as authors (Table 1). Although histochemical classifications are based at present on the affinity of the pituitary cells for the periodic acid-Schiff (PAS) staining (*McManus* 1946), the terms »acidophils« and »basophils« are still frequently

Table 1.
Histochemical nomenclatures of human adenohypophysial cells.

Cell types	Terminologies[1] and staining patterns of human adenohypophysial cells characterized by					
	Acid fuchsin & anilin blue (Mallory 1938)	Resorcine, fuchsin & Heidenhain's azan (Romeis 1940)	Aldehyde thionine, PAS[2] & orange G (Ezrin & Murray 1963)	Alcian blue, PAS & orange G (Pearse & van Noorden 1963)	Aldehyde thionine. PAS & orange G (Purves 1966)	Alcian blue, PAS & orange G (Herlant & Pasteels 1967)
Acidophils — Red	α Red	—	Light orange Orange G +	α Yellow	α Yellow Orange G +	α Yellow Orange G +
	ε Orange				ε Red erythrosinophil[3]	ε Red erythrosinophil
						»Corticotrophs« Thin granulated erythrosinophil

Group					
Basophils or Mucoids	β Brown violet	β1 Large red; PAS + aldehyde thion. —	R mucoid PAS +	ζ Purple β; PAS +	Classic β purple; PAS +
	Blue	β2 Large polyhedral dark blue; PAS +; aldehyde thionine +	S2 mucoid purple blue	Θ Blue β angular; aldehyde thionine +	»Thyrotrophs« Polyhedral dark blue; PAS +; alcian blue +
	δ Anilin blue	δ1 Small oval purple; PAS +; aldehyde thionine +	S1 mucoid purple	δ Round purple PAS +; aldehyde thion. +	δ Oval violet; PAS +; alcian blue +
		δ2 Small red; PAS +			
	γ Light purple	β3 Light purple; degranulated		γ Weakly PAS +	γ Weakly PAS +; lipidic inclusions
Chromophobes	Pale grey	Colourless	Colourless	Colourless	Colourless
	Colourless	Colourless			

1) Equivalent cell types in the different terminologies are on the same horizontal lines.

2) PAS = Periodic acid Schiff.

3) Erythrosinophil only when stained by Herlant's tetrachrome technique (*Herlant* 1960).

171

used. The trichrome techniques combining alcian-blue or aldehyde thionine with PAS and orange G are mostly used to characterize the basophils or mucoids. The Herlant's tetrachrome technique combining erythrosin, anilin blue, orange G and alizarin blue (*Herlant* 1960) is most convenient for characterizing the acidophils.

As can be seen from Table 1 most of the classifications of the human adenohypophysial cell types to a Greek alphabetical terminology are proposed by *Romeis* (1940). This author has described five cell types in the human adenohypophysis: α, β, γ, δ and ε. Later, other investigators have used the same Greek alphabet, however, to designate quite different staining patterns of the cells. An attempt to correlate the existing morphological nomenclatures is also presented in Table 1. There is a high degree of correlation between all staining methods when considering the characterization of acidophils and chromophobes. However, the limits between the subgroups of basophils are very hazy and vary from one author to another.

No specific chemical staining reaction is available for any pituitary hormone. Therefore, the histochemical procedures could not provide direct proofs for crediting a particular cell with the formation of a given hormone. Most arguments to support the functional significance of the nomenclature of human adenohypophysial cells were derived from the modifications of the morphology and of the staining patterns of well defined cell types in endocrine disorders. The acidophilic adenoma of the pituitary associated with acromegaly contains and secretes large amounts of STH. Such tumours are made of hyperactive and partially degranulated α cells (*Ross & Bahn* 1960). Therefore these cells were considered as secreting STH. The modifications of the β cells in Addison's disease and their transformation into Crooke cells (*Crooke* 1935) in Cushing's disease were correlated with the alterations of ACTH and MSH secretions occurring in these disorders (*e. g. Herlant & Pasteels* 1967). Castration is followed by striking morphological changes in basophilic cell types indicating their gonadotrophic function (*e. g. Herlant & Pasteels* 1967). Furthermore endocrinologists have devised clever experimental models in several mammalian species to elucidate more accurately the intracellular location of hormones. In the rat pituitary LH, FSH and TSH secretion were assigned to three different types of basophils on the basis of morphological changes occurring in these cell types following thyroidectomy and following castration combined with injection of steroids (*Halmi* 1952; *Purves & Griesbach* 1951, 1954).

Similar conclusions were reached from experimental findings in several other mammals (*Herlant* 1956, 1959; *Herlant & Canivenc* 1960). The extrapolation to the human pituitary of these data derived from indirect experiments in animals was the origin of increasing confusion in the identification of the secretory functions of the human basophils where the discrimination

172

between subgroups is not clearcut. The danger of such extrapolation is further emphasized by the fact that »based on experimental procedures combined with chemical staining or electron microscopy, the secretion of corticotrophin, has been attributed to acidophils, basophils and chromophobes« (*Baker* 1970). More recently, experimental data on the identification of human adenohypophysial cells were obtained from *in vitro* cultures of foetal pituitaries. *Pasteels* (1962, 1970) showed that during the first week of such cultures the prolactin of the medium increased whereas the STH activity decreased concomitantly with the decrease in number of the α cells. The cultures were then made up almost exclusively of hypertrophied ε cells. These cells were considered to be secreting the large amounts of prolactin.

For a detailed review of morphological and histochemical data on the hormonal secretions of the pituitary collected from human endocrine disorders and from animal experiments, the papers by *Halmi* (1963), *Pearse & van Noorden* (1963), *Purves* (1966) and *Herlant & Pasteels* (1967) should be consulted.

2. *Immunohistochemical techniques.* – Immunohistochemistry can be defined as the intracellular detection of antigens by the use of specific antibodies labelled with a tracer. The choice of the tracer is such that the sites of antigen-antibody reactions can be visualized by microscopic examination.

2.1. *Tracer.* – The credit goes to *Coons et al.* (1942) for the introduction of the first immunohistochemical technique using antibodies conjugated with fluorescein isocyanate. This procedure has been improved by the conjugation of antibodies with other tracers such as fluorescein isothiocyanate (*Marshall et al.* 1958), rhodamine (*Silverstein* 1957) and enzymes (*Nakane & Pierce* 1966; *Avrameas* 1968). Using these tracers, the cellular sites of the antigen-antibody reaction were examined under light microscope. Electron microscopic studies became also possible with the use of antibodies conjugated with electron dense substances : ferritin (*Singer & Schick* 1961) and peroxydase (*Nakane* 1970). Most immunohistochemical studies of the human pituitary were conducted using fluorescein isothiocyanate as tracer.

2.2. *Fixation.* – The fixation procedure must preserve the morphological structure of the tissue and maintain the antigen *in situ*. The first immunohistochemical investigations of the pituitary were carried out on frozen sections. It was presumed that classical histological fixations would denature the antigenic structure of proteins (*Coons et al.* 1942; *Coons & Kaplan* 1950; *Marshall* 1951; *Cruikshank & Currie* 1958; *Leznoff et al.* 1960). Although the immunofluorescent stainings obtained on frozen sections were very satisfactory, it was almost impossible to establish any precise correlation between the fluorescent positive cells and the cell types of the histochemical nomenclatures. Indeed the morphology and the staining patterns of the glandular cells were not preserved on frozen sections. Most recent immunohistochemical studies of

173

the pituitary were conducted on conventional paraffin sections. *Midgley &* *Pierce* (1962) have shown that the antigenicity of human gonadotrophins was preserved after fixation in formalin and Bouin's solutions. In our experience, Hollande Bouin and Helly fixatives (*Langeron* 1942) were the most suitable for immunohistochemical studies of the pituitary (*Robyn et al.* 1964; *Leleux &* *Robyn* 1970). It is, however, essential to wash off all traces of fixative from the glands for one to three days under running water (*Midgley* 1966; *Bain &* *Ezrin* 1970; *Leleux & Robyn* 1970). Whenever omitting this step, a very intense non specific fluorescence of all tissue structures masked the specific reaction. After the last step of the immunofluorescent technique, the paraffin sections are treated according to the classical histochemical procedures without significant alterations of the staining properties of the adenohypophysial cells. Correlations between the cells reacting specifically with the anti-hormone antibodies and the cell types of the nomenclatures can be investigated with accuracy.

2.3. *Controls.* – A further advantage of the paraffin sections is the possibility of easily obtaining serial sections of 4.0 and even 2.0 μm. The specificity of the immunofluorescent staining is readily demonstrated by the incubation of pairs of adjacent serial sections with a specific antiserum and with one of the control sera as listed in Table 2, respectively. In this situation, the same cells are fluorescent positive on the first section and fluorescent negative on the second.

The use of serial sections does not only improve the reliability of the controls but also facilitates the observations of the immunoreactivity of the same cells incubated with antisera of different specificities. As illustrated in Fig. 2 (c and e; g and i) when covering two consecutive serial sections with an anti-LH and anti-FSH serum, respectively, the same cells reacted to both antisera.

2.4. *Direct and indirect stainings.* – In the first description of the immunofluorescent technique by *Coons et al.* (1942), the histological sections were covered with the specific antibodies conjugated with the tracer. In the indirect or sandwich technique proposed by *Weller & Coons* (1954) the sections were incubated in a first step with the unconjugated antiserum obtained against the cellular antigen to be detected. In a second step the immunoglobulins bound to the cellular antigen were stained by an anti-immunoglobulin serum conjugated with the tracer. The sandwich technique has several advantages. Provided all antisera prepared against cellular antigens were obtained in the same species, only one fluorescent antiglobulin serum is required to detect any of the antigen-antibody reacting sites. The anti-immunoglobulin sera are usually of high titer and the antibody losses caused by the conjugation procedure are negligible. Finally, the sandwich staining is some 4 to 12 times more sensitive than the direct technique (*Coons* 1956; *Pressman et al.* 1958). The additional combining sites introduced with the unconjugated antibodies are likely to be

Table 2.

Specificity controls in immunofluorescence studies of adenohypophysial cells conducted on tissue sections incubated with an anti-hormone serum and with an anti-immuno-globulin serum, successively.

First incubation with a serum obtained in an animal of species A	Second incubation with an antiserum obtained in an animal of species B against the immunoglobulins of species A	Results
1) Non immune serum	Unconjugated antiserum	Tissue autofluorescence
2) Non immune serum	Antiserum conjugated with fluorescein isothiocyanate	Non specific fluorescence
3) Anti-hormone serum	,,	Specific immunofluorescence in individual cells
4) Anti-hormone serum + hormone used for immunization	,,	Extinction of specific immunofluorescence
5) Anti-hormone serum + other hormones	,,	Decrease of specific immunofluorescence in case of cross reactions
6) Anti-hormone serum + other proteins	,,	Extinction of non specific immunofluorescence due to non anti-hormone antibodies
7) Anti-hormone serum	Unconjugated antiserum followed by the conjugated one	No immunofluorescence; no antigenic sites available for the fluorescent antibodies

responsible for this improved sensitivity of the indirect technique (*Nairn* 1964).

2.5. *Microphotography.* – Photographic record is essential owing to the short life of the fluorescent antibody staining and to its complete disappearance during the further histochemical staining.

Very short exposure times (20 to 120 s) are critical for the sharpness of the pictures of the fluorescent positive cells. Furthermore the high energy ultraviolet light decreases dramatically the affinity of the hypophysial cells for the delicate histochemical stainings when the exposure time exceeds 120 s. In our experience such high speed exposures could only be achieved by the sandwich technique.

2.6. *Specificity of the antisera.* – In immunohistochemistry the definition of the reactive cells is implicit in the specificity of the antisera obtained against the cellular antigens. Therefore any conclusion drawn from immunohisto-chemical data has to be balanced by the degree of specificity of the antisera.

First, the specificity is influenced by the degree of purity of the hormonal preparations injected for immunization. With an exception for ACTH and MSH which have been synthesized as polypeptides, the adenohypophysial hormones are not isolated in an immunochemically pure state and their biochemical characterization has not been achieved. Therefore the immunological homogeneity of all antisera even when obtained following immunization with the most purified preparations should be carefully studied by techniques such as quantitative immunoprecipitation and immunoelectrophoresis. Usually in addition to the hormone-antihormone reaction several other antigen-antibody reactions are detected. The unspecific antibodies can be removed by absorption with protein extracts containing large amounts of the corresponding non hormonal antigens.

In the definition of the antisera the next step is the estimation of their neutralizing potencies tested against the biological activity of the hormone injected for immunization. »The classic definition of a hormone is . . . implicit in its bioassay« (*Albert* 1968). Therefore the definition of an anti-hormone serum should be implicit in the biossay of its hormone neutralizing activity. The biological characterization of antisera should be based on partial neutralization of a given hormone and on specific and statistically valid bioassay of the fraction of hormone left unneutralized. Such a method has been successfully used for the characterization of antigonadotrophic sera (*e. g. Robyn* 1969).

Another difficulty in assessing the specificity arises from the cross reactions which have been established between ACTH and MSH (*McGarry et al.* 1962; *Kracht & Hachmeister* 1967), between STH and prolactin (*Hayashida* 1962) and between LH, FSH and TSH (*Schlaff et al.* 1968; *Odell et al.* 1969). Here too, quantitative evaluations of the cross reacting antibodies are essential if

---

Fig. 1.

Localization by immunofluorescence of somatotrophin (STH) and luteinizing hormone (LH) in human (a and b), porcine (c and d), dog (e and f), castrated rat (g and h), goat (i) and bat (j) adenohypophyses. A pituitary section of a 46 year old man was incubated with an anti-human STH serum (a). The fluorescent positive cells are identified as orangeophilic when stained by the erythrosin, analin blue, orange G, alizarin blue tetrachrome method (b). The sections of animal pituitaries were incubated with anti-human STH serum (c. e and g) or with an antiserum neutralizing specifically the human LH activity (d, f, h, i and j). The antisera obtained against human hormones reacted specifically with adenohypophysial cells of all mammalian pituitaries investigated.

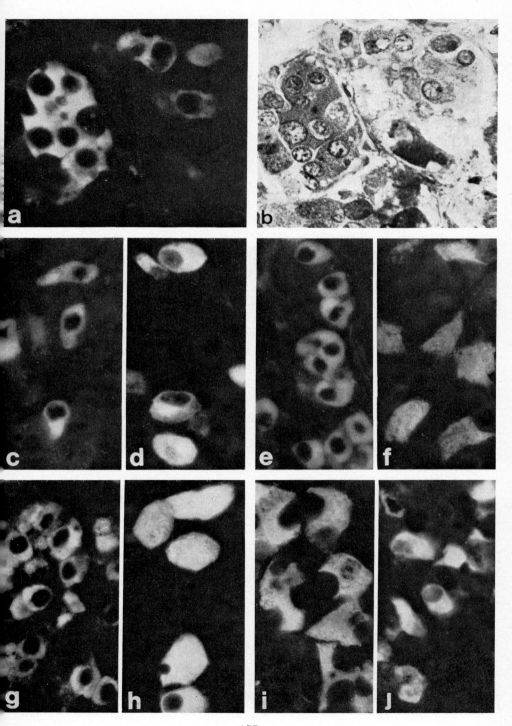

one wishes to prepare biologically and immunologically specific antisera by selective neutralization of these antibodies. Absorption procedures carried out on a strictly quantitative basis have been employed to prepare antisera neutralizing specifically the biological activity of LH or that of FSH (*Robyn & Leleux* 1969, 1971). The problem of selective neutralization of cross reacting antisera has been recently reviewed by *Petrusz* (1969).

Finally one should bear in mind that the specificity found in an immunochemical system where antigen-antibody reactions take place in buffer solutions is not necessarily the same as in an immunohistochemical system where the antigen-antibody reactions take place on the solid phase of the tissue section. Different antibody populations or different parts of the antigen-antibody reaction could be involved in these two systems. In an immunofluorescence system, the gonadotrophic cells of the rat pituitary were specifically stained by anti-human gonadotrophin sera (*Monroe & Midgley* 1966, 1969; *Leleux et al.* 1968). However, this interspecies cross reaction could never be shown by any other immunochemical technique.

3. *Identification of individual adenohypophysial cells by immunohistochemistry.* – In the critical review of the experimental data we shall refer most of the time to the human species or to cross reactions between pituitary hormones of the human and those of other mammals.

It should also be emphasized that the detection of a hormonal antigen in a cell only indicates storage and not necessarily synthesis or secretion of the hormone by this cell.

3.1. *ACTH and MSH.* – The first immunohistochemical studies of the pituitary were conducted by *Marshall* (1951). A fluorescent anti-porcine ACTH serum reacted with some basophilic cells of porcine pituitaries. This author, however, failed to identify more precisely the basophilic cells on frozen sections stained by the aldehyde-fuschin method. *Leznoff et al.* (1962) localized ACTH in basophils of the human pituitary. *Pearse & van Noorden* (1963) combining immunochemistry and histochemistry reported that ACTH was confined to mucoid cells of the R type equivalent to Romeis β cells (see Table 1). This author found also an important proportion of fluorescent positive cells infiltrating the pars nervosa. The mucoid cells of the R type and the Crooke cells were also reported by *Kracht & Hachmeister* (1967) to be fluorescent positive when incubated with antisera obtained following immunization of rabbits with extracted and synthesized ACTH.

In the mammalian species the intermediate lobe is considered to be responsible for the secretion of MSH (*e. g. Herlant & Pasteels* 1967). *Purves* (1961) and *Herlant & Pasteels* (1967) suggested that in the human the basophils of Romeis β type, some of them invading the pars nervosa, corresponded to the intermediate lobe which is absent in this species. Owing to the cross reactions between ACTH and MSH the identification of a secreting cell for

178

each of these hormones was not possible by immunohistochemistry so far. *Robyn & Leleux* (1969, 1971) reported that some non specific antisera obtained against human hypophysial gonadotrophin preparations (anti-HHG sera) reacted in immunofluorescence with Romeis β cells. They emphasized the fact that these non specific antisera also reacted consistently with the intermediate lobe of rats, monkeys and dogs. These data would favour the hypothesis that the β cells or R mucoids contain not only ACTH but also MSH.

3.2. *STH and prolactin.* – Using rabbit antisera obtained following immunization with a human STH preparation (*Raben* 1957), *Leznoff et al.* (1960) found a specific fluorescence in the acidophils of the human adenohypophysis. Frozen sections were used and no precise correspondence should be established between the fluorescent positive cells and the α or the ε acidophilic types by the use of subtle histochemical stainings. *Grumbach et al.* (1962) reported that STH was located only in the acidophils of the α type (Table 1). In immunohistochemical studies on several animal pituitaries combining the use of anti-human STH sera with that of the Herlant's tetrachrome staining, it has repeatedly been shown that STH was confined to orangeophilic cells equivalent to the human α cells (*Nayak et al.* 1968; *Baker et al.* 1969; *Baker* 1970; *Herbert & Hayashida* 1970). We also found extensive cross reactions between human STH and STH of several other mammalian species. An antiserum produced against Raben human STH (Batch No. 11) reacted specifically in immunofluorescence with the α cells of the human pituitary and with orangeophilic cells of canine, ovine, porcine, simian, rat and bat pituitaries (see examples on Fig. 1). In the adenohypophysis of a dwarf swine strain, no fluorescent cells could be found. Concomitantly, no orangeophilic cells were demonstrable by the tetrachrome staining. Finally, by immunohistochemistry we detected STH cells in human foetal pituitaries from the third month of pregnancy at a time when all adenohypophysial cells were still chromophobic.

The only immunohistochemical study of the human pituitary conducted with an anti-human prolactin serum has been reported by *Breustedt et al.* (1965). This antiserum obtained following immunization with prolactin isolated from human pituitaries by *Apostolakis* (1965) cross reacted with STH and failed to discriminate between α and ε acidophils. However, in immunohistochemical studies of several animal pituitaries using antianimal prolactin sera, this hormone has been repeatedly localized in erythrosinophilic cells equivalent to the human ε cells (*Nayak et al.* 1968; *Baker et al.* 1969; *Baker* 1970). In the pituitary of primates, *Herbert & Hayashida* (1970) by a similar technique recently localized prolactin in acidophilic cells very different from the orangeophilic α cells containing STH.

3.3. *LH, FSH and TSH.* – Taking advantage of the immunological cross reaction between human chorionic gonadotrophin (HCG) and human pituitary

179

LH, *Midgley* (1964) and *Robyn et al.* (1964) located LH by immunofluorescence in PAS positive cells of the human adenohypophysis. *Robyn* (1965) reported that the fluorescent positive cells reacting with anti-HCG antibodies were basophils equivalent to Romeis δ cells when stained with the trichrome alcian blue-PAS-orange G technique (Table 1 and Fig. 2). Using a similar staining method, *Midgley* (1966) described the fluorescent positive cells as »turquoise colored« and identified them as the S1 mucoids of Pearse. It seems that according to *Purves* (1966) the S1 mucoids are closely related to the Romeis δ cells (see Table 1). More recently, *Bain & Ezrin* (1970) found a specific fluorescence with conjugated anti-HCG sera in »basophilic cells having PAS and aldehyde thionine positive granules«. They could not identify the cells as a well defined cell type of their previous nomenclature. The LH cells represented only a part of Ezrin δ_1 subgroup of basophils (Table 1).

Kofler & Fogel (1964) endeavoured to discriminate between FSH and LH cells using »purified« anti-HCG and anti-human menopausal gonadotrophin (anti-HMG) sera on frozen sections of human pituitaries. In immunofluorescence, each of the two types of antisera reacted with different populations of cells. However, the anti-LH and the anti-FSH activities of the antisera were not estimated by bioassays and the fluorescent positive cells were not characterized by histochemical methods classically used to stain the human basophils. *Midgley* (1964, 1966) also indicated that two different adenohypophysial cell types reacted with anti-HCG sera neutralizing LH and with an anti-HMG serum neutralizing FSH, respectively. When stained with the alcian blue-PAS-orange G method, the LH cells slightly PAS positive were blue (S1 mucoids of Pearse) and the FSH cells more strongly PAS positive were purple blue (S2 mucoids of Pearse; see also Table 1). The problem of the identification of the gonadotrophic cells of the human pituitary becomes even more confused when considering that anti-HCG and anti-HMG sera cross reacted both with LH and with FSH as tested by bioassays of neutralizing potencies (*Robyn & Diczfalusy* 1968) and by radioimmunological methods (*Faiman & Ryan* 1967; *Midgley* 1967; *Taymor et al.* 1967; *Rosen et al.* 1969;

Fig. 2.

Photomicrographs of the same human gonadotrophic cells stained first by an immunofluorescence technique (a, c, e, g and i) and consecutively by the alcian blue, PAS, orange G method (b, d, f, h and j). A pituitary section from a 46 year old man was incubated with an anti-human chorionic gonadotrophin serum (a). The fluorescent cells are alcian blue and PAS positive (b). Two adjacent serial sections from a 32 year old man with testicular atrophy were incubated with antisera neutralizing specifically the human LH activity (c and g) or the human FSH activity (e and i). The same PAS and blue alcian positive cells are fluorescent with both anti-LH and anti-FSH sera (d, f, h and j).

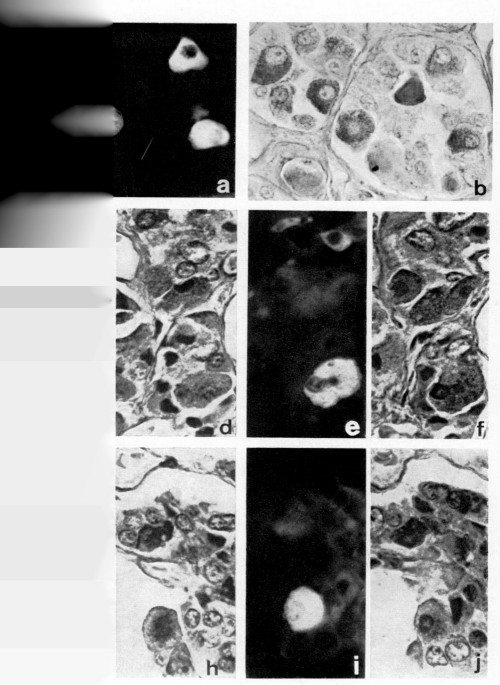

Fig. 2.

Butt & Lynch 1969). *Jeffcoate* (1970) has even developed a radioimmuno-assay of human FSH using an anti-HCG serum.

As illustrated in Fig. 2, *Robyn & Leleux* (1969, 1971) have shown that an absorbed anti-HCG serum neutralizing specifically LH and an absorbed anti-HHG serum neutralizing specifically FSH reacted in immunofluorescence both with the same adenohypophysical cells : Romeis δ cells.

In pathological cases (castration, testicular atrophy) the population of fluorescent positive cells with both anti-LH and anti-FSH antibodies showed all degrees of hypertrophy and degranulation when stained with the alcian blue-PAS-orange G method (Fig. 2). Some cells were typical purple δ cells, others were identical to Romeis γ cells but all intermediate forms were also found (*Robyn & Leleux* 1971). This diversification of the basophils in patho-logical cases could reflect different functional states of the same cell type or an exacerbation of slight morphological differences undetected in normal pituitaries.

Monroe & Midgley (1966) and *Leleux et al.* (1968) have shown that anti-human gonadotrophin sera reacted in immunofluorescence with cells of the rat pituitary. These cells were characterized by the alcian blue-PAS-orange G method and were identical with the »gonadotrophs« described by *Purves & Griesbach* (1954). Furthermore following castration they increased in number and in size together with degranulation and vacuolization of their cytoplasm. As found for the human pituitary, anti-LH and anti-FSH sera did not dis-criminate between two types of rat adenohypophysial cells (*Leleux & Robyn* 1969, 1970; *Nakane* 1970). The concept »one hormone – one cell« has perhaps to be challenged and as indicated by *Nakane* (1970) the difference in localiza-tion of LH and FSH could lie at the subcellular level rather than at the cellular one.

Furthermore we also found extensive cross reactions in immunofluorescence between human gonadotrophins and gonadotrophins of all mammalian species tested: ovine, porcine, canine, simian, rat and bat (Fig. 1). Similarly, the gonado-trophic cells of sheep foetuses were identified by the use of anti-HCG sera (*Dubois & Mauleon* 1969).

Finally the functional identification of the basophils of the human pituitary reach an even greater confusion when considering the intracellular localization of TSH. *McGarry et al.* (1964) concluded from immunohistochemical studies that ACTH and TSH were both confined to the R mucoids of Pearse (see Table 1). This finding is in contradistinction to data obtained in experi-mental and pathophysiological conditions such as thyroidectomy and myx-oedema suggesting that the source of TSH could be in the S2 mucoids of Pearse (*Herlant & Pasteels* 1967). The presence of TSH in a population of cells morphologically closely related to the gonadotrophic cells would be in agree-ment with the cross reactions found between gonadotrophins and TSH (*Odell et al.* 1969). Further experimental data are required before more definite conclusions on the identification of TSH cells by immunohistochemistry can be reached.

ACKNOWLEDGMENTS

The expenses of the investigations presented in this report were defrayed by Research Grants to Prof. P. O. Hubinont from the Ford Foundation and from the »Fonds National de la Recherche Scientifique Médicale« (Belgium).

REFERENCES

Albert A.: J. clin. Endocr. *28* (1968) 1683.

Apostolakis M.: Acta endocr. (Kbh.) *49* (1965) 1.

Avrameas S.: Bull. Soc. chim. biol. (Paris) *50* (1968) 1169.

Bain J. & Ezrin C.: J. clin. Endocr. *30* (1970) 181.

Baker B. L.: J. Histochem. Cytochem. *18* (1970) 1.

Baker B. L., Midgley A. R., Gersten B. E. & Yu Y. Y.: Anat. Rec. *164* (1969) 163.

Breustedt H. J., Apostolakis M. & Kracht J.: Acta endocr. (Kbh.) Suppl. *100* (1965) 163.

Butt W. R. & Lynch S. S. In: Margoulies M., Ed. Protein and Polypeptide Hormones, Excerpta med. (Amst.) Int. Congr. Ser. *161* (1969) 134.

Coons A. H.: Int. Rev Cytol. *5* (1956) 1.

Coons A. H. & Kaplan M. H.: J. exp. Med. *91* (1950) 1.

Coons A. H., Creech H. J., Jones R. N. & Berliner E.: J. Immunol. *45* (1942) 159.

Crooke A. C.: J. Path. Bact. *41* (1935) 339.

Cruickshank B. & Currie A. R.: J. Immunol. *1* (1958) 13.

Dubois M. & Mauleon P.: C. R. Acad. Sci. (Paris) *269* (1969) 219.

Ezrin C. & Murray S. In: Benoit J. and Da Lage C., Eds. Cytologie de l'adénohypophyse, No. 128, Ed. Centre National de la Recherche Scientifique, Paris (1963) 183 and 346.

Faiman C. & Ryan R. J.: J. clin. Endocr. *27* (1967) 444.

McGarry E. E., Ballantyne A. & Beck J. C. In: Wolstenholme G. E. W. and Cameron M. P., Eds. Ciba Foundation Colloquia on Endocrinology, vol. *14.* Immunoassay of Hormones. Churchill J. & A., London (1962) 273.

McGarry E. E., Ambe L., Nayak R., Birch E. & Beck J. C.: Metabolism *13* (1964) 1154.

Grumbach M. M., Kaplan S. L., Hsu K. & Elftman H. In: Wolstenholme G. E. W. and Cameron M. P., Eds. Ciba Foundation Colloquia on Endocrinology, vol. *14.* Immunoassay of Hormones. Churchill J. & A., London (1962) 373.

Halmi N. S.: Endocrinology *50* (1952) 140.

Halmi N. S. In: Benoit J. and Da Lage C., Eds. Cytologie de l'Adénohypophyse No. 128, Ed. Centre National de la Recherche Scientifique, Paris (1963) 19.

Hayashida T. In: Wolstenholme G. E. W. and Cameron M. P., Eds. Ciba Foundation Colloquia on Endocrinology, vol. *14*. Immunoassay of Hormones. Churchill J. & A., London (1962) 338.

Herbert D. C. & Hayashida T.: Science *169* (1970) 378.

Herlant M.: Arch. Biol. (Liège) *67* (1956) 89.

Herlant M.: C. R. Acad. Sci. (Paris) *248* (1959) 1033.

Herlant M.: Bull. Microsc. appl. *10* (1960) 37.

Herlant M. & Canivenc R.: C. R. Acad. Sci. (Paris) *250* (1960) 606.

Herlant M. & Pasteels J. L. In: Bajusz E. and Jasmin G., Eds. Methods and Achievements in Experimental Pathology, vol. *3*. Karger S., Basel (1967) 250.

Jeffcoate S. L. In: Kirkham K. E. and Hunter W. M., Eds. Radioimmunoassay Methods. Livingstone E. & S., London (1970) 90.

Koffler D. & Fogel M.: Proc. Soc. exp. Biol. (N. Y.) *115* (1964) 1080.

Kracht J. & Hachmeister U.: Endokrinologie *51* (1967) 164.

Langeron M.: Precis de Microscopie, 6th ed.. Masson & Cie, Paris (1942).

Leleux P. & Robyn C.: Acta endocr. (Kbh.) Suppl. *138* (1969) 198.

Leleux P. & Robyn C.: Ann. Endocr. (Paris) *31* (1970) 181.

Leleux P., Robyn C. & Herlant M.: C. R. Acad. Sci. (Paris) *267* (1968) 438.

Leznoff A., Fishman J.. Goodfriend E., McGarry E. E., Beck J. C. & Rose B.: Proc. Soc. exp. Biol. (N. Y.) *104* (1960) 232.

Leznoff A., Fishman J., Talbot N., McGarry E. E.. Beck J. C. & Rose B.: J. clin. Invest. *41* (1962) 1720.

Mallory F. B.: Pathological Technique, Saunders W. Co., Philadelphia (1938).

Marshall J. M.: J. exp. Med. *94* (1951) 21.

Marshall J. D., Eveland W. C. & Smith C. W.: Proc. Soc. exp. Biol. (N. Y.) *98* (1958) 898.

McManus J. F. A.: Nature (Lond.) *158* (1946) 202.

Midgley A. R.: J. Cell Biol. *23* (1964) 59A.

Midgley A. R.: J. Histochem. Cytochem. *14* (1966) 159.

Midgley A. R.: J. clin. Endocr. *27* (1967) 295.

Midgley A. R. & Pierce G. B.: J. exp. Med. *115* (1962) 289.

Monroe S. E. & Midgley A. R.: Fed. Proc. *25* (1966) 315.

Monroe S. E. & Midgley A. R.: Proc. Soc. exp. Biol. (N. Y.) *130* (1969) 151.

Nairn R. C.: Fluorescent Protein Tracing, 2nd ed. E. & S. Livingstone Ltd., Edinburgh (1964).

Nakane P. K.: J. Histochem. Cytochem. *18* (1970) 9.

Nakane P. K. & Pierce G. B.: J. Histochem. Cytochem. *14* (1966) 929.

Nayak R., McGarry E. E. & Beck J. C.: Endocrinology *83* (1968) 731.

Odell W. D., Reichert L. E. & Bates R. W. In: Margoulies M., Ed. Protein and Polypeptide Hormones, Excerpta med. (Amst.) Int. Congr. Ser. *161* (1969) 124.

Pasteels J. L.: C. R. Acad. Sci. (Paris) *254* (1962) 4083.

Pasteels J. L. In: Hubinont P. O., Leroy F., Leleux P. and Robyn C., Eds. Ovoimplantation, Human Gonadotrophins and Prolactin, 2nd International Seminar on Reproductive Physiology and Sexual Endocrinology. S. Karger, Basel (1970) 279.

Pearse A. G. E. & van Noorden S.: Canad. Med. Ass. J. *88* (1963) 462.

Petrusz P.: Acta endocr. (Kbh.) Suppl. *142* (1969) 77.

Pressman D., Yagi Y. & Hiramoto R.: Int. Arch. Allergy *12* (1958) 125.

Purves H. D. In: Young W. C., Ed. Sex and Internal Secretions, 3rd ed., vol. *1*. Morphology of the Hypophysis related to its Function. The Williams & Wilkins Co., Baltimore (1961) 161.

Purves H. D. In: Harris G. W. and Donovan B. T., Eds. The Pituitary Gland, vol. *1*. Anterior Pituitary. Butterworth & Co., London (1966) 147.

Purves H. D. & Griesbach W. E.: Endocrinology *49* (1951) 244.

Purves H. D. & Griesbach W. E.: Endocrinology *55* (1954) 785.

Raben M. S.: Science *125* (1957) 883.

Robyn C.: Rev. belge Pathol. Méd. exp. *31* (1965) 334.

Robyn C.: Acta endocr. (Kbh.) Suppl. *142* (1969) 31.

Robyn C. & Diczfalusy E.: Acta endocr. (Kbh.) *59* (1968) 277.

Robyn C. & Leleux P.: Acta endocr. (Kbh.) Suppl. *138* (1969) 197.

Robyn C. & Leleux P.: Acta endocr. (Kbh.) (1971) in press.

Robyn C., Bossaert Y., Hubinont P. O., Pasteels J. L. & Herlant M.: C. R. Acad. Sci. (Paris) *259* (1964) 1226.

Romeis B. In: von Möllendorf W., Ed. Handbuch der Mikroskopischen Anatomie des Menschen, vol. *6* (3). Die Hypophyse. J. Springer, Berlin (1940) 1.

Rosen S. W., Schlaff S. & Roth J. In: Margoulies M., Ed. Protein and Polypeptide Hormones, Excerpta med. (Amst.) Int. Congr. Ser. *161* (1969) 396.

Ross G. T. & Bahn R. C.: Proc. Mayo Clin. *35* (1960) 400.

Schlaff S., Rosen S. W. & Roth J.: J. clin. Invest. *47* (1968) 1722.

Silverstein A. M.: J. Histochem. Cytochem. *5* (1957) 94.

Singer S. J. & Schick A. F.: J. biophys. biochem. Cytol. *9* (1961) 519.

Taymor M. L., Tamada T., Soper M. & Blatt W. F.: J. clin. Endocr. 27 (1967) 707.

Weller T. H. & Coons A. H.: Proc. Soc. exp. Biol. (N. Y.)) *86* (1954) 789.

ADDENDUM

Very recently, using the immunofluorescence technique, *Leleux, van Haelst & Robyn* (in preparation) have shown that, in human pituitary sections incubated with an anti-bovine TSH serum absorbed with HCG only a few Romeis δ cells are fluorescent positive. These δ cells contained the largest amounts of alcian blue positive granules and are probably equivalent to the S2 mucoids of Pearse.

DISCUSSION

Lunenfeld: You showed that in your antiserum you got rid of anti-LH in the FSH antiserum and of anti-FSH in your LH antiserum by biological neutralization. Did you investigate whether after neutralization you do not have present any immunochemically active material which may still cross react with FSH or with LH?

Robyn: The establishment of reliable criteria of specificity for antisera to be used in immunohistochemistry is a very difficult problem. This is even more true for anti-LH and anti-FSH sera. The specificity of the antigonadotrophic sera employed in our study has been tested by immunoprecipitation and by neutralization of the biological

185

activities. However, it has to be emphasized that when the specificity has been characterized in one immunological test, the results are not necessarily the same in another immunological test. For example, the cross reactions between human and rat gonadotrophins were systematically detected by immunohistochemistry, with all antisera tested, but not by immunoprecipitation, by neutralization of the biological activity (*Monroe & Midgley* 1966, 1969; *Leleux et al.* 1968) and not consistently by radioimmunological techniques (*Niswender et al.* 1968; *Monroe et al.* 1968). Therefore one should be careful in the generalization to immunohistochemistry of conclusions drawn from specificity controls conducted in other immunological systems.

Lunenfeld: You use biological criteria for characterizing your antibody and you use immunohistological techniques in your actual experimentation. I think it may be wise to check the immunospecificity of the antisera before reaching binding conclusions, *e. g.*, demonstrating absence of binding of FSH to an antiserum to gonadotrophins, presumably devoid of anti-FSH, or vice versa, with LH. Otherwise, one could argue that your results, demonstrating the presence of cells containing both FSH and LH, may be due to contamination with immunochemical binding material. This could give a totally different interpretation of your immunohistological results.

Robyn: Indeed, we would like to test the specificity of our antigonadotrophic sera by radioimmunological techniques. However, highly purified LH and FSH for iodination were only very recently available to us. Still the fact remains that the radioimmunological criterion, as previously indicated, is also of no absolute value. Highly purified protein hormones may be immunologically different from the native hormone contained in the adenohypophysial cells. The radioimmunological tests are probably as different from immunohistochemistry as the neutralization of the biological activities.

Eshkol: In your slides you used the term anti-LH when you actually used anti-HCG sera. Is it because the anti-HCG serum was the one which was absorbed with FSH to render it specific to react with LH?

Leleux: Yes, it is; as »LH« is a biological definition, when we say anti-LH sera, we mean to say that our antibodies are neutralizing the biological activity of LH.

Eshkol: In your last slide you pointed out the various criteria which one should consider when using immunological techniques. One of them was biological assessment of the specificity of the antiserum. I wonder whether you did this when you used antirat gonadotrophin, that is, whether your antirat gonadotrophin really neutralized human gonadotrophin, and vice versa, namely, whether antihuman gonadotrophin neutralized rat gonadotrophins. In our experience, antisera to rat gonadotrophins did not neutralize either HMG or HCG (*Lunenfeld et al.* 1967), and anti-HMG and anti-HCG did not neutralize rat gonadotrophins (*Eitan Lunenfeld and A. Eshkol*, unpublished data).

Leleux: The immunohistochemical cross reaction between human and rat gonadotrophin does exist but cannot be found in other immunological systems. We didn't succeed in neutralizing the rat LH activity by an anti-HCG serum. The cross reaction between hormones of different species is shown more easily by immunohistochemistry than by other immunological methods. The controls of specificity are thus also to be found inside the immunohistochemical systems, as I have shown by the extinction of the fluorescence after neutralization of the antibodies by the hormonal preparation to be detected.

Robyn: As already pointed out in this discussion, the cross reaction between the same pituitary hormones of several mammalian species are not always easily detectable. Immunohistochemistry seems to be the most sensitive technique in this respect. Considering the results obtained by Dr. Leleux on rat pituitary sections incubated with antihuman gonadotrophic sera, the specificity of the reaction could only be based on the fact that the fluorescent positive cells were identified as gonadotrophic cells by their staining properties when using classical histochemical techniques and by their modifications following castration.

Coming back to the neutralization of the biological activity, although we could not show any cross reaction between human and rat gonadotrophin by this technique, *Parlow* (personal communication) found partial inhibition.

Means: Recent data have indicated that for TSH, LH and FSH there is at least one identical subunit. Have you tested your antisera for subunit specificity?

Robyn: The problem is how to obtain enough highly purified human gonadotrophins in order to perform such studies on subunits.

Nakane: Each time I have to give a lecture to students, it takes me approximately 30 minutes to explain the nomenclature. Since the method has at least advanced to the point where, except gonadotrophin secreting cells, all other cells can be identified according to their hormone content, I am a strong supporter of the concept that from now on one should start using the cell types according to their hormone content.

Leleux: We have always to correlate our results with previous data based on animal experiments and on human physiopathology cases which are described in terms of histochemical nomenclatures. It is the purpose of this review to correlate the hormonal content with the previous morphological nomenclatures.

Eshkol: I wonder whether Drs. Leleux and Robyn would not tend to think that actually there are no differences in the specificities of the cross reacting antisera when checked in different systems, but that cross reacting antibodies have different association and dissociation constants. Therefore, in an *in vitro* system, you can probably pick up a binding between an antigen and an antibody, but due to a high dissociation constant, you cannot detect it in a biological system and express it as biological neutralization.

Robyn: The experimental conditions are very different in radioimmunological tests, in neutralization of the biological activities, in immunoprecipitation tests and in immunohistochemistry. The reaction takes place in buffer solutions in the case of the first two techniques, in agar gel in the case of the third one and in a kind of solid phase system in the case of the last one. In addition, the antigen and the antibody concentrations vary from one technique to the other. Therefore, the antigen and the antibody populations involved in the reaction may be very different in each type of immunological tests. This could provide an explanation for the differences in specificity from one test to the other.

Stumpf: There are some differences in the intensity of the fluorescence in your slides, and I was wondering what this reflects. Is it a different content of hormones in the cells, or can you modify the fluorescence by the time of incubation? Can you, for instance, increase the number of cells that fluoresce if you increase your incubation time? On the other hand, is the method sensitive enough to demonstrate all of those specific cells?

Leleux: The fluorescence is influenced by several technical factors, such as the thickness of the section, for example. During the last washing in buffer solution, you are doing a »differentiation« which removes the excess of fluorescein. This removal is very labile and can be very different from one section to another. Fluorescence is fading quickly and is diminishing during the time you are trying to measure it. All we can say is that there is no direct correlation between the intensity of the fluorescence and the staining affinities of the cells for any histochemical stain.

Nakane: Based on the theoretical calculations made by *Ornstein et al.* (1957) on the fluorescence of Acriflavin, it is possible to suggest that under an ideal condition, the indirect fluorescence antibody method is capable of detecting at least 50 per cent of existing antigenic molecules. The higher sensitivity of the method is not required when you reach a point where you can localize one molecule at a time.

Johannisson: Would there be any possibility to make a quantitation of this type of fluorescence? Do you have any experience of the grade of fading of these preparations?

Leleux: No, I have no quantitative data.

Lunenfeld: Dr. Robyn, after what you showed now, do you really believe that the same cells produce FSH and LH? Though I do not doubt your data, do you really believe that these are conclusive?

Robyn: On the basis of their biological specificity, our anti-LH and anti-FSH sera reacted with the same cells of the human adenohypophysis. Dr. Nakane also found by immunohistochemistry that FSH and LH were located in the same cells of the rat pituitary. However, his anti-LH and anti-FSH sera did not react uniformly with the same subcellular structure. More comprehensive studies on specificity are required to determined if LH and FSH have different localizations on the cellular or on the subcellular level.

Diczfalusy: I think there is an increasing body of evidence indicating that the relationship between biological and immunological activities of gonadotrophin preparations is at best tenuous. This raises the question whether or not scientists at this stage would not profit from the introduction of inernational standards, or at least reference preparations of antisera. What would the general reaction of this group be to such a proposition?

Lunenfeld: As a member of the WHO Expert Committee on Biological Standardization, I would like to mention that the problem of standard preparations for antisera has been raised several times. The general opinion was not very favourable. It would be useful if members of this group here would express their opinion on this subject.

Diczfalusy: I think that it is fair to say that all gonadotrophin preparations we have seen thus far, including those for which the highest purity was claimed, in terms of bioassay results, contained a significant amount of what we described as immunological activity, which was sometimes unrelated to the biological activity. Dr. Robyn indicated an HCG preparation exhibiting almost 18 000 IU per mg. This preparation still neutralized large quantities of anti-FSH sera and when used for immunization gave rise to very potent anti-FSH sera. So, if Dr. Lunenfeld could convey to his colleagues the simple message that we think that all the gonadotrophin preparations that we use today are highly heterogeneous, and that antisera might perhaps be less so, maybe you could create a more favourable atmosphere.

Eshkol: I think that it will be a very difficult task to get homogeneous preparations. If we remember the presentation, this morning, by Dr. Kohler who showed that even single clone cultures of choriocarcinoma cells produced different populations of HCG molecules (namely, with different properties), I think that even purified preparations, prepared from pooled pituitaries or pooled urine, will show even more heterogeneity. This will also be reflected in antisera produced against gonadotrophic preparations, and heterogeneity of antibodies will also be influenced by the individual immune response of each animal. Thus not even a uniform heterogeneity of antibody populations can be anticipated. (For antibody purification, see General discussion).

Kohler: I think it would be very difficult to arbitrarily assign antisera to gonadotrophins as standards without a clear understanding of the specific portion of the molecule to which each antibody was directed.

References:

Leleux P., Robyn C. & Herlant M.: C. R. Acad. Sci. (Paris) *267* (1968) 438.

Lunenfeld B., Eshkol A., Baldratti G. & Suchowsky G. K.: Acta endocr. (Kbh.) *54* (1967) 311.

Monroe S. E. & Midgley A. R.: Fed. Proc. *25* (1966) 315.

Monroe S. E. & Midgley A. R.: Proc. Soc. exp. Biol. (N. Y.) *130* (1969) 151.

Monroe S. E., Parlow A. F. & Midgley A. R.: Endocrinology *83* (1968) 1004.

Niswender G. D., Midgley A. R. & Reichert L. E. In: Rosemberg E., Ed. Gonadotropins 1968, Geron-X Inc., Los Altos, Calif., p. 299.

Ornstein L., Mautner W., Davis B. J. & Tamura R..: J. Mt. Sinai Hosp. (1957) 1066.

University of Colorado, School of Medicine, 4200 East Ninth Avenue,
Denver, Colorado 80220, U. S. A.

APPLICATION OF PEROXIDASE-LABELLED ANTIBODIES TO THE INTRACELLULAR LOCALIZATION OF HORMONES

By

*Paul K. Nakane**

ABSTRACT

Hormones were localized immunoenzymocytochemically at the ultra-structural level directly on ultrathin sections of anterior pituitary glands of rats which had been fixed and embedded in either methacrylate or Epon. GH, LTH, ACTH and LH are best localized on methacrylate embedded glands and GH and LTH on Epon embedded glands. GH and LTH were found in secretion granules, and depending on the activity of the cells, the hormones could be found in the Golgi apparatus and in the cisternae of endoplasmic reticulum. The grids on which hormones have been localized may also be processed for electron radioautography, an approach particularly useful to study simultaneously substrate uptake as well as product synthesis.

The peroxidase-labelled antibody method has been useful for the localization of tissue antigens both at the light and electron microscopic levels. The use of peroxidase as a marker for immunoglobulins possesses unique advantages. At the light microscopic level, the preparations are permanent and require no special equipment (*Nakane & Pierce* 1966) and several tissue antigens may be localized simultaneously in a single specimen (*Nakane* 1968). At the ultra-structural level, the small molecular weight of horseradish-peroxidase (40,000)

* Career Development Awardee of the United States National Institutes of Health, Grant GM46228.

in contrast to that of ferritin (molecular weight, 700,000) causes less interference with the penetration of labelled antibody into tissue sections (*Nakane & Pierce* 1967). This is a prerequisite for immunoelectron microscopy when the thick sections are to be impregnated with reactant. In addition, the amplifying ability of the enzymatic reaction makes the method extremely sensitive, and the method may be modified to localize tissue antigens directly on ultrathin sections for electron microscopy (*Kawarai & Nakane* 1970). This approach not only eliminates the problem of penetration of antisera through the tissues, but allows the use of serially sectioned material. Thus one antigen may be localized on one section and other antigens on succeeding sections, resulting in better control. Small amounts of tissue and antisera are required to carry out the procedures and the results may be compared directly by light and electron microscopy.

The localizations of polypeptide hormones in the anterior pituitary glands permit a positive identification of cell type with respect to its hormone content (*Nakane* 1970).

In this present paper, I wish to report the development of the method for the localization of hormones on ultrathin sections of anterior pituitary glands which have been embedded in Epon.

MATERIALS AND METHODS

Adult male and female albino rats (Sprague-Dawley), purchased from Simonsen's Laboratory, Gilroy, California, were used for these studies. The rats were maintained in a temperature controlled room on Purina laboratory chow and water *ad libitum* for two weeks before sacrifice.

Anterior pituitary glands of the male rats were diced and fixed for eight hours in 4 % paraformaldehyde-picric acid phosphate buffer solution (*Zamboni & De Martino* 1967). This fixative was prepared in the following manner: Twenty g of paraformaldehyde was dissolved in 150 ml of a saturated aqueous solution of picric acid. The solution was warmed to 60°C and 2.52 % sodium hydroxide was added dropwise until the solution became clear. The solution was filtered and allowed to cool. The above mixture was made up to one liter with phosphate buffer (3.31 g $NaH_2PO_4 \cdot H_2O$ and 33.77 g $Na_2HPO_4 \cdot 7\ H_2O$ per liter). The final fixative had an osmotic pressure of approximately 780 m osmoles or slightly higher with a pH of 7.3 to 7.4. The tissues were washed overnight with 0.01 M phosphate buffered saline[1] (PBS) and dehydrated in increasing concentrations of alcohol and cleared in hydroxy-

---

[1] 0.9 % NaCl solution buffered with 0.01 M sodium phosphate at pH 7.2 to 7.3.

1968) as a substrate for peroxidase instead of the conventional 3,3'-diamino-benzidine (*Graham & Karnovsky* 1966) gave better results. For this, one-tenth concentration of a solution of saturated 4-Cl-1-naphthol in 0.05 M tris buffer at pH 7.6 with 0.001 % hydrogen peroxide solutions was used. The addition of 4-Cl-1-naphthol to this buffer reduces its pH, so the pH of the incubation medium should be checked and readjusted with either 0.05 M tris base or with 0.01 N NaOH to pH 7.4. The developed grids were subsequently washed with distilled water within the apparatus with slightly faster flow rate and dried. The dried grids were then exposed briefly to 1 % OsO_4 solution for 1–2 min, washed with distilled water, placed on a droplet of 1 % copper sulphate solu-

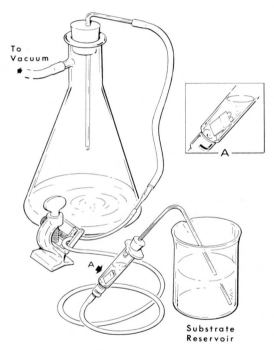

To
Vacuum

A

A

Substrate
Reservoir

Fig. 1.

Grid incubation apparatus: Grids which have been reacted with antisera were placed on an edge of a cover-slip (11 × 22 mm) by means of a double-surfaced Scotch tape. Up to three grids were mounted in this manner. The cover-slip was then placed in a 5 ml glass syringe (box A). The substrate solution was passed through the syringe at a rate of 25 ml/min. Care was taken so that the solution in the syringe always covered the grids. The rate of flow was regulated by a variable clamp, and the effluent was discarded into a trap. Usually the trap was connected to a vacuum line or to a water aspirator.

tion in distilled water for 5 min in order to enhance the contrast of the reaction product and washed with distilled water. The sections were observed directly in the electron microscope or after counterstaining with lead hydroxide.

d) *Radioautography*

The pituitary gland from the pregnant rat was used for this study. LTH was localized first on the ultrathin section, then the stained grid was processed for radioautography. A thin layer of carbon was evaporated on the grids to prevent dislocation of the reaction products. The grids were stuck to a glass slide by means of double-surfaced Scotch tape, dipped into Ilford radioautographic emulsion and kept in the dark for 12 weeks. The silver grains were developed by conventional radioautographic methods.

RESULTS

I. *Effect of Fixation and Embedding on the Antigenicity of Hormones*

In our previous study, it was found that all six hormones known to exist in the anterior pituitary gland of rats retain their antigenicity when the glands were fixed in p-formaldehyde-picric acid fixative (*Nakane* 1970). Therefore failure to obtain positive results when the glands were embedded either in methacrylate or Epon was considered to be due to either the impregnation of polymer or the polymerization of plastic polymers.

GH, LTH, ACTH and LH could be localized on ultrathin sections of tissues fixed in paraformaldehyde-picric acid fixative and embedded in methacrylate. FSH lost its activity during this embedding procedure. Most preparations of TSH failed to react with anti-TSH, but occasionally TSH retained its antigenic activity. Antigenicity of GH, LTH and ACTH was retained in tissues fixed in paraformaldehyde-picric acid and embedded in Epon but that of LH was lost. Only GH and LTH retained their antigenic activities when anterior pituitary glands were fixed in paraformaldehyde-picric acid, post-fixed in osmium tetroxide and embedded in Epon.

II. *Localization of Hormones in Tissues Embedded in Methacrylate*

Ultrastructure of secretion granules of all cell types was well preserved, however, the membranous cell organelles, such as Golgi apparatus, mitochondria, and smooth endoplasmic reticulum were very difficult to recognize. The usual positive appearance of the membranes obtained when osmium tetroxide was used as the fixative was absent. The rough surfaced endoplasmic reticulum was detected by the presence of attached ribosomes. The secretion granules always contained hormones. Occasionally the hormones were also found on or in the cisternae of the endoplasmic reticulum depending upon the stage of protein synthesis (Figs. 2 and 3).

The sizes of the reaction products deposited at the antigenic sites were considerably larger than those deposited in tissues when thick sections were used.

III. *Localization of Hormones in Tissues Embedded in Epon*

The ultrastructural morphology of the tissues fixed in paraformaldehyde-picric acid and post-fixed in osmium tetroxide and embedded in Epon appeared almost identical to those tissues prepared by the conventional method for

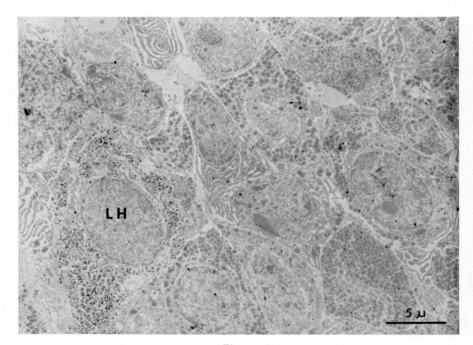

Fig. 2.
A male pituitary gland fixed in p-formaldehyde-picric acid solution and embedded in methacrylate. LH was localized using rabbit anti-human chorionic gonadotrophin (a gift from Dr. A. R. Midgley, University of Michigan) and peroxidase-labelled sheep anti-rabbit IgG. 4-Cl-1-naphthol and H_2O_2 were used as substrate. The granular electron dense reaction products mark the LH cell (LH). Other cell types are virtually free of reaction product.

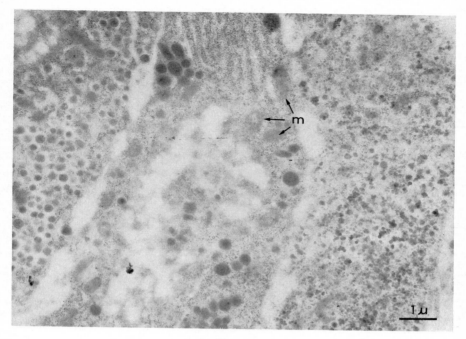

Fig. 3.

A male pituitary gland fixed in p-formaldehyde-picric acid solution and embedded in methacrylate. ACTH was localized directly using rabbit anti-porcine ACTH and peroxidase-labelled sheep anti-rabbit IgG. 4-Cl-1-naphthol and H_2O_2 were used as substrate. Portions of three different cells are shown. A portion of the cell at the right is densely stained for ACTH, whereas the cell in the center (morphologically appears to be an LTH cell) and the cell at the left (morphologically appears to be a gonadotrophic cell) were not stained. A slightly negative appearance of mitochondria (m) is visible in the center cell.

electron microscopy. The membranous structures such as Golgi apparatus and mitochondria were well preserved by this method. The secretion granules of growth hormone cells always contained growth hormone (Fig. 4) and those of prolactin cells always contained prolactin (Figs. 5 and 6). Shape and size of secretion granules, Golgi apparatus and endoplasmic reticulum varied considerably. At one stage the cytoplasm of the prolactin cell was filled with small vesiculated endoplasmic reticulum. Frequently, the reaction products were found in the cisternae of endoplasmic reticulum. Small membrane-bound secretion granules were scattered throughout the cell and frequently the Golgi sacs contained the reaction product indicating the presence of hormone in them. The mitochondria were dispersed among the secretion granules. The

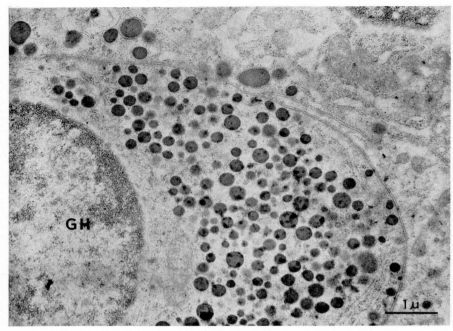

Fig. 4.

A female pituitary gland fixed in p-formaldehyde-picric acid solution, post-fixed in osmium tetroxide and embedded in Epon. GH was localized indirectly using rabbit anti-rat GH (a gift from Dr. J. Furth, Columbia University) and peroxidase-labelled anti-rabbit IgG. 4-Cl-1-naphthol and H_2O_2 were used as substrate. The GH was localized on secretion granules of the GH cell (GH). A portion of an unstained cell (appears to be an LTH cell) is seen at the upper half of this photograph.

large secretion granules were dispersed throughout the cytoplasm and occasionally they were found in the process of secretion (Fig. 6).

IV. *Radioautography*

The enzymatic reaction products remained intact while the grids were processed for radioautography. The silver grains were found frequently on the secretion granules of LTH cells (Fig. 7).

DISCUSSION

The use of ultrathin sections for the localization of tissue antigens offers several unique advantages over the use of thick sections. The problem of penetration of antisera through tissue slices is completely eliminated in this method and one is able to run well defined controlled experiments by using serial sections. Radioautography may be used in conjunction with this method and will provide a powerful tool for the cell biologist. In this way one will be able to determine not only the biosynthetic route but the incorporation of the tracer into the product as well.

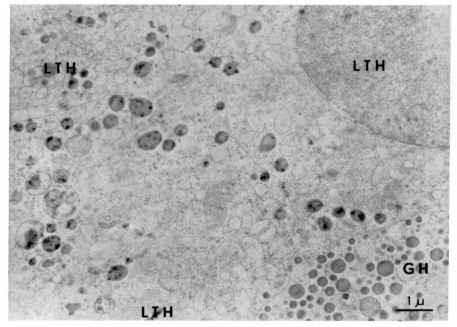

Fig. 5.

A female pituitary gland fixed in p-formaldehyde-picric acid solution, post-fixed in osmium tetroxide and embedded in Epon. LTH was localized indirectly using rabbit anti-rat prolactin (a gift from Dr. J. Furth, Columbia University) and peroxidase-labelled sheep anti-rabbit IgG. 4-Cl-1-naphthol and H_2O_2 were used as substrate. The sites of LTH were marked by the reaction products of peroxidase on secretion granules of LTH cells (LTH). A cell which appears to be a GH cell (GH) in the right bottom of this photograph was unreactive to the antiserum. Endoplasmic reticulum of LTH cells was vesiculated. Well preserved mitochondria were scattered among the stained secretion granules.

199

However, other antigens which are denatured easily during the tissue preparation may require some modification in procedure either by altering the conditions of fixation or the type of polymer employed. Provided that the antigen will withstand the tissue treatment and antibody against antisera satisfies immunological criteria specificity, the method described here is a powerful tool for the ultrastructural localization of antigens, especially that of hormones.

ACKNOWLEDGMENTS

The author wishes to gratefully acknowledge Dr. Yasuyuku Kawarai for the expert technical assistance, Dr. G. Barry Pierce for reading the manuscript, and Mrs. LaVonne King for preparing the manuscript.

This investigation was supported in part by Grants AI 09109 and AM 13112 from the United States Public Health Service and Grant E 105 from the American Cancer Society.

REFERENCES

Avrameas S.: Immunochemistry 6 (1969) 43.
Graham R. C. & Karnovsky M. J.: J. Histochem. Cytochem. *14* (1966) 291.
Kawarai Y. & Nakane P. K.: J. Histochem. Cytochem. *18* (1970) 161.
Mittler J. C. & Meites J.: Endocrinology *78* (1966) 500.
Nakane P. K.: J. Histochem. Cytochem. *16* (1968) 557.
Nakane P. K.: J. Histochem. Cytochem. *18* (1970) 9.
Nakane P. K. & Pierce G. B.: J. Histochem. Cytochem. *14* (1966) 929.
Nakane P. K. & Pierce G. B.: J. Cell Biol. *33* (1967) 307.
Singer S. J. & McLean J. D.: Lab. Invest. *12* (1963) 1002.
Zamboni L. & DeMartino C.: J. Cell Biol. *35* (1967) 148A.

DISCUSSION

Leleux: Dr. Nakane, using your very sensitive method, have you tried to detect the pituitary hormones in the target organs, like ovaries, testis, etc.?

Nakane: No. I believe that somebody in Dr. Midgley's laboratory has tried, and I think they were successful in localizing them in the ovaries of pseudopregnant animals. We haven't tried simply because my major interest lies in the pituitary, not in the target.

Stumpf: Can you do without fixation? Did you try?

Nakane: If the protein you are interested in is stable in aqueous solution and is not washed away, I don't think there is any reason why not. But usually tissue disintegrates in water.

Stumpf: Some people incubate sections or tissue slices in isotonic saline solution. Quite a segment of research is based on treatment of tissue in aqueous solutions. And the fixative is a solvent too. A fixative does not necessarily immobilize. This is a misconception many investigators have.

Nakane: I am aware that some people localize antigens on sections, but they usually do it on frozen, air dried sections. By air drying many materials become rather stabilized. However, some of the mitochondrial enzymes I have tried to localize in the past simply denature by freezing, and it becomes rather impossible to localize them.

Lunenfeld: Mrs. Eshkol and myself have attempted to localize exogeneously administered [^{125}I] HCG in mouse ovaries. It was found in follicular envelopes and corpora lutea, but the grains were so large that it was difficult to say where in the cell it was. Later on, Mrs. Eshkol tried to label HCG with tritium, but the specific activity was very low.

Nakane: I think labelling of these hormones with radioactive material is a very sensitive way to trace them. However, if one wishes to know whether the label is on intact molecules or on disintegrated molecules, it becomes impossible, unless one can recover this material and test its specificity either immunologically or biologically. I feel that the method I have described here can localize hormones at the target site if the hormone retains its antigenicity upon contact with the target. This has not been well documented elsewhere. Another problem is that it is rather difficult to obtain a peroxidase labelled gammaglobulin which has total enzymatic as well as immunological activities.

Lunenfeld: I fully agree that after labelling, the material has to be checked for integrity, but the only thing we can state is that prior to injection, the labelled material was biologically and immunologically active.

Johannisson: A question about the formation of these granules: Have you been able to see any connection between the Golgi zone and the endoplasmic reticulum? Have you been able to localize any specific hormone in these organelles?

Nakane: Yes. One can localize prolactin in endoplasmic reticulum, occasionally on ribosomes, on the cisterns of the Golgi apparatus and in secretion granules. From established data on the formation of secretion granules by Drs. *Jamieson & Palada* (1967a,b) with labelled amino acids as precursors, I assume that the migration of protein is in the direction just stated. However, our study on this with precursor has not been completed yet.

Robyn: Do your anti-ACTH react with the intermediate lobe of the rat pituitary?

Nakane: Yes. This also includes anti-14-39 ACTH. This means that the intermediate lobe perhaps makes ACTH, if the previous data, that MSH is only secreted from the intermediate lobe, are correct, then one can assume that there is an intercellular degradation of ACTH to MSH.

Robyn: Some anti-human hypophysial gonadotrophins (anti-HHG) sera tested in immunofluorescence reacted not only with the gonadotrophic cells of the rat pituitary but also with the intermediate lobe and with some small angular cells of the anterior lobe (*Leleux & Robyn* 1970). It is likely that these antisera contained some anti-MSH and (or) anti-ACTH antibodies. In immunofluorescence studies of the human adenohypophysis, all these non-specific anti-HHG sera stained, in addition to the gonadotrophic cells, the large PAS positive Romeis β cells.

Nakane: I think it would be quite extraordinary if you didn't find cross reaction between anti-MSH and anti-ACTH. Incidentally, I would like to add a word about the specificity of LH and FSH and how perhaps one could handle it. Maybe we should wait until the sequence of LH, FSH and TSH are completed. Upon that completion, one should be able to make any portion or fragment you wish and make antibody to it, and it should cross react. Therefore I suggest that if there is to be standardization, it should be based on a polypeptide sequence rather than on biologically isolated materials.

Stumpf: In the posterior lobe there are »ectopic« invaginated cells. Nobody really knows where they come from. Current believe is that they stem from the intermediate lobe. Did you study them too? We found that these invaginated cells are labelled with oestradiol, and I wonder what the immunological properties of these cells are?

Dr. Nakane, did you count the percentage of gonadotrophs and various other cell types, so that a comparison can be made with tinctorial counts, as provided by Dr. *Halmi* (1950), for instance?

Nakane: Yes, I reported it in that conference at the NIH on the percentage of FSH and LH cells (October, 1970). It is somewhere around 17.5 %.

Robyn: I would like to come back to Dr. Stumpf's question concerning the nature of the cells invaginated into the posterior lobe of the human pituitary. These cells were fluorescent positive with the antigonadotrophic sera cross reacting with ACTH and (or) MSH, as just mentioned. Further studies on the specificity of this reaction are required.

Wira: In your slide of an LH secreting cell, Dr. Nakane, you showed that antiserum reaction granules appear as light granules above the LH secretion granules. When I first saw this slide, I would have thought that since these cells are actively secreting LH, the antiserum reaction would have completely blocked out the secretory granules. Does the presence of only one or two antiserum reaction granules represent an artifact of fixation, or could it suggest that perhaps LH or FSH in the secretory granules are not in forms that are sensitive to the antiserum reaction?

Nakane: I think that the major reason for this spotty distribution is in the loss of antigenicity of the hormone because of the fixation and the procedure it went through, since when one uses 40 micron thick sections, one gets complete granular staining. And please remember that these tissues went through considerable drastic changes. I was extremely amused just to find some.

References:

Halmi N.: Endocrinology *47* (1950) 289.
Jamieson J. D. & Palade G. E.: J. Cell Biol. *34* (1967a) 577.
Jamieson J. D. & Palade G. E.: J. Cell Biol. *34* (1967b) 597.
Leleux P. & Robyn C.: Ann. Endocr. (Paris) *31* (1970) 181.

Laboratories for Reproductive Biology,
Departments of Anatomy and Pharmacology,
University of North Carolina, Chapel Hill, N. C., U. S. A.

AUTORADIOGRAPHIC TECHNIQUES FOR THE LOCALIZATION OF HORMONES AND DRUGS AT THE CELLULAR AND SUBCELLULAR LEVEL*

By

Walter E. Stumpf

ABSTRACT

The paper describes four autoradiographic techniques which can be recommended, not without restrictions, for the study of the cellular and
subcellular hormone or drug distribution in tissues. In all of the techniques desiccated slides are used which are precoated with photographic
emulsion. The techniques are (I) Dry-mounting of freeze-dried sections
on emulsion precoated slides; (II) Thaw-mounting of frozen sections on
emulsion precoated slides; (III) Smear-mounting on emulsion precoated
slides; and (IV) Touch-mounting on emulsion precoated slides. The techniques are designed to avoid or minimize translocation of the labelled
molecules during preparation and during the application to photographic
emulsion. Cited examples of application of these techniques demonstrate
their utility in hormone research.

GENERAL CONSIDERATIONS

Autoradiography has the potential to provide information about the cellular
and subcellular distribution of radioactively labelled substances in individual

---

* Supported by U. S. Public Health Service Grant No. AM-12649 and U. S. Atomic
Energy Commission Contract No. AT-(40-1)-4057 as well as a grant from the Rocke-
feller Foundation for the Laboratories for Reproductive Biology, Chapel Hill, North
Carolina.

cells. This histochemical technique permits compartmental analysis with simultaneous recognition of the tissue topography, the type of cell, and the subcellular organel, with which the labelled substances are associated. The metabolic and transport processes can be arrested at any given time by freezing of the tissue. Thus the *in vivo* or *in situ* distribution of certain compounds can be studied and followed at time sequences as it had been shown in the case of [³H] oestradiol (*Jensen et al.* 1968), and [³H] urobilinogen (*Stumpf & Lester* 1966). Autoradiography provides morpho-physiologic information that may not be obtainable otherwise, implementing at its best data on a time-substance-topography relationship.

Autoradiography, like other localization techniques, such as centrifugal fractionation of tissue homogenates, does not inform about the chemical nature of the localized radioactivity. These techniques must be supplemented by chemical assay procedures in order to ascertain purity of the injected material and chemical identity of the bound or compartmentalized radioactive label demonstrated in the tissues. For the elucidation of hormone and drug action, biochemical and histochemical techniques require and supplement each other, with the former yielding more chemical and the latter more histologic information.

Autoradiography is one of the most sensitive techniques regarding the detection of substances in tissues. The information, stemming from the disintegrations of the radioactive label, is stored in the photographic emulsion and thus amplified over a period of time. The limit of detectability of a given number of molecules is remarkably low and exceeds most of the available assay techniques. For instance, tritium labelled oestradiol, systematically administered at 0.1 μg per 100 g rat body weight, can be discovered in the nucleus of a single target cell from, *e. g.*, the uterus, the granulosa cells of the ovary, interstitial cells of the testis, and others (*Stumpf* 1968*a*, 1969*a*, 1970*a*). The average number of disintegrations required, in order to obtain the latent image for a silver grain, varies, depending on the type of emulsion, the isotope, the section thickness, the humidity content, exposure, and other factors. Not every radioactive disintegration of tritium results in a silver grain. For instance, *Maurer & Primbsch* (1964) reported that 16 disintegrations of tritium resulted in one silver grain, when 3 μm thick methacrylate sections on stripping film were used. Every modification in technique will give a different ratio, that is, another *specific sensitivity*.

Autoradiography is a time consuming process. The main limiting factors are the sensitivity of the photographic emulsion, the *specific activity* of the compound used, and the *specific concentration* of the compound in the tissue. Since some of the important factors are unknown, the exposure time cannot be calculated in advance, but will have to be found out through autoradiographic experiments. Unfortunately, under the conditions of the present state of the art, increased sensitivity of the photographic emulsion can be accomplished mainly by loss of resolution, due to the larger size of the silver halide crystals. Different modifications of the photographic emulsion have been tried, without yielding satisfactory results. Here is an area for improvement. Progress may ultimately depend on the development of an entirely different photographic procedure, which may not be based on the silver halide principle, but, hopefully permits visualization of the latent image without the need for elaborate processing of the radiation sensitive layer.

The high sensitivity of autoradiographic techniques has been demonstrated in many contributions. This sensitivity has, on the other hand, caused many problems in the interpretation of autoradiograms. The alluring pictorial approach, seemingly easy, often has ensnared propulsive and unwary investigators into a quick study. If it were not for continued disregard for reasonable prerequisites in the localization of non-covalently bound substances, the reiterated warnings (*Stumpf* 1968*b*, 1969*b*, 1970*b*) could be deemed hypercritical.

Autoradiographic techniques

Considering the available information, and with cautious extrapolation beyond our own experience, only a few of the many autoradiographic techniques in the literature can be recommended for the light microscopic cellular and subcellular localization of chemically unbound substances:

I. Dry-mounting of freeze-dried sections on emulsion precoated slides;
II. Thaw-mounting of frozen sections on emulsion precoated slides;
III. Smear-mounting on emulsion precoated slides;
IV. Touch-mounting on emulsion precoated slides.

I. Dry-mounting of freeze-dried sections on emulsion precoated slides

This technique has been described in detail in two previous accounts (*Stumpf* 1968*b*, 1970*c*), and applied for the localization of radioactivity after the injection of [³H] oestradiol (*Stumpf* 1968*a*, 1968*c*, 1968*d*, 1969*a*, 1970*a*; *Stumpf et al.* 1971), [³H] norethynodrel *(Stumpf* 1968*a)*, [³H] testosterone (*Sar et al.* 1970; *Stumpf & Sar* 1971), [³H] cortisol (*Stumpf & Sar* 1971) [³H] progesterone. [¹²⁵I] thyroxine (both unpublished) as well as non-hormonal substances (*Grossman & Stumpf* 1969). The dry-mount autoradiography technique appears superior to other techniques which were proposed for the localization of hor-

207

mones, as can be concluded from the published evidence, our own comparative studies with six autoradiographic techniques (*Stumpf & Roth* 1966), and most important, the exclusion of all steps that are known to be potential sources of diffusion artifacts. Although this technique may show pressure artifacts, produced during the dry-mounting, this type of artifact can be controlled and recognized by virtue of its variability between different sections of the same tissue, and by its association with folds, compressed areas, or structures of high density. Freezing of tissue optimally arrests metabolism and preserves a given situation at a given time. However, ice crystal formation, fracturing and loss of large samples, may be complicating factors. Thus, freezing limits the size of the tissue blocks to about 2 mm diameter for light microscopic and to about 1 mm for electron microscopic studies. Freeze-drying can not be applied when volatile compounds are to be assayed. There are, however, only very few drugs that fall under this category.

The dry-mount autoradiography technique consists of the following steps:

(1) *Simultaneous freeze-quenching and mounting.* A tissue block of 1–2 mm³ is excised and placed on a tissue holder using minced liver as an adhesive. Tissue with tissue holder are immersed in liquified propane cooled by liquid nitrogen to about –180°C. If larger tissue blocks are used, slower cooling or the use of a different coolant is required in order to avoid fracturing of the specimens. The mounted tissue is stored in a liquid nitrogen refrigerator until further use.

(2) *Cryostatic sectioning.* The tissue is transferred in a liquid nitrogen Dewar from the liquid nitrogen storage tank to the cryostat (Fig. 1), mounted on the microtome, and trimmed for cutting. The cut sections are transferred from the knife with a fine brush to a vial in the vicinity of the knife. The vial is covered with a fine punched out wire mesh which permits wiping the section from the brush and prevents section loss during freeze-drying and breaking of the vacuum. Several vials may be contained in a tissue carrier which is transferred by a long and precooled forceps to the sample chamber of the cryosorption pump (Thermovac Industries Corp., Copiaque, Long Island, New York) within the cytostat.

(3) *Freeze-drying.* Sample chamber and cryo-pump are assembled within the cryostat with the help of a vacuum produced by an outside forepump, which facilitates self-seating of the O-ring joint and activation of the molecular sieve of the cryo-pump. After brief evacuation of 5 to 10 minutes, the cryosorption chamber of the assembled cryo-pump is inserted into a Dewar which is filled with liquid nitrogen. The liquid nitrogen Dewar with the cryo-pump are kept within the cryostate which provides the cooling temperature for the specimen chamber of the cryo-pump. A microtome-cryostat (Fig. 1) which provides the

desired features for the cutting of thin frozen sections and freeze-drying is manufactured (Harris Manufacturing Company, Cambridge, Mass.). In case a suitable microtome cryostat is not available, freeze-drying microtome is not available, freeze-drying may be performed outside of the cryostat. In this case two Dewars are prepared, one filled with liquid nitrogen as a coolant for the molecular sieve, and the other one filled with alcohol-dry ice slush as a coolant for the specimen. After the forepumping within the cryostat, the cryo-pump is disconnected from the forepump and transferred to the two outside Dewars, immersing simultaneously, without delay, the two fingers of the cryo-pump into the Dewars. A vacuum between 10^{5-} to 10^{-6} torr is obtained. Freeze-drying may be terminated safely after about 15 to 20 hours by breaking the vacuum with nitrogen gas. Before the vacuum is broken, the sample chamber has been removed from the coolant and allowed to equilibrate to room temperature for about 1 hour. The tissue carrier is removed and stored in a desiccator until further use. The cryo-pump is then removed from the liquid nitrogen and the

Fig. 1.

Wide-range microtome cryostat for cutting of frozen sections and freeze-drying within the cryostat chamber. A dissecting microscope may be mounted on the left or right top ledge. Thus cutting may be performed under observation through a dissecting microscope. Temperature range: $-10°$ C to $-55°$C; cutting range: 1 μm to 18 μm. (Harris Manufacturing Co., Cambridge, Mass.).

209

molecular sieve will desorb the trapped water and reactivate within the pump at room temperature or in an oven at about 80°C for 2 hours.

(4) *Dry-mounting of sections.* Histologic slides which have been coated with liquid photographic emulsion (Kodak NTB 3) are used. They were air-dried, and stored over Drierite. At room temperature of 20° – 22°C and under conditions of a relative humidity between 20 % and 40 % for the avoidance of electrostatic discharge artifacts, if too low, and diffusion artifacts, if too high, sections are placed on clean pieces of Teflon (Crane Packing Co., Morton Grove, Illinois) using a fine forceps. Although handling of sections should be minimal, checking under a dissecting microscope may be especially important for judging the quality of thin and small sections, their positioning, and in order to remove folds. Under safelight an emulsion-coated slide is placed over the Teflon (Fig. 2, top) and Teflon and slide are pressed together between forefinger and thumb (Fig. 2, bottom). After release of the pressure, the Teflon falls off with the tissue slightly impressed and adhering to the emulsion. The

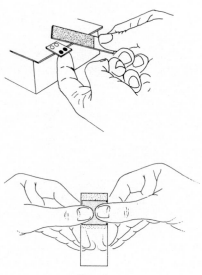

Fig. 2.

Dry-mounting of freeze-dried sections: The radioactivity-containing sections, ●, and control sections without radioactivity, ○, are placed on a Teflon piece. Under safelight a dried emulsion-coated slide is placed over the Teflon (upper picture) and both are pressed together by perpendicular pressure (lower picture).

Reproduced from *Stumpf* (1970c).

210

mounted slides are stored in a black box (modified Clay-Adams box) with a Drierite compartment and exposed at –15°C.

(5) *Photographic processing and staining*. At the end of exposure the slide containing box is allowed to adapt to room temperature before opening. A slide is removed and the section area is breathed on, once or twice, to briefly moisten the emulsion for better adherence of the section to the emulsion. If the breathing step is not included, loss of sections may occur during photographic processing or staining. The slide is developed with Kodak D 19 developer for about 1 minute at 21°C, briefly rinsed in tap water, fixed in Kodak fixer for 4–5 minutes, gently rinsed in tap water for 5–10 minutes, and stained. Immediate staining with a single step staining procedure such as methyl green-pyronin (*Stumpf* 1970c) is optical for most autoradiographs, since it does not introduce silver grain fading and provides good histologic differentiation without obscuring of silver grains. After a few seconds of staining and brief rinsing, the slide is air-dried and a coverslip is mounted with Permount. It is important during photographic processing and staining to keep the temperature of the different fluids within a close range in order to avoid reticulation of the emulsion. Histologic fixation of the sections prior to or after development is not necessary since it may affect the latent image of the silver grains.

II. *Thaw-mounting of frozen sections on emulsion precoated slides*

This technique has been described (*Stumpf & Roth* 1966; *Stumpf* 1970b) and compared with the above dry-mount procedure. Among six different auto-radiographic techniques which were used to study the localization of [³H] oestradiol and [³H] mesobilirubinogen – two diffusible substances known to be concentrated at distinct subcellular sites or tissue compartments – the thaw-mounting procedure was found to give results close to those obtained with the dry-mount technique. The subcellular resolution is, however, inferior to the one obtained with the dry-mount technique. The thawing of the section is accompanied by some disruption of tissue structures and a limited amount of diffusion of unbound labelled molecules. The degree of the latter depends on the section thickness and the compound used. Less diffusion can be expected in thinner sections. Since it is a wet procedure, the possibility of chemographic artifacts due to interactions between enzymes or other active tissue constituents and the photographic emulsion must be considered. The technique of thaw-mounting of frozen sections is as follows:

Freezing and sectioning of the tissue, photographic exposure, development

conventional liquid »fixatives«, it is conceivable that polypeptide and protein hormones may be precipitated and trapped during the denaturing of the tissue proteins. Leaching and redistribution are likely to occur to a lesser degree, however, artificial binding of *in situ* unbound material may result as a consequence of »fixation«. This has been demonstrated for amino acids (*Peters & Ashley* 1967). The short biological half life of at least some of the polypeptide hormones and their rapid metabolism may impose other problems, and will probably make it difficult to put meaning to localization data, if one expects visualization at target sites. There is no indication for retention and concentration of polypeptide hormones, due to binding to carrier proteins, in target cells, as appears to be the case for steroid hormones.

Electron microscope autoradiography

No technique is available which permits localization under electron microscopic magnification of chemically unbound hormones at their target sites. Unless the hormone under investigation is trapped in granules, classical tissue embedding procedures are likely to lead to translocation artifacts. Dry application of photographic emulsion appears to be another obstacle. Progress in frozen sectioning and freeze-drying at low temperatures in our laboratory (*Stumpf & Roth* 1965a, 1965b, 1967) and other laboratories (*Christensen* 1969) justifies hope that a useful technique for electron microscopic localization of hormones and drugs can be developed.

In vitro studies

The described four autoradiographic procedures may be used in conjunction with *in vitro* experiments. The dry-mount technique has been applied to the localization of [3H] oestradiol in rat uterus after incubation under varying conditions of time and temperature (*Jensen et al.* 1968; *Stumpf* 1968b). The uptake of oestradiol into the cytoplasm and nuclei of uterine cells could be followed. Incubation at 37°C gave data similar to those obtained in the *in vivo* experiments. However, even after 1 hour incubation at 37°C only a marginal portion, less than 100 μm, of the longitudinally slit uteri, showed the typical picture as *in vivo* of nuclear concentration of radioactivity. In deeper, surface remote layers, the radioactivity appeared diffusely distributed, in the cytoplasm and extracellular space, following a diffusion gradient. The results demonstrate, that apparently only a marginal portion of the tissue was functioning intact.

214

A similar observation has been reported in the literature. When thyroid tissue, prelabelled with ^{131}I was incubated, almost entire loss of the radio-iodine occurred from degenerating central follicles. Non-prelabelled lobes accumulated radioiodine only in the peripheral follicles when incubated with [131]I (*Grimm & Greer* 1966).

In the *in vitro* autoradiograms with [³H] oestradiol another observation has been made that did not occur in the *in vivo* experiments. Irregular islands of uterine tissue appeared free of radioactivity. Apparently, these tissue areas were damaged during handling with the forceps and had lost the capacity to take up and to bind the hormone. These, and other possible artifacts during *in vitro* autoradiography have been reported (*Stumpf* 1968*b*).

New findings and concepts related to progress in technique

The sensitive histochemical approach of dry-mount or dry autoradiography has furnished information which probably could not have been obtained otherwise. Among these is the identification of target cells for oestradiol and gluco-corticoid in the pituitary (*Stumpf* 1968, 1971*a*), and for oestradiol, androgen, and glucocorticoid in the brain. It has become possible to identify hormone-neurons in the brain and to precisely determine their topography. For the first time, a map of the brain for »oestrogen-neurons« has been provided (*Stumpf* 1970*a*) and information on the distribution of »androgen-neurons (*Sar & Stumpf* 1971; *Stumpf* 1971*b*; *Stumpf et al.* 1971) and »glucocorticoid-neurons« (*Stumpf* 1971*a,b*) has been obtained. This information will advance experimental design in neuroendocrinology and neurophysiology and will be essential for our understanding of brain functions as related to the »feed-back« regulation of endocrine gland, behaviour, production and release of hypo-physiotrophic hormones and others. In this context, the concept of the *peri-ventricular brain* with *hormone-neuron systems* (*Stumpf* 1970*a*) has been advanced and the current view of a single or dual sex »center« in the basal hypothalamus and preoptic region questioned.

REFERENCES

Bogoroch R. In: Roth L. J. and Stumpf W. E., Eds. Autoradiography of Diffusible Substances, Academic Press, New York (1969) 99.
Christensen A. K. In: Roth L. J. and Stumpf W. E.. Eds. Autoradiography of Diffusible Substances, Academic Press, New York (1969) 349.
Grimm Y. & Greer M. A.: Endocrinology 79 (1966) 469.

Grossman S. P. & Stumpf W. E.: Science 166 (1969) 1410.
Jensen E. V., Suzuki T., Kawashima T., Stumpf W. E., Jungblut P. W. & DeSombre E. R.: Proc. Nat. Acad. Sci. 59 (1968) 632.
Maurer W. & Primbsch E.: Exp. Cell Res. 33 (1964) 8.
Peters Jr. T. & Ashley C. A.: J. Cell Biol. 33 (1967) 53.
Sar M., Liao S. & Stumpf W. E.: Endocrinology 86 (1970) 1008.
Sar M. & Stumpf W. E.: Fed. Proc. (1971) in press.
Stumpf W. E.: Endocrinology 83 (1968a) 777.
Stumpf W. E. In: Hayes R. L., Goswitz F. A. and Murphy B. E. P., Eds. Radioisotopes in Medicine: In Vitro Studies, U. S. Atomic Energy Commission (1968b) 633.
Stumpf W. E.: Science 162 (1968c) 1001.
Stumpf W. E.: Z. Zellforsch. 92 (1968d) 23.
Stumpf W. E.: Endocrinology 85 (1969a) 31.
Stumpf W. E.: Science 163 (1969b) 958.
Stumpf W. E.: Amer. J. Anat. 129 (1970a) 207.
Stumpf W. E.: J. Histochem. Cytochem. 18 (1970b) 21.
Stumpf W. E. In: Wied G. L. and Bahr G. F., Eds. Introduction to Quantitative Cytochemistry-II, Academic Press, New York (1970c) 507.
Stumpf W. E.: Am. Zoologist (1971a) in press.
Stumpf W. E.: Fed. Proc. (1971b) in press.
Stumpf W. E. & Lester R.: Lab. Invest. 15 (1966) 1156.
Stumpf W. E. & Roth L. J.: Nature (Lond.) 205 (1965b) 712.
Stumpf W. E. & Roth L. J.: J. Histochem. Cytochem. 14 (1966) 274.
Stumpf W. E. & Roth L. J.: J. Histochem. Cytochem. 15 (1967) 243.
Stumpf W.E. & Sar M. In: Proceedings of the Third International Congress on Hormonal Steroids. Excerpta Med. (Amst.) (1971) in press.
Stumpf W. E., Baerwaldt C. & Sar M. In: Hubinont P. O. and Leroy F., Eds. Basic Action of Sex Steroids on Target Organs, Third International Seminar on Reproductive Physiology and Sexual Endocrinology, S. Karger, Basel (1971) in press.

DISCUSSION

Diczfalusy: Dr. Stumpf, is there anything known about qualitative differences in certain tissue constituents which are lost by fixation?

Stumpf: Yes. Most of the investigators who are quoted in Table A (p. 218) analysed for loss of nucleic acids, RNA or DNA, amino acids or protein. When I elaborated on the astounding percentage of loss, I indeed indicated what has been studied by the various investigators. I think that macromolecules are not as easily lost as smaller tissue constituents. The amount of loss depends also on the fixative used. There are differences in the precipitation. For hormone studies it is noteworthy that it seems, from what has been published in the literature, that classical fixation can be used for the study of polypeptide and protein hormone localization. Since fixatives precipitate these larger molecules, they may be maintained to a large degree. The best would be if one had a technique where one preserved everything. On the other hand, someone could state, O. K., I wash out what is not bound, since I want to see only what is bound – and many people argue this way. But, how do you know that you have washed out every-

216

thing that is not bound? How do you know that you did not wash out an undefined portion of what has been bound, and how do you know that there was no redistribution? So, this is the problem. For comparative studies, that is, if one treats all of the tissues the same way, one may get away with dunking of the tissues into the various media. Most of the histological sections we look at are only residues.

Ryan: Have you done control experiments of the time course of radioactive steroids going into cells? Can you drive them out? What is the time factor in relationship to this? You stated in your discussion that the steroids go there and they never stick.

Stumpf: Possibly they never stick to the receptor proper.

Ryan: Have you done studies which would give us some idea of the specificity of your oestradiol labelling? Can you drive it out with unlabelled oestradiol? Finally, I am intrigued by your figures, and if they have been published, I would like to have the references.

Stumpf: I don't think I can answer satisfactorily your question, because this is at present under investigation. In our laboratory, Dr. *Tchernitchin* is attempting to study uptake kinetics and competitive binding in *in vivo* experiments, using quantitative autoradiography. He injects [³H] oestradiol and removes uterine tissue at early and short time intervals. The path of oestradiol uptake, its dependence on the hormonal state of the animal, its interference with antioestrogens, etc., can be followed. Preliminary data indicate that the nuclear concentration of [³H] oestradiol as obtained in uterine cells in the immature rat and castrated mature rat, is less pronounced in an animal with an endogenous hormone level. In the real *in vivo* situation, you probably have a more overall distribution. Although the hormone seems to »stick« to macromolecules to some degree, as displacement studies indicate, it is still questionable whether this represents the receptor site, if we agree that the receptor is the site of hormone-protein interaction where hormone actions are initiated.

Ryan: Have you published the figures you showed of the distribution of the oestrogen?

Stumpf: Yes – in Science *162* (1968) 1001, and in the Am. J. Anat. *129* (1970) 207.

Hansel: Dr. Stumpf, there are supposed to be a »chronic« and a »cyclic« center in the hypothalamus for LH release. Have you seen anything in the pattern of oestrogen binding that would suggest this? The argument still goes on as to whether oestrogen feedback is entirely on the hypothalamus, or whether it is, in part, directly on the pituitary. What are your comments on this?

Stumpf: The tonic and the cyclic center are postulated to exist. We find at the postulated sites in the brain localization and high accumulation of oestrogen neurons and also androgen neurons. But these sites are ill defined by the endocrine physiologists – some say that the cyclic center is in the preoptic region, or others say, in the anterior hypothalamic region, while the tonic center is localized in the basal tuberal region. The question is an anatomical one, and one has to be specific. For instance, is it in the median eminence, in the ventromedial nucleus or in the nucleus paraventricularis or periventricularis, the bednucleus of the stria terminalis, the nucleus suprachiasmaticus, etc.? All these questions are relevant. With our histochemical approach we can specify and exclude some of the nuclei. There is a fair agreement with the areas proposed by endocrine physiologists. In addition to the cyclic and tonic »centers«,

217

Table A.

Loss of tissue constituents by fixation*.

Authors	Fixatives	Duration	Temperature	Labelled molecules	Loss of tissue or radioactivity
Sylvén (1)	(1) Saline 0.9 % (2) Formaldehyde soln. 5 % (3) Abs. alcohol (4) Carnoy solution	24 h	Room temp.	—	10–30 % Loss of the total tissue mass of fresh organs Slices from perfused rabbit liver, lung, skeletal muscle, and spleen were used
Merriam (2)	(1) 10 % Formalin	19–20 h	Room temp.	—	With formalin: 25 % (liver), 22 % (muscle) loss of total dry weight, 5–8 % further loss during subsequent dehydration and infiltration, 0.2–0.6 % of total dry weight protein loss in water after embedding
	(2) Acetic acid-alcohol				With acetic acid-alcohol similar loss
Dallam (3)	OsO_4 buffered	20 h	—	—	10.2–16.9 % Loss of protein from rat heart and kidney pieces (50–150 mg) during whole tissue preparation 29.2–31.8 % Loss from isolated mitochondria and 13.8–14.9 % loss from isolated liver microsomes
Ostrowski et al. (4)	Formalin or Carnoy's fluid Absolute alcohol or acetone	24 h	Room temp.	—	1 % 2.3 % } Protein elution from rat liver or kidney pieces of fresh tissue weight

Droz and Warshawsky (5)	Bouin's fluid and treatment with ethanol and dioxane	1-leucine-^{14}C	Room temp.	48 h	10–50 %	Loss of total radioactivity from tissue of mice sacrificed and exsanguinated at 30 min or 24 h after intraperitoneal injection
Morgan and Huber (6)	s-Collidine-buffered OsO$_4$	Choline-methyl-^{3}H Cl	Room temp.	2 h	66.9 %	Loss of total radioactivity from 1-mm cubes of lung tissue, excised 0.5–30 hour after ip injection, fixed in 10 volumes of fixative; 9.9–37.8 % was lipid-soluble radioactivity
	4 % Buffered formalin followed by OsO$_4$		Room temp.	3 h and 2 h	46.5 %	
	2 % Glutaraldehyde followed by OsO$_4$		Room temp.	24 h and 2 h	39 %	
	Tricomplex fixation		Room temp.	2 h	51.3 %	
Schneider and Schneider (7)	Formol 10 % Formol 40 %	–	Room temp.	180 days		21 % dry weight loss from 2-cm brain slices (including loss of protein, DNA and RNA)
	Carnoy solution					40 % dry weight (90 % of the extractable lipoids)

* Reproduced from Stumpf W. E., in Introduction to Quantitative Cytochemistry, Vol. 2, Academic Press, New York, 1970, pp. 507–526.

References:

(1) Sylvén B.: On the advantage of freeze-vacuum dehydration of tissues in morphological and cytochemical research. Acta, Unio Intern. Contra Cancrum 7, 708–712 (1951).

(2) Merriam R. W.: Standard chemical fixations as a basis for quantitative investigations of substances other than deoxyribonucleic acid. J. Histochem. Cytochem. 5, 43–51 (1957).

(3) Dallam R. D.: Determination of protein and lipid lost during osmic acid fixation of tissues and cellular particulates. J. Histochem. Cytochem. 6, 178–181 (1958).

(4) Ostrowski K., Komender J. and Kwarecky K.: Quantitative investigations on the solubility of proteins extracted from tissues by different chemical and physical methods. Experientia 17, 183–184 (1961).

(5) Droz B. and Warshawsky H.: Reliability of the radioautographic technique for the detection of newly synthesized protein. J. Histochem. Cytochem. 11, 426–435 (1963).

(6) Morgan T. E. and Huber G. L.: Loss of lipid during fixation for electron microscopy. J. Cell Biol. 32, 757–760 (1967).

(7) Schneider G. and Schneider G.: Qualitative und quantitative Untersuchungen über Stoffverluste bei Formol- und Carnoy-Fixierung von menschlichem Hirngewebe. Acta Histochem. 28, 227–242 (1967).

there are sites in the brain with hormone neurons that have not been considered by most of the endocrine physiologists. From our autoradiographic results on the distribution of »oestrogen-neurons« and »androgen-neurons«, the concept of a single or dual sex »center« seems untenable. To which »center«, for instance, would the oestradiol concentrating neurons belong which we find in the nucleus paraventricularis, the nucleus periventricularis, the organon subfornicale, the thalamic commissure, the nucleus habenulae lateralis, the periaqueductal gray, or the different parts of the amygdala?

Sex hormone neurons are found in many portions of the *periventricular brain*, the phylogenetically old part of the mammalian brain. We may indeed have the anatomical substrate for the »feedback« regulation of the gonads, for the production of specific hypophysiotrophic hormones and for the influence of the sex hormones on the various aspects of behaviour (sex, maternal, aggressive, emotional and others), temperature regulation and other vegetative functions. Perhaps even Freud's concept of the subconscious' relation to sex may have a substrate here.

Martini: You maintained that testosterone does not appear to be bound to the anterior pituitary. There are »in vitro« data which indicate that the pituitary does contain the protein which binds testosterone (*Samperez et al.* 1969).

Stumpf: Testosterone binds to many proteins. Is this a specific protein?

Martini: It is believed to be specific.

Stumpf: Implantation of testosterone into the pituitary was shown to be ineffective (*Davidson & Sayer* 1961; *Lisk* 1962), and this agrees with our autoradiographic data (together with Dr. *M. Sar*) that there is no androgen concentration and retention in the pituitary.

Martini: You mentioned that testosterone was bound to the amygdala and that it might be transformed into dihydrotestosterone there. Are these our own results (*Kniewald et al.* 1970), or do you have new information on this point?

Stumpf: We have not done chemical identification. You have done it (*Kniewald et al.* 1970) and, actually, this remark was based on your publication.

Martini: You mentioned that feedback mechanisms might operate outside the hypothalamus. Could you elaborate a little bit on whether the distribution of oestrogens is modified by castration, previous administration of unlabelled oestrogen, or whether you can displace your label by giving antioestrogenic compounds?

Stumpf: This is still under investigation. We have no data on competitive binding, although together with Dr. *Eisenfeld* we have begun these studies about a year ago. Dr. Eisenfeld has biochemical evidence of competitive binding with clomiphene and norethynodrel. With clomiphene, the competition with oestradiol in various parts of the brain, including the amygdala, is comparable to the peripheral target tissues. To elaborate on the outside »feedback« effect of oestradiol, I may quote here that *Tindal et al.* (1967) implanted oestradiol into the amygdala and thus stimulated prolactin secretion. There are a number of studies on sex behaviour, but also on effects on gonadotrophin secretion. This has been reviewed in our recent publication on oestrogen-neurons in the amygdala (*Stumpf & Sar* 1971). Our localization of oestrogen-neurons in the periaqueductal gray of the brain stem (*Stumpf* 1970) is parallelled by observations of lesion effects on gonadotrophin secretion (*Appeltauer et al.* 1966).

There is also the work by *Endröczi & Hilliard* (1965), which suggests that LH releasing activity may be obtained from tissue outside the hypothalamus.

Rodesch: A technical question: What do you do to avoid the pressure artifact, and if you get some, what do they look like?

Stumpf: We have pressure artifacts where there are folds, and also at compressed areas of the section. Usually, when you cut, the initial part of the section is thicker, that is, at one margin of the section you may get pressure artifacts. But you recognize the pressure artifacts by virtue of association of those artifacts with the described areas as well as by their variability. Pressure artifacts can therefore be controlled, and we have had no serious problems.

Concerning Dr. Hansel's question about the oestrogen-feedback I would think that, from the localization data with oestradiol, both the pituitary and brain seem to be included in the feedback – but, I just don't know what »feedback« is. I think, on the basis of the nuclear concentration, that it is a stimulatory »feedback«. I have discussed this view in earlier publications.

Gurpide: One of your slides showed that after incubation of tissue with labelled steroids the isotope was localized mainly on the edges of the section, while the rest of the radioactivity was diffusely distributed. Does this preparation indicate that there was a lack of penetration of the steroids or diffusion during fixation? What was the thickness of the incubated material and how long was the exposure to radioactive steroids?

Stumpf: These were longitudinally slit uteri. How thick is the immature uterus – 1 mm? Probably it was too thick for optimal penetration. In addition to the penetration problem, the diffusion gradient, you also have problems of oxygen and nutrient supply. We have the same picture in the center of the tissues after incubation at 37°C as we have after incubation at 2°C. So, the hormone stays in the cytoplasm and only little enters the nucleus. Probably, energy is necessary to transport it to the nuclei, and this is impaired when the tissue is thicker than 0.4 to 0.5 mm.

Gurpide: For how long do you incubate?

Stumpf: The incubation was done at 37°C for one hour and at 2°C for five minutes (*Jensen et al.* 1968).

Baulieu: Have you any evidence for a nuclear localization of cortisol in any organ? Secondly, have you any evidence for progesterone uptake in any organ? You said that you have nothing in the brain, but what about other organs, in any species?

You are obviously aware of the very difficult problem of the location of the so called *receptors*, or of binding proteins in the target cells. I was interested to hear that when you inject 0.5 µg of oestradiol together with the radioactive tracer, you find a decrease of the nuclear binding, as expected if you have a limited number of sites, and also an increase of the cytoplasmic labelling. Have you any evidence that the cytoplasmic localization of the grains that you observed represents some bound radioactive material? Is it possible to do some isotopic dilution experiments which could prove that point? Again, when you heat at 37°C after preincubation in the cold and you see some shift of the radioactivity and some nuclear uptake, what is your opinion about that change? Couldn't it be artifactual, since you said that any *in vitro* incubation is bad compared to the *in vivo* situation?

Stumpf: Concerning your first question, I don't know if it is cortisol. However, at 30 minutes and one hour after injection of 0.5 μg of tritium labelled cortisol, we found nuclear concentration of radioactivity in various parts of the brain, such as the gyrus denatus, the hippocampus, and the amygdala, and it seems that there is some nuclear concentration also in anterior pituitary cells (*Stumpf* 1971). I do not have evidence of any other peripheral tissue where there is a special concentration. We have studied the thymus, but so far our results are not conclusive. The autoradiographic localization experiments with cortisol are still under way and it is premature to put the cards down.

For progesterone: in the brain we have so far no conclusive evidence for concentration at any subcellular site, which would resemble what we have seen with other steroids. But in the rat uterus and oviduct we find some selective nuclear concentration of radioactivity after [³H] progesterone injection (together with *M. Sar,* unpublished).

Baulieu: In the rat we have not studied the progesterone localization in the nuclei, so we don't know. In the uterine nuclei of guinea pigs primed with oestrogen, Dr. *Milgrom* found it, for sure. In the rat uterus cytosol, we have binding sites, so, in the cytoplasm you may have something.

Stumpf: So far we have found pronounced nuclear concentration in the muscularis of the uterus.

Baulieu: What is your feeling about the real significance of the grains that are observed in cytoplasmic areas?

Stumpf: The answer to this, I think, only the biochemists can provide. It would be beyond my capacity to make any statement here.

Ryan: Dr. Davies in our Department has studied the distribution of progesterone in the pregnant rat myometrium. At least a good portion of the radioactivity is in fact progesterone, which remains there for quite a while, so it is highly likely that you are seeing what we are measuring.

References:

Appeltauer L. C., Reissenweber N. J., Dominguez R., Grinó E., Sas J. & Benedetti W. L.: Acta neuroveget. *29* (1966) 75.
Davidson J. M. & Sawyer C. H.: Proc. Soc. exp. Biol. Med. *107* (1961) 4.
Endröczi E. & Hilliard J.: Endocrinology 77 (1965) 667.
Jensen E. V., Suzuki T., Kawashima T., Stumpf W. E., Jungblut P. W. & DeSombre E. R.: Proc. Nat. Acad. Sci. (U. S. A.) *59* (1968) 632.
Kniewald Z., Massa R. & Martini L.: Excerpta med. Intern. Congr. Ser. *210* (1970) 59.
Lisk R. D.: Endocrinology *41* (1962) 195.
Samperez S., Thieulant M. L. & Jouan P.: C. R. Acad. Sci. (Paris) *1268* (1969) 2965.
Stumpf W. E.: Amer. J. Anat. *129* (1970) 207.
Stumpf W. E.: Fed. Proc. (1971) in press.
Stumpf W. E. & Sar M.: Proc. Soc. exp. Biol. Med. *136* (1971) 102.
Tindal J. S., Knaggs G. S. & Turvey A.: J. Endocr. *37* (1967) 297.

Unité de Recherches sur le Métabolisme Moléculaire
et la Physio-Pathologie des Stéroides de l'Institut National de la Santé
et de la Recherche Médicale, Département de Chimie Biologique,
Faculté de Médecine de Paris-Sud, 78 Avenue du Général Leclerc – F 94 Bicêtre

EVALUATION OF TISSUE STEROID BINDING IN VITRO

By

C. R. Wira, H. Rochefort and E. E. Baulieu

ABSTRACT

The definition of a RECEPTOR* in terms of a receptive site, an executive site and a coupling mechanism, is followed by a general consideration of four binding criteria, which include hormone specificity, tissue specificity, high affinity and saturation, essential for distinguishing between specific and nonspecific binding. Experimental approaches are proposed for choosing an experimental system (either organized or soluble) and detecting the presence of protein binding sites.

Techniques are then presented for evaluating the specific protein binding sites (*receptors*) in terms of the four criteria. This is followed by a brief consideration of how *receptors* may be located in cells and characterized when extracted.

Finally various examples of oestrogen, androgen, progestagen, glucocorticoid and mineralocorticoid binding to their respective target tissues are presented, to illustrate how researchers have identified specific corticoid and mineralocorticoid binding in their respective target tissue *receptors*.

INTRODUCTION

The concept that hormones interact with target tissues and that this interaction is the primary step which eventually results in hormone effects, is generally accepted. It is not clear, however, that only *some* forms of binding to

---

* An argument concerning the use of »RECEPTOR«, »*receptor*«, »neo-nuclear« is found in *Baulieu et al.* (1971).

Brinck-Johnsen 1968), then a similar saturation phenomenon would be expected if the extracted proteins studied really are target cell *receptors*.

EXPERIMENTAL APPROACHES

Detection of receptors

The detection of *receptors* consists of demonstrating a specific interaction between a hormone and a macromolecule. Since hormones under physiological conditions act at very low concentrations, the use of tritiated steroids of high specific activity is essential. For this reason, steroids labelled with 1 or even 2 molecules of tritium (50–100 Ci/mmole) are most effective for detecting specific binding, which in general occurs within the same range as endogenous tissue levels of hormone. Since endogenous hormone may compete with radioactive steroids for specific binding, thereby preventing detection of *receptor* sites, possible endogenous sources may be removed by surgery (example: ovariectomy, adrenalectomy, etc. . .) or by using tissues of immature animals. Further, it is suggested that preparation and handling of tissues, cells and subcellular components be carefully controlled, in light of numerous results indicating that *receptors* are very fragile.

Choice of experimental system

Hormone binding in a given tissue may be studied by working either with an *organized system,* such as intact tissue, slices or isolated cells, or with a *cell free system* of organelles or soluble fractions.

With an *organized system,* the preparation is exposed to tritiated steroids either for short or long term incubation (tissue culture). In either case, parameters such as O_2, CO_2, temperature, pH, etc. . . should be controlled in an effort to duplicate *in vivo* conditions. Following incubation, incorporation into tissues or cell fractions can be measured directly. It should be noted, however, that the possibility of steroid translocation exists whenever fractions are prepared. As a result, data from such studies are most meaningful when compared to *in vivo* and cell free results.

In *cell free* studies, tissues are homogenized in buffer and centrifuged at various speeds to obtain subcellular fractions which are then exposed to tritiated steroids. Products of high speed centrifugation that do not sediment are referred to as cytosol. With differential centrifugation, organelles such as nuclei, mitochondria and ribosomes can be obtained. Extracts of these fractions can then be obtained eventually with high ionic strength solvents and exposed directly to steroids for evidence of binding (*Baulieu et al.* 1970). One advantage of cell free studies is that quantitative results of direct hormone-protein interactions are obtained without the problem of compartmentalization. as in tissue and intact cell studies. Cell free data, nevertheless, should be evaluated with great caution. This suggestion is prompted by results obtained from oestrogen studies demonstrating that a cytosol *receptor* was essential for specific binding of oestradiol to uterine nuclei (*Brecher et al.* 1967).

It is worthwhile mentioning that knowledge of the active form of a hormone is important for insight into the mechanism of action of steroids. Chromatographic studies have indicated that oestradiol in the uterus (*Jensen & Jacobson* 1962) and cortisol in thymus cells (*Munck & Brinck-Johnsen* 1968) exert their effects as such and not *via* one of their metabolites. In contrast, androstanolone and other metabolites of testosterone have been identified as active in prostate tissue (*Baulieu et al.* 1968).

Determination of binding criteria

Hormone specificity

Specificity can be determined by incubation of tritiated steroids with either tissues, cells or cell free systems. Techniques for direct measurements of binding in tissues (*Jensen & Jacobson* 1960), whole cells (*Munck & Brinck-Johnsen* 1968) and cell free systems (*Baulieu et al.* 1970) have been reported previously. In addition to direct binding, studies of competition for suspected specific tritiated steroids with other unlabelled steroids or with the same unlabelled steroids (*i. e.* lowered specific activity) are of value. They may provide further evidence of specificity and at the same time indicate whether the suspected protein sites are saturable. Binding results from tissue, cell and cell free experiments should be similar to *in vivo* binding data.

Tissue specificity

Hormone specificity studies similar to those discussed above, can be undertaken with other tissues. With non-target tissues, evidence for binding would be expected to be negative when care is taken to compare similar fractions.

High affinity

High affinity binding, while most readily observed at low levels of steroid concentration, may not be measurable due to the presence of nonspecific binding. In this case, slow dissociation (an important characteristic of most high affinity binding) can be used with organized systems, as illustrated in

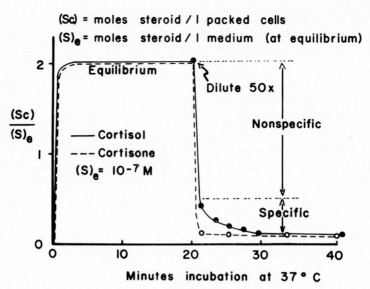

Fig. 3.

Steroid binding to cells. Outline of a typical pair of binding experiments, one with cortisol and one with cortisone. A thymus cell suspension was incubated at 37°C in Krebs-Ringer bicarbonate buffer, with 3 mM glucose and the tritium-labelled steroid at a concentration $(S)_e$ in the medium of about 10^{-7} M. After an initial equilibration period of 20 min, for which the binding curves are indicated schematically, the suspension was diluted 50-fold into buffer without steroid. The values of (Sc) at various times were measured by centrifuging aliquots of the suspensions and determining the tritium bound to the cells (*Munck et al.* 1970).

Fig. 3 (*Munck & Brinck-Johnsen* 1968) or with soluble preparations (*Truong & Baulieu* 1971; *Wira & Munck* 1970a,b), as illustrated in Fig. 4.

Overall affinity can be determined from binding *equilibrium* studies if the relationship of specific to nonspecific binding is taken into consideration. That is, if the specific fraction is masked by the nonspecific fraction, the latter can be partially removed by an adsorbtion technique (»differential dissociation«: see *Baulieu et al.* 1970). Once again, these findings should be compatible with results obtained from organized systems and *in vivo* experiments.

Saturability

Another means of distinguishing between specific and nonspecific binding is to look for evidence of limited capacity. The absence of saturation coupled with binding of a number of biologically unrelated steroids, would indicate

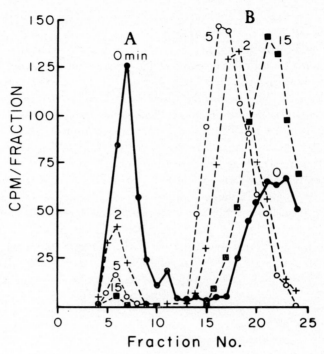

Fig. 4.

Slow dissociation of specifically bound cortisol from the *receptor* complex. Separation on a Sephadex column of the cortisol-nuclear *receptor* complex (peak A) from free cortisol (peak B), and progressive dissociation of the complex at 37°C. Nuclear extracts, prepared as described in the text from thymus cells incubated with [³H] cortisol (8 nM) for 20 min at 37°C, were chromatographed on Sephadex G-25 columns. The solid line gives the elution curve of an aliquot of extract that was kept at 3°C throughout the procedure. The dashed lines gives the elution curves of aliquots that were warmed at 37°C for 2 min (+), 5 min (o), and 15 min (■); then recooled to 3°C and chromatographed (*Wira & Munck* 1970).

a lack of specificity. When saturation is studied tritiated steroids with increasing amounts of the same steroids in the non-radioactive form are either administered *in vivo* or incubated with cells or subcellular fractions. Evidence of saturability would be a decrease in tritiated steroid binding with increasing concentrations of non-labelled steroid.

Characterization of receptors

Experiments with enzymatic digestion are of value for preliminary identification of hormone-receptor complexes. All receptors examined to date, have been found to be at least in part protein because of their rapid degradation by pronase and insensitivity to deoxyribonuclease, ribonuclease, lipase and neuraminidase. Further characterization may include measurements of protein sensitivity to heat and the effect that various agents (*i. e.* SH blockers) have on specific binding, since nonspecific binding is often relatively insensitive to such treatments. It should be noted that hormone-receptor interaction, in general stabilizes the receptor against heat denaturation, proteolysis, etc. . . ., as illustrated in Fig. 5, and therefore is potentially another tool for distinguishing between specific and nonspecific proteins.

Since proteolysis in organized and cell free systems occurs rapidly, studies to obtain intact (native) binding proteins should be undertaken at low temperatures with proteolytic inhibitors. Another source of protein alteration is illustrated in Fig. 6. When the protein-hormone complex was exposed to solutions of increasing concentrations of KCl, multiple forms of oestradiol *receptor* complex were found. Manipulations such as freezing, thawing and column chromatography tend to provoke other forms, such as aggregates.

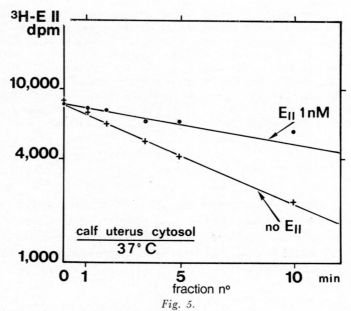

Fig. 5.

Protection by oestradiol of calf uterus cytosol *receptor* from alteration by heat (*Rochefort & Baulieu* 1971, to be published, cited in *Baulieu et al.* 1971).

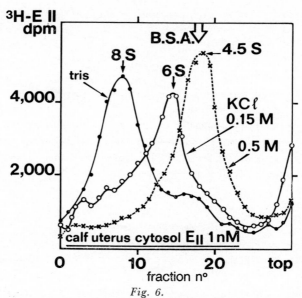

Fig. 6.

Effects of salt on cytosol *receptor* conformation. Sedimentation patterns of tritiated oestradiol cytosol *receptor* complexes in tris buffer and following exposure to 0.15 M and 0.5 M KCl (*Rochefort & Baulieu* 1971, to be published, cited in *Baulieu et al.* 1971).

Localization of receptors

Autoradiography and cellular fractionation are two techniques available for determining the location of *receptors* in cells. In both cases support for nuclear sites can be obtained if care is taken to diminish steroid translocation, which may occur either during homogenization or fixation. Use of these techniques for identification of cytoplasmic *receptors,* however, remains an unsolved question. In fractionation studies, the possibility is always present that either buffer (solvent) or homogenization solubilizes some portion of the organelles, which subsequently appear in the cytosol (cytoplasmic) fraction. Likewise, with autoradiography, grains above the cytoplasm may not be due to the presence of cytoplasmic *receptors.* Evidence for specific cytoplasmic binding by auto-radiographic analysis would, however, be more meaningful if carried out in conjunction with saturation, and time course studies.

The state of the tissue examined must be considered. This suggestion is based on evidence indicating that translocation of cytosol bound steroid is temperature sensitive. That is, on warming to 37°C, binding appears in the nucleus (»neonuclear binding«) as it simultaneously decreases in the cytosol.

This will be considered in greater detail in the oestrogen and glucocorticoid sections.

STEROID HORMONE RECEPTORS

The following section on steroid hormone *receptors* is presented with the intent of illustrating how various problems of determining hormone specificity have been approached and resolved in different biological systems and is not to be considered a review of the literature.

Oestrogen receptors

The retention and eventual fate of oestrogens in various rat tissues was measured in studies designed to explore hormone action (*Jensen* 1958; *Glascock & Hoekstra* 1959). Following synthesis of tritiated oestradiol (*Jensen & Jacobson* 1962), physiological doses were injected into immature rats. By measuring the concentration of radioactivity in various tissues, oestrogen-responsive tissues, *i. e.* uterus, vagina and anterior pituitary, were found to have characteristic patterns of rapid hormone uptake and preferential retention not shared by non-target tissues such as liver, blood and skeletal muscle (Fig. 7). Subsequent chromatographic analysis indicated that no chemical transformation of the oestradiol molecule had occurred. When this experimental procedure was repeated with radioactive oestrone, a steroid with only one-tenth as much oestrogenic activity as oestradiol, the radioactivity retained by the target tissues was found to be oestradiol, metabolically derived from oestrone.

Autoradiography and cell fractionation studies have shown that of the tritiated oestradiol retained by uterine tissue, the majority was associated with the nuclei of endometrial and myometrial cells (*Stumpf & Roth* 1966; *Jensen et al.* 1967). Analysis of the supernatant fraction with Sephadex chromatography indicated that the oestradiol present was bound to a macromolecule (*Talwar et al.* 1964).

Toft & Gorski (1966) were the first to characterize this cytosol macromolecule complex as having a sedimentation coefficient of 8–10 S by means of ultracentrifugation in a sucrose density gradient. Furthermore, this macromolecule, which is at least in part a protein, was found to have a high affinity ($K \cong 1.10^{10} M^{-1}$, at 4°C), to be stereospecific for oestrogen molecules (*Baulieu et al.* 1967) and saturated at concentrations of oestradiol above physiological levels (*Jensen et al.* 1968). Extraction of a nuclear oestradiol *receptor* sedimenting at about 5 S was accomplished with dilute KCl (*Jensen et al.* 1967a).

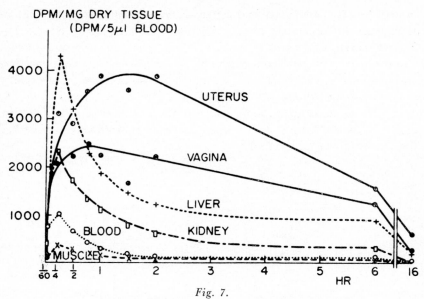

DPM/MG DRY TISSUE
(DPM/5μl BLOOD)

Fig. 7.

In vivo retention of oestradiol by target tissues. Concentration of radioactivity in dried tissues of 23-day-old rats after single subcutaneous injection of 0.1 μg (11.5 μCi) [6,7-³H] oestradiol in 0.5 ml saline. Liver and kidney points are mean values of 3 aliquot samples of pooled tissue: other points are median values of individual samples from 6 animals. Blood data plotted as dpm/5 μl. Muscle in all experiments is *M. quadriceps femoris*. Radioactivity incorporation patterns paralleling that of blood are shown in this or in analogous experiments by bone, adrenal, lung, diaphragm, hypothalamus and cerebrum (*Jensen & Jacobson* 1960).

The 8–10 complex was produced *in vitro* by direct addition of [³H] oestradiol to the cytosol, whereas the neo-nuclear 5 S complex required uterine nuclei exposed to the oestradiol 8–10 complex, and was found to be temperature dependent (*Jensen et al.* 1968; *Schyamala & Gorski* 1969).

More recently, the cytosol 8 S complex has been demonstrated to contain 4 S binding subunits distinguishable from the neo-nuclear 5 S complex (*Erdos* 1968; *Rochefort & Baulieu* 1968; *Jensen et al.* 1969). At present, indirect evidence suggests that the cytosol *receptor* becomes the nuclear 5 S *receptor*. However, the exact sequence of events as well as the eventual fate of the *receptor* and oestradiol at the chromatin level remain to be established.

Androgen receptors

Androgen *receptors* have been studied almost exclusively in the rat ventral prostate, although preliminary evidence suggests that they may also be present

235

in seminal vesicles. A fundamental difference that exists between the binding of androgens and the binding of other steroids to their respective target tissues is that the active form does not appear to be testosterone, but rather androstanolone (5α-dihydrotestosterone). This metabolite, which can originate from several precursors in addition to testosterone, has been found to accumulate selectively *in vivo* (*Bruchovsky & Wilson* 1968), *in vitro* (*Anderson & Liao* 1968) and in tissue culture (*Baulieu et al.* 1968). Furthermore, in the latter experiments, 5α-androstane-3β,17β-diol as well as androstanolone have been implicated in testosterone activity.

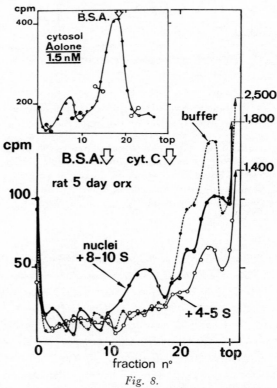

Fig. 8.

Neo-nuclear *receptor* in rat ventral prostate. Glycerol gradient sedimentation patterns showing the formation of neo-nuclear 3S *receptor* from 8–10 S cytosol *receptor*. Prior to labelling with tritiated androstanolone two regions (8–10 S and 4–5 S) of cytosol from 1 day orchidectomized rat prostate were prepared by ultracentrifugation (small panel). Each region was then incubated separately with prostate nuclei of 5 day orchidectomized rats. As seen in the large panel, formation of neo-nuclear 3 S *receptor* occurs when nuclei are exposed to 8–10 S (●——●) and not to 4–5 S (○——○) fractions or buffer (● – – ●) (*Baulieu et al.* 1970a).

236

When ventral prostate tissue of one day castrate rats is disrupted in hypotonic tris buffer, a *receptor* (8–10 S) can be recovered from the cytosol. This *receptor,* which has an equilibrium binding constant for androstanolone of the order of $10^{10}M^{-1}$ at 4°C, also binds testosterone, but does not bind 5α- or 5β-androstanediol. In addition, oestradiol (but not diethylstilboestrol), progesterone, cyproterone and R-2956 (an anti-androgen) have been found to be competitors of androstanolone binding (*Baulieu & Jung* 1970).

A reversible conversion of 8–10 S androstanolone complex binding protein to 4–5 S has been obtained on 0.5 M KCl exposure. This *receptor* complex was found to be less stable than its corresponding oestrogen *receptor* in the rat uterus cytosol and therefore was analyzed at temperatures of less than 4°C in solutions containing glycerol (*Mainwaring* 1969). Recently, two androstanolone binding proteins were obtained by another procedure (*Liao & Fang* 1970) and found to have sedimentation coefficients of approximately 4 S. Only one binds selectively androstanolone and can be converted to neo-nuclear *receptor* (as will be discussed shortly) whereas the second, which does not change to neo-nuclear, may even be inhibitory to neo-nuclear formation.

Evidence for a 3 S neo-nuclear *receptor* was obtained from examination of rat ventral prostate nuclei at various tissue intervals after castration. Nuclear 3 S binding of androstanolone was observed in 1–2 day castrates but absent 5–7 days after orchidectomy (*Baulieu & Robel* 1970). More recently, conversion of 8–10 S but not 4–5 S cytoplasmic *receptor* to neo-nuclear 3 S *receptor* in cell free experiments was observed with androstanolone (Fig. 8) but not with testosterone (not shown).

Preliminary data (*Robel & Blondeau,* unpublished) indicate that small particles (microsomes?) of rat ventral prostate also bind androstanolone, 3α- and 3β-androstanediol with high affinity, but not testosterone. Further, 3β-androstanediol and androstanolone compete for binding in the microsomes. Finally, from *in vitro* studies, androstanolone, testosterone and the two androstanediols have been found to bind in the 4 S region of the cytosol, although no saturation can be demonstrated (*Baulieu & Jung* 1970). It is likely that there are several unidentified proteins with sedimentation coefficients similar to 4 S, since other steroids, such as oestradiol and cortisol, are also bound to this region.

Progesterone receptors

A progesterone binding protein has been identified in cytosol fractions of immature, cycling, pregnant and oestradiol primed rat uteri which, based on physico-chemical criteria, is very similar to plasma Corticosteroid Binding Globulin (CBG) (*Milgrom & Baulieu* 1970a). This protein is present at concentrations that cannot be explained simply by plasma contamination. The demonstration that CBG like protein is intracellular, comes from tissue in-

237

cubation experiments which have shown that CBG binds radioactive progesterone but not radioactive cortisol. The diminished availability of cortisol to intracellular sites was due either to decreased entry or greater metabolism of the corticosteroids. Contrary to the circulating plasma CBG, *in vivo* studies with radioactive progesterone and cortisol have indicated selective labelling of uterine CBG by progesterone and not by cortisol (*Milgrom & Baulieu* 1970*b*).

Cytosol *receptors* with high affinity for progesterone in the guinea pig (approximately $5.10^8 M^{-1}$ at 4°C) have been reported (*Milgrom et al.* 1970). This receptor is very similar to other steroid *receptors* in that it has a sedimentation coefficient of 6.7 S and is converted to 4 S when exposed to 0.5 M KCl. Further, it is specific since it binds 5α-pregnane-3,20-dione and 17α-ethynyl-19-nortestosterone, a synthetic progestagen, but does not bind 20α-reduced progesterone, glucocorticoids or oestradiol. While only small amounts of this *receptor* are present in castrate uterus cytosol, formation is readily stimulated by oestradiol (*i. e.* 5 μg × 3 days). Similar results have been obtained in rabbit and human endometrium (*Rao & Wiest* 1970).

Only recently has a nuclear *receptor* with a 4 S sedimentation coefficient been extracted by 0.3 M KCl following *in vivo* injections of tritiated progesterone (*Milgrom et al.* 1970).

Glucocorticoid receptors

The binding of glucocorticoids to thymus cells was studied (*Munck & Brinck-Johnsen* 1966, 1968) in an effort to identify the factors responsible for glucocorticoid effects on glucose uptake (*Munck* 1968). The term binding implied no particular physiological or molecular mechanisms but rather was used to describe the nature of the association that existed between hormones and thymus cells. Differences among glucocorticoids and nonglucocorticoids were determined by *in vitro* measurements of their rates of release from cells into supernatant following a shift in equilibrium. In this way, two sets of binding sites were identified. One set, a minor portion of the total, was found to be specific for glucocorticoids while a second set, the nonspecific sites, accounted for the majority of the bound steroid (Fig. 3). This latter set was unrelated to physiological glucocorticoid activity but was related to nonspecific metabolic effects (*Munck* 1965). The specific sites were distinguished from the more numerous nonspecific sites by their relatively slow rates of dissociation at 37°C (a 3 minute half-life time constant for the specifically-bound fraction as compared to one of less than 15 seconds for the nonspecific fraction). The conclusion that the slowly-dissociating fraction represents those molecules bound to physiological *receptors* which produce specific metabolic effects was based upon the following observations: (1) saturation of the specific sites occurs

238

over the range of glucocorticoid concentrations that give a graded metabolic response *in vivo* and *in vitro* (10 nM to 3000 nM); (2) glucocorticoids such as cortisol, corticosterone and dexamethasone, which produce specific hormonal effects *in vitro*, dissociate slowly; whereas a nonglucocorticoid such as cortisone, which is metabolically inactive, lacks a slowly-dissociating fraction; (3) the specific fraction is competed for by other steroids in rough proportion to glucocorticoid activity; (4) cortexolone, a steroid shown to prevent the binding of the slowly-dissociating fraction (but not the nonspecific fraction), also blocks the metabolic effects of cortisol on thymus cells; (5) the specific fraction becomes bound rapidly enough (7–10 minutes) to account for the earliest glucocorticoid effects (15–20 minutes) on thymus cells that have been observed so far (*Munck et al.* 1970).

When thymus cells containing specifically-bound cortisol were disrupted by hypotonic shock in 1.5 mM $MgCl_2$ following incubation at either at 20°C or 37°C, the majority of the specifically bound fraction was found in the nuclei. However, when cells were incubated at 3°C and then disrupted, the specific fraction was found in the supernatant. Although the exact location of the supernatant fraction was not identified, it was referred to as »cytoplasmic« (*Munck & Wira* 1970). Specifically bound cortisol was found to dissociate at 37°C from nuclear (extracted with 0.6 M KCl) and »cytoplasmic« *receptors* (Fig. 4) at rates similar to the slow dissociation of the specific fraction bound to whole cells indicating that slow dissociation is an intrinsic property of the *receptor* complexes (*Wira & Munck* 1970*a,b*). It has further been demonstrated that both *receptors*, which bind glucocorticoids directly, are specific and have saturation properties that are very similar to those of whole cells. Evidence for an obligatory temperature sensitive translocation of »cytoplasmic« to nuclear *receptor* has been obtained from whole cell studies.

From studies designed to identify the location of the nonspecific fraction, several lines of evidence have indicated that thymus cells are readily permeable to glucocorticoids. In this context, it has been suggested that the primary hormone interaction in some way directs the *receptor* to its nuclear or executive site rather than the *receptor* transferring glucocorticoids to the nucleus (*Munck & Wira* 1970) and that it is the hormone *receptor* complex that is active rather than the *receptor* alone (*Munck & Wira* 1970).

Similar glucocorticoid *receptors* have also been found in responsive cells (thymus cells: *Schaumburg & Bojesen* 1968; hepatoma cells (»HTC«): *Baxter & Tomkins* 1971).

Aldosterone receptors

Evidence for nuclear aldosterone *receptors* in the toad bladder was first obtained from autoradiographic studies. Following exposure of toad hemibladders

239

to tritiated aldosterone, selective localization of grains was found above mucosal epithelium cell nuclei (*Edelman et al.* 1963). Subsequent aldosterone displacement studies, also in the total bladder, resulted in evidence for two sets of binding sites, one with high and one with low affinity (*Sharp et al.* 1966). Since the low affinity set was saturated at concentrations of hormone corresponding to levels used to obtain maximal physiological activity, it was concluded that this set was responsible for effects on sodium transport. The physiological significance of the high affinity set was not established because saturation occurred at concentrations well below the minimal levels of aldosterone needed to produce mineralocorticoid effects. When tritiated aldosterone cells were disrupted (*Ausiello & Sharp* 1968), a major fraction of the radioactivity was associated with the nuclei, thus supporting the earlier autoradiographic evidence of a nuclear receptor.

In an attempt to elucidate the action of mineralocorticoids in mammalian tissues, studies of aldosterone binding to the kidney of the adrenalectomized rat were undertaken (*Fanestil & Edelman* 1966). When unmetabolized aldosterone was measured in nuclear, supernatant, mitochondrial and microsomal fractions, only the nuclear fraction showed evidence of saturation. Further it was found that nuclei were half-saturated at 6 nM or well within the physiological range and that only aldosterone binding in the nuclear fraction was competed for by other mineralocorticoids. More recently, aldosterone-macromolecular complexes from nuclear and cytosol fractions of the rat kidney have been demonstrated (*Edelman & Fimognari* 1968).

These complexes were recovered following injection of [³H] aldosterone into adrenalectomized rats and after incubation of labelled aldosterone with renal nuclear extracts and cytosol fractions *in vitro*. Binding experiments, following *in vivo* injection or *in vitro* incubation with other mineralocorticoids and spirolactone, were found to decrease the formation of the [³H] aldosterone nuclear and cytosol complexes in proportion to their potencies in regulating renal tubular transport of sodium. In this way a positive relationship was demonstrated between binding and metabolic effects.

Studies on the extraction of three aldosterone-bound proteins from nuclei of toad bladder mucosal cells have been reported (*Alberti & Sharp* 1969). Two appear to be nonspecific while the third, which dissociated rapidly and is specific for mineralocorticoids, is believed to be the *receptor* responsible for stimulation of sodium transport.

ACKNOWLEDGMENTS

This report is based on experiments partially supported by the Ford Foundation, the Délégation Générale à la Recherche Médicale Française, and Roussel – UCLAF.

240

REFERENCES

Alberti K. G. M. M. & Sharp G. W. G.: Biochim. biophys. Acta (Amst.) *192* (1969) 335.

Anderson K. D. & Liao S.: Nature (Lond.) *219* (1968) 277.

Ausiello D. A. & Sharp G. W. G.: Endocrinology *82* (1968) 1163.

Baulieu E. E. & Jung I.: Biochem. Biophys. Res. Commun. *38* (1970) 599.

Baulieu E. E. & Robel P. In: Griffiths K., Ed. Some aspects of the aetiology and biochemistry of prostatic cancer. Cardiff (1970) in press.

Baulieu E. E., Alberga A. & Jung I.: C. R. Acad. Sci. (Paris) *265* (1967) 354.

Baulieu E. E., Lasnitzki I. & Robel P.: Nature (Lond.) *219* (1968) 1155.

Baulieu E. E., Raynaud J. P. & Milgrom E.: Acta endocr. (Kbh.) Suppl. No. *142* (1970) 104.

Baulieu E. E., Alberga A., Jung I., Lebeau M. C., Mercier-Bodard C., Milgrom E., Raynaud J. P., Raynaud-Jammet C., Rochefort H., Truong-Richard-Foy H. & Robel P.: Recent Progr. Hormone Res. (1971) in press.

Baxter J. & Tomkins G. In: Baulieu E. E., Ed. Schering symposium on steroid *receptors* (1971) in press.

Brecher P. I., Vigersky R., Wotiz H. S. & Wotiz H. H.: Steroids *10* (1967) 635.

Bruchovsky N. & Wilson J. D.: J. biol. Chem. *243* (1968) 2012.

Edelman I. S. & Fimognari G. M.: Recent Progr. Hormone Res. *24* (1968) 1.

Edelman I. S., Bogoroch R. & Porter G. A.: Proc. Natl. Acad. Sci. (U.S.A.) *50* (1963) 1169.

Erdos T.: Biochem. Biophys. Res. Commun. *32* (1968) 338.

Fanestil D. D. & Edelman I. S.: Proc. Natl. Acad. Sci. (U.S.A.) *56* (1966) 872.

Glascock R. F. & Hoekstra W. G.: Biochem. J. *12* (1959) 673.

Herman T. S., Fimognari G. M. & Edelman I. S.: J. biol. Chem. *243* (1968) 3849.

Jensen E. V.: Proc. 4th Int. Congr. of Biochem., Vienna, Pergamon Press, London, Vol. *15* (1958) 119.

Jensen E. V. & Jacobson H. I. In: Pincus G. and Vollmer E. P., Eds. Biological activities of steroids in relation to cancer. Academic Press, New York (1960) 161.

Jensen E. V. & Jacobson H. I.: Recent Progr. Hormone Res. *18* (1962) 387.

Jensen E. V., DeSombre E. R. & Jungblut P. W. In: Wissler R. W., Dao T. L. and Wood Jr.. Eds. Endogenous factors influencing host-tumor balance. U. Chicago Press, Chicago (1967a) 15.

Jensen E. V., Hurst D. J., DeSombre E. R. & Jungblut P. W.: Science *158* 1967b) 385.

Jensen E. V., Suzuki T., Numata M., Smith S. & DeSombre E. R.: Steroids *13* (1969) 417.

Liao S. & Fang S.: Excerpta med. Internat. Congr. Ser. No. 210. Third International Congress of Hormonal Steroids (1970) Abstract No. 53.

Mainwaring W. I. P.: J. Endocr. *45* (1969) 333.

Milgrom E. & Baulieu E. E.: Endocrinology *87* (1970a) 276.

Milgrom E. & Baulieu E. E.: Biochem. Biophys. Res. Commun. *40* (1970b) 723.

Milgrom E., Atger M. & Baulieu E. E.: Steroids *16* (1970) 741.

Munck A.: Endocrinology 77 (1965) 356.

Munck A.: J. biol. Chem. 243 (1968) 1039.

Munck A. & Brinck-Johnsen T.: Proceedings of the Second International Congress on Hormonal Steroids, Excerpta med. Internat. Congr. Ser. *132* (1966) 472.

Munck A. & Brinck-Johnsen T.: J. biol. Chem. *243* (1968) 5556.

241

Munck A. & Wira C. R.: Schering Symposium on Steroid Receptors (1970) in press.
Munck A., Young D. A., Mazur K. & Wira C. R.: Proceedings of the Nottingham Conference on Hormones and Development, Appleton-Century-Crofts, New York (1970) in press.
Rao B. R. & Wiest W. G.: Excerpta med. Internat. Congr. Series No. 210. Third International Congress of Hormonal Steroids (1970) Abstract No. 314.
Rochefort H. & Baulieu E. E.: C. R. Acad. Sci. (Paris) 267 D (1968) 662.
Sharp G. W. G., Komack C. L. & Leaf A.: J. clin. Invest. 45 (1966) 450.
Schyamala G. & Gorski J.: J. biol. Chem. 244 (1969) 2306.
Schaumburg B. P. & Bojesen E.: Biochim. biophys. Acta (Amst.) 170 (1968) 172.
Stumpf W. & Roth L. R.: J. Histochem. Cytochem. 14 (1966) 274.
Talwar G. P., Segal S. L., Evans A. & Davidson O. W.: Proc. Natl. Acad. Sci. (U.S.A.) 52 (1964) 1059.
Toft D. & Gorski J.: Proc. Natl. Acad. Sci. (U.S.A.) 55 (1966) 1574.
Truong H. & Baulieu E. E.: Biochim. biophys. Acta (Amst.) (1971) in press.
Wira C. R. & Munck A.: Fed. Proc. 28 (1970a) 832.
Wira C. R. & Munck A.: J. biol. Chem. 245 (1970b) 3436.

DISCUSSION

Ryan: I think it migh be helpful in the proceedings to have some critique or discussion of the methods which you use for measuring binding. You mentioned several methods, but you didn't discuss equilibrium dialysis. How do you choose between these methods when you are trying to decide to study a binding function?

Wira: The choice of a method for measuring binding really depends on the system with which one is working. If one is dealing with an organized system, such as intact tissues, slices or isolated cells, steroid retention can be measured directly. However, with a free cell system consisting of organelles or soluble fractions, the choice of techniques will vary with the stability, purity, affinity and type of information desired (equilibrium or kinetic measurements). When equilibrium is maintained, equilibrium dialysis can be used for the detection of different binding systems if a wide concentration of steroid is used. The main disadvantage of this system is the time required for the steroid to diffuse through the membrane. Another technique is the batchwise use of Sephadex, which is more rapid than equilibrium dialysis and enables one to separate free from bound steroid.

If equilibrium is not maintained, bound from free steroid can be separated by Sephadex columns. It should be noted, however, that without care being taken to remove non-specifically bound steroid prior to elution both specific and non-specific complexes will eventually be present in the excluded volume. Another means of removing free steroid is by the use of adsorbents, such as charcoal, florisil, or Fuller's earth. Such adsorbents may be added to soluble systems at equilibrium or prior to equilibrium for short periods of time to measure the kinetics of binding. In such experiments, conditions such as temperature, contact time etc. must be carefully controlled. I should say that this subject of evaluating steroid binding by various techniques is excellently presented by *Baulieu et al.* (1970) in the 2nd Karolinska Symposium.

Lerner: I thought that it was proved that glucocorticoids act upon enzyme systems by changing their activity. This was proved by *Weber* (1964), *Shrago et al.* (1963), *Lardy et al.* (1964), and others. There are other hypotheses too, claiming that hormones might have some sort of allosteric behaviour. How do you relate these effects to your glucocorticoid system?

Secondly, in your Table 1, you refer to progesterone as a compound exhibiting no metabolic activity. There is some evidence that progesterone has metabolic activity upon enzyme systems as well as upon nucleotides (*Velfin et al.* 1961). Now, for some enzyme systems involved in carbohydrate metabolism, it is known that progesterone has to act together with oestrogens. There are other proofs (*Tomkins & Vielding* 1961) indicating that progesterone, like some oestrogens and androgens, acts upon glutamic dehydrogenase by changing the configuration of the enzyme. We know, for example, that adrenalin and glucagon are in some way working together with insulin as metabolic regulators of glycogen metabolism. Also these effects are mediated through enzyme systems. Would you say that all these effects are mediated through receptors?

Wira: I think that both aspects of your question can be considered together. One point I should have made is that glucocorticoid actions on lymphoid tissue, skin and adipose tissue are catabolic and the result of decreased transport on phosphorylation of glucose. The studies you are speaking of concern anabolic effects seen mainly in the liver and kidneys. While at a first glance, these effects, both anabolic and catabolic, would seem to be divergent, on closer examination, a similarity of events preceding the onset of metabolic effects, whether it be a stimulation of enzymes or inhibition of glucose uptake, can be observed. I am referring to preliminary evidence by *Young* (1970), suggesting that cortisol in the thymus stimulated RNA synthesis as well as protein synthesis (*C. Hallahan, D. Young & A. Munck,* unpublished) prior to the effects of cortisol on glucose uptake. From these studies, the effects of glucocorticoids on catabolic tissues as well as those you mentioned, which occur in anabolic tissues, appear to be similar in that both result in the synthesis of a protein. It would appear then that the difference lies in the action of the protein synthesized, which in the thymus leads to inhibition of glucose transport, whereas in the liver maybe the production of a certain enzyme. The differences that exist between steroid specificity of thymus and the hepatoma tissue Dr. Lee is working with are not yet resolved. Once again, tissues such as tumours, tumour preparations, culture preparations, and liver cells seem to bind steroid with a specificity that is distinct from that of the lymphoid tissue. Whether the receptors in both types of systems differ in other ways, such as sedimentation coefficients, etc., remains to be examined.

Stumpf: It has been stated by *Jensen* (1965) that »estrogenic hormones initiate and stimulate growth processes in responsive tissues without undergoing chemical transformation.« Is there really enough evidence that this is so? What happens to the oestradiol? Is it reused after the action? How is it transported out? If unmetabolized, it should be trapped on the way out by the cytoplasmic 4s or 8s protein. The closest I can think of is that there may be a mechanism which is comparable to chemical nerve transmission, where there are storage sites. Some messenger molecule portion is released constantly – in addition to impulse firing in the nerve – which is in part metabolized but in part taken up again by the storage sites and reused. It is quite possible that something like this might exist in the uterus for the steroid hormones. It may be released from storage proteins and act, not according to the *occupation*

243

theory, but rather according to the *rate theory*. I wonder what your comments are to this?

Wira: Chromatographic studies of oestrogens bound to uteri (*Jensen & Jacobson* 1962), glucocorticoids bound specifically to thymus cells (*Munck & Brinck-Johnsen* 1968) and aldosterone bound to toad bladders (*Sharp & Leaf* 1966) and rat kidney (*Fanestil & Edelman* 1966) all indicate that of the steroid recovered, very little, if any, at all, has been converted to metabolites as binding and physiological effects are produced. It is conceivable that a very small fraction consisting of only a few molecules, might be responsible for producing physiological effects. However, if one considers the standard log dose response curves of receptor occupation to metabolic responses, it turns out that the magnitude of the metabolic response increases roughly in proportion to the number of binding sites unoccupied. This would suggest that the greater part of the steroid-receptor complex, that identified as unchanged steroid on the basis of chromatographic analysis, is essential for producing physiological effects. The only evidence for a steroid being metabolized to an active form has been obtained with testosterone, which is metabolized to androstanolone. This metabolite, as mentioned in our paper, appears to be active in the rat ventral prostate.

Ryan: Dr. Stumpf, I think that the implication of most of these binding studies was that there was no metabolism of oestradiol. We know that this is not true, as 20 years ago we showed that oestradiol is converted to oestrone in the human myometrium, and other people have now demonstrated this in the rabbit. Obviously, the oestradiol is not used in perpetuity, but is in fact metabolized. The question is whether or not it is bound as oestradiol. Now I think that question has clearly been answered: It is bound as oestradiol.

Stumpf: My question is: Does it act without being metabolized or does the action imply metabolism? I am not raising the question whether or not it is metabolized prior to action. The question is: Is it metabolized while acting, and then, by virtue of being metabolized, allowed to diffuse out of the cell? This has been denied for oestradiol, but I thought that one might question this.

Ryan: Jensen, as you recall, made a 17α-tritiated derivative of 17β-oestradiol and showed that this compound was bound without loss of that tritium group. All this indicates is that it was bound without being changed. It says nothing about its action. Dr. Wira's title is »Tissue steroid binding«. He is talking about receptors, but he is in fact describing only binding.

Lee: Dr. Wira, you are talking about specific binding. Even with specific binding the dissociation half-life is about 3 minutes. How can you quantitate the specific binding?

Wira: The procedure for estimating specific binding quantitatively was published by *Munck & Brinck-Johnsen* (1968). Briefly, the slow dissociation curve was analyzed exponentially. This analysis assumes that the non-specifically bound steroid dissociates within one minute, so that the only remaining steroid is the slowly dissociating specific fraction. This component, which has a time constant of three minutes, was extrapolated back to 0 minute to give the value A_1. In Dr. Munck's paper, A_1, which is the magnitude of the specific fraction at the time of dilution, was used to estimate quantitatively the specific binding of a variety of steroids to thymus cells.

Lee: Dr. Lerner, you said that glucocorticoids have their effect on gluconeogenesis through the change of enzyme activity. I wonder whether you can elaborate a little more on this. I thought that this is not generally accepted.

Lerner: What Weber did was just to put together some proofs of glucocorticoid action and to elaborate his so called functional genomal hypothesis, but there are many proofs of glucocorticoid action on enzymes in the carbohydrate metabolism. This is not under discussion. Weber's work is under discussion, since his hypothesis is not well established.

Lee: What I mean is the primary action of glucocorticoids on gluconeogenesis mediated through enzyme induction or through something else. It seems to me that the regulation of activity has not been accepted as a primary action of glucocorticoids on gluconeogenesis.

Hansel: Is it clear that the progesterone binding protein in the uterus is a different protein from the cortisol binding protein in the plasma?

Wira: This is under investigation in Dr. Baulieu's laboratory, so I would defer the answer to Dr. Baulieu.

Baulieu: In the rat there is no difference, as seen in Dr. *Milgrom*'s recent work (*Milgrom & Baulieu* 1970a). However, in the guinea pig uterus there is a distinct progesterone binding protein, which does not bind corticosteroids and is increased when priming is made by oestrogens (*Milgrom & Baulieu* 1970b). This may also be true for the rabbit and the human (even if the evidence for the human is still slight). This uterine protein in the guinea pig is different from the Progesterone Binding Protein (PBP) found in pregnant guinea pig plasma.

Gurpide: You indicated that a correlation was found in *in vitro* systems between the extent of saturation of cortisol receptors in thymocytes and the response to the hormone. Have you attempted to measure the concentration of cortisol in thymus to determine the level of saturation of the receptors under physiological conditions?

Wira: Experiments in which cortisol is administered *in vivo* and then measured *in vitro* have yet to be undertaken. From results reported by *Munck & Brinck-Johnsen* (1968), however, it would not be anticipated that glucocorticoid specific binding would be measured. This conclusion is based on results which indicate that of the total amount of steroid bound under equilibrium conditions, only about one-fifth is bound specifically. If a scheme was devised to remove most of the non-specifically bound steroid, then one would still be faced with the problem that the specific fraction, while dissociating slowly, nevertheless has a time constant of about three minutes. In this context then, meaningful *in vivo* measurements of glucocorticoid binding would be extremely difficult.

Ferin: The antagonism between oestrogens and androgens is well known. In ovariectomized women, for instance, it is possible to suppress the proliferative effect of oestrogens by simultaneous administration of androgens (*Ferin* 1953). My question is: Have you any data concerning this neutralizing effect *in vitro*? Is there a competition at the binding sites?

Wira: Perhaps Dr. Baulieu would care to answer this question.

Baulieu: For the uterine oestradiol binding protein in the rat, the calf and the pig, there is not, as far as I know. Even, there might be some small affinity of the oestradiol binding protein for androstanolone. The evidence today is that it will not account for a very clear hormone antagonism. To generalize, if there are certain intracellular binding proteins which may bind steroids having two different activities, eventually antagonistic, it cannot be considered as a general feature. Continuing with the guinea pig progesterone *receptor* of the uterus, which does not bind cortico-steroids, this protein binds progesterone and 5α-dihydroprogesterone with high affinity, but also binds other steroids, which have no progestative activity. The question is therefore not solved, whether there is not always a unique specificity for intracellular binding proteins.

References:

Baulieu E. E., Raynaud J. P. & Milgrom E.: Acta endocr. (Kbh.) Suppl. *142* (1970) 104.

Fanestil D. D. & Edelman I. S.: Proc. Nat. Acad. Sci. (U. S. A.) *56* (1966) 872.

Ferin J.: Ann. Endocr. *14* (1953) 919.

Jensen E. V. In: Canadian Cancer Conference, Pergamon Press (1965) 143.

Jensen E. V. & Jacobson H. I.: Recent Progr. Hormone Res. *18* (1962) 387.

Lardy H. A., Foster D. O., Shrago E. & Ray P. D.: Advances in Enzyme Regulation 2 (1964) 39. MacMillan (New York) – Pergamon (Oxford).

Milgrom E. & Baulieu E. E.: Endocrinology *87* (1970*a*) 276.

Milgrom E. & Baulieu E. E.: Biochem. Biophys. Res. Comm. *40* (1970*b*) 1723.

Munck A. & Brinck-Johnsen T.: J. biol. Chem. *243* (1968) 5556.

Sharp G. W. G. & Leaf A.: Physiol. Rev. *46* (1966) 593.

Shrago E., Lardy H. A., Nordlie R. C. & Foster D. O.: J. biol. Chem. *238* (1963) 3188.

Tomkins G. M. & Yielding K. L.: Cold. Spr. Harb. Symp. quant. Biol. *26* (1961) 331.

Volfin P., Clauser H., Gautheron D. & Ebove D.: Bull. Soc. Chim. Biol. *43* (1961) 107.

Weber G., Bhide S. V. & Manwaring S.: Biochem. Biophys. Res. Comm. *16* (1964) 167.

Young D.: Fed. Proc. *29* (1970) 3006.

KAROLINSKA SYMPOSIA ON RESEARCH METHODS IN REPRODUCTIVE ENDOCRINOLOGY

3rd Symposium . In Vitro Methods in Reproductive Cell Biology

January 25–27, 1971

From the Departments of Obstetrics & Gynecology and of Biochemistry,
University of Minnesota, Minneapolis, Minnesota 55455, U.S.A.

QUANTITATIVE STUDIES OF TISSUE UPTAKE
AND DISPOSITION OF HORMONES

By

Erlio Gurpide, Ann Stolee and Linda Tseng

ABSTRACT

A two-tracer continuous flow perfusion experimental design has been used
to measure the entry of steroids (oestradiol, oestrone, progesterone, 20α-
dihydroprogesterone, testosterone, androstenedione, cortisol, cortisone) and
nucleic acid precursors (uridine, cytidine, UMP) into several tissues, using
slices (human endometrium, endometrial adenocarcinoma, placenta, foetal
membranes, rat and rabbit liver) or cell suspensions (chorion, amnion,
liver, choriocarcinoma Be/Wo). Rates of interconversion between the perfused compounds and rates of release into the medium were also measured.
The response of the system to additions of hormones, drugs and plasma
proteins was evaluated by measuring rates and concentrations. The entry
of oestrogen sulphates and UMP into tissues was compared with the entry
of the corresponding unesterified compounds.

Measurements of rates at which the hormones are formed or metabolized and
elucidation of the relative importance of branched metabolic pathways have
been attempted with batch incubations of steroidogenic or target tissues with
labelled hormones. A recurring criticism of most of these experiments is that
the results are dependent upon the incubation time. To eliminate one of the
pitfalls of the usual *in vitro* experimental design the tracers may be perfused
(superfused) at a constant rate through tissue slices and the rates may then
be calculated from data obtained during the isotopic steady state.

Perfusion experiments have other desirable characteristics, emphasized by
Orti et al. (1965), which are unrelated to the use of tracers. A continuous flow

247

of medium removes metabolic products formed during the incubation which may alter enzymatic systems. Furthermore, continuous flow incubations of tissue slices or fragments are particularly convenient to evaluate the effect of agents added to the medium on the production of hormones, as demonstrated by the studies on gonadal and adrenal steroidogenesis conducted by *Tait et al.* (1967, 1970), *Saffran et al.* (1967), *Huibiegtse & Ungar* (1970), *Ungar et al.* (1970), and others.

The studies to be reported here are based on an experimental design involving the exposure of tissue slices or cell suspension contained in small chambers to a continuous, unrecycled flow of a solution of two metabolically related compounds, one labelled with ^3H, and the other with ^{14}C (*Gurpide & Welch* 1969; *Giorgi et al.* 1970).

With this system the fraction of a perfused tracer that enters the tissue can be estimated. If the compound entering the tissue were totally and irreversibly metabolized, only one tracer would be needed since measurement of the ratio of the concentration of the labelled compound in the perfusate (outflowing) and in the perfusion medium (inflowing) would be sufficient to calculate the fraction of tracer entering the tissue. However, as will be described in the section on calculations, a second isotope is necessary to trace that fraction of the compound which may enter the cell, undergo reversible metabolism and then be released, apparently unchanged, back into the medium. Examples of reversible entry into cells have been provided by previous studies which show that a large part of oestrone, as well as of androstenedione, enter slices of human endometrium and return to the medium.

The determination of the unidirectional rate of entry of a compound into cells is essential for studies of cell permeability. This rate can be measured with a two-tracer perfusion system and distinguished from the »net uptake« of the compound by the cell, which represents the difference between rates of entry and release.

In the field of reproductive physiology there are several pertinent questions related to permeability which could be investigated with such a system. Some of these are the following: do target tissues have a selective permeability for some hormones?; does the permeability change in various physiological or pathological states?; do hormones influence the entry of compounds which are normally present in blood?; is the permeability of the tissue different for the free and conjugated forms of the hormone?; do steroid-specific plasma binding proteins facilitate or prevent the entry of hormones into tissues?; are there saturable systems involved in the entry of hormones into cells, and if so, what is their capacity and specificity?; what agents modify the entry of hormones into target tissues? Experimental data pertinent to some of these questions will be presented in the section on results.

Not only rates of entry and exit can be calculated from the isotopic data provided by the two-tracer perfusion system; in addition, the same isotopic data can be used to determine the rates of interconversion between the two perfused compounds and to calculate the rates at which these compounds are metabolized to other products. By evaluation of all these parameters it is possible to obtain a dynamic picture of intracellular processes and to study the influence of these processes on the concentration of the hormones in the tissue.

Such a comprehensive picture helps to interpret physiologic events occurring in target tissues and to search for agents which could modify hormonal action by altering the entry, the metabolism, or the release of the hormone.

Previously published studies (*Gurpide & Welch* 1969) of perfusion of slices of human endometrium with oestrone (E_1), oestradiol (E_2), testosterone (T), and androstenedione (Δ) have now been extended to include other compounds and tissues indicated in Table 1.

The new experiments also include perfusions of cell suspensions which provide the opportunity of working with homogeneous cell populations. These preparations also offer the advantage of allowing more uniform access of tracers, oxygen and nutrients to each cell. The possibility of artifactual results produced by the activity of enzymes trapped in the intercellular spaces of the tissue slices is practically eliminated. Furthermore, a quantitative estimation of the viability of the cells in suspension can be obtained by dye exclusion techniques (*Merchant et al.* 1964) which are not applicable to tissue slices.

To obtain cells for these experiments several techniques were utilized. Rat

Table 1.
Tissues and Compounds Perfused.

Slices	*Cell Suspensions*
Human endometrium	Human amnion
Proliferative	Human chorion laeve
Secretory	Human placenta
Postmenopausal	Choriocarcinoma, Be/Wo line
Hyperplastic	Rat liver
Decidua	Rabbit liver
Adenocarcinoma	
Human Placenta	*Compounds*
Term	Oestrone: oestradiol
Early (12–18 wks.)	Oestrone sulphate: oestradiol-3-sulphate
Human foetal membranes	Progesterone: 20α-dihydroprogesterone
Chorion laeve	Testosterone: androstenedione
Amnion	Cortisol: cortisone
Rat liver	Uridine: cytidine
Rabbit liver	Uridine: uridine-5′-phosphate

and rabbit hepatocytes were prepared by using sodium tetraphenylboron (*Rappaport & Howze* 1966). Cells from human amnion were conveniently obtained by trypsinization (*Duncan & Bell* 1961). Preparation of cell suspensions of chorion laeve were accomplished by using trypsin. Drs. P. Carbajal, G. Fontan and B. Parks in Dr. R. Good's laboratories at the University of Minnesota collaborated with us in the isolation and culture of these cells.

We have been privileged to obtain cultures of the Be/Wo line of choriocarcinoma cells (*Pattillo & Gey* 1968) from Dr. R. Pattillo and his collaborators at the Marquette School of Medicine, Milwaukee, Wisconsin.

EXPERIMENTAL DESIGN

About 300 mg of tissue slices (prepared with a Sorvall TC-2 tissue slicer set at 200 μm) or about the same amount of cell suspensions are placed in a chamber. Oxygenated Krebs-Ringer bicarbonate glucose buffer (pH 7.4, 37°C) containing the tracers is forced upward at 12 or 18 ml/h through the fritted glass disk at the base of the chamber. The perfusate is collected in tubes immersed in a methanol-ice bath. The perfusion is continued for 90–120 min and 4–6 fractions are collected. When the perfusion is stopped, the tissue or cells are rapidly washed with buffer and homogenized in a methanolic solution of carriers. Carriers in methanol are also added to aliquots of the perfusate fractions. The compounds are isolated from these samples and purified by paper and thin layer chromatography. The final experimental data are concentrations of the individual ^{3}H and ^{14}C labelled compounds in the samples, expressed as cpm/ml of perfusate or cpm/g of tissue. In some experiments, concentrations of the compounds (in ng/ml of medium or ng/g of tissue) are determined before and after perfusion using radioimmunoassay methods.

From these data, several parameters are calculated using the formulae described in the next section.

CALCULATIONS

Suppose that, as indicated in Fig. 1, tritiated compound A is perfused over the tissue, together with a ^{14}C labelled compound B. B is enzymatically converted to A in the tissue. At the steady state the ^{3}H/^{14}C ratio of compound A released by the tissue into the medium will likely be the same as the ^{3}H/^{14}C ratio of A present in the tissue. This ratio can be measured experimentally. Therefore the concentration in the perfusate of [^{3}H] A from the tissue can

Models and Symbols

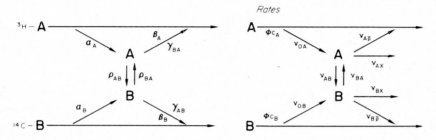

Rates

Fig. 1.

Left: Scheme showing symbols which denote the fraction of perfused tracer A that enters the tissue (a_A) or is released back into the medium either as A (β_A) or as B (γ_{AB}), and the fraction of A entering tissue that is converted to B »for the first time« (ϱ_{AB}). Similar meanings are assigned to a_B, β_B, γ_{BA}, and ϱ_{BA}.

Right: Scheme showing the symbols for rates of perfusion (φc_A and φc_B), entry into tissue (v_{BA} and v_{oB}), interconversion (v_{AB} and v_{BA}), release to medium ($v_{A\bar{p}}$ and $v_{B\bar{p}}$) and metabolism to other products (v_{Ax} and v_{Bx}).

be calculated from the concentration of [^{14}C] A in the perfusate and the ^{3}H/^{14}C ratio in A in the tissue, *i. e.*

$$(c\,^{3\!}\!\!A_{\bar{p}})\text{ from tissue} = c\,^{14\!}\!A_{\bar{p}}\,(\tfrac{^3H}{^{14}C})\text{ A in tissue} \tag{1}$$

where $\bar{p}$ is a subscript used to indicate perfusate (see glossary for the explanation of symbols).

The fraction of perfused compound A that did not enter the tissue is given by the ratio of the concentration of [^{3}H] A in the perfusate that bypassed the tissue and the concentration of [^{3}H] A perfused. Then, if a_A is the fraction of perfused A that entered the tissue, it follows from Equation 1 that

$$1 - a_A = \frac{c\,^{3\!}\!A_{\bar{p}} - (c\,^{3\!}\!A_{\bar{p}})\text{ from tissue}}{c\,^{3\!}\!A} = \frac{c\,^{3\!}\!A_{\bar{p}} - c\,^{14\!}\!A_{\bar{p}}\,(\tfrac{^3H}{^{14}C})\text{ At}}{c\,^{3\!}\!A} \tag{2}$$

Therefore, a_A can be determined simply from the concentrations of labelled A in the perfusate (cpm/ml) and the isotope ratio of A isolated from the tissue at the end of the perfusion.

The fraction β_A represents that part of perfused A that is released back into the medium as A. Therefore, it is given by the ratio of the concentration of

[³H] A coming out from the tissue and the concentration of [³H] A in the perfusion medium, $i.\,e.$

$$\beta_A = \frac{(c\,{}^{3H}_{A_{\bar{p}}})\ \text{from tissue}}{c^{3H}_A} = \frac{c^{14C}_{A_{\bar{p}}}\,(\frac{{}^{3H}}{{}^{14C}})\ At}{c^{3H}_A} \tag{3}$$

The difference $\alpha-\beta$ represents the net uptake of the compound by the tissue or, equivalently, the fraction of the perfused tracer which is irreversibly metabolized.

The fraction of perfused A that is released into the medium as metabolite M is called γ_{AM}. This fraction is simply calculated from the concentration of tritiated M in the perfusate, $i.\,e.$

$$\gamma_{AM} = \frac{c^{3H}_M}{c^{3H}_A}. \tag{4}$$

If the α values for both perfused compounds are known, the fraction of compound A entering the tissue which is converted to B (ϱ_{AB}) can be estimated by measuring the ³H/¹⁴C ratio of compound B isolated from the tissue (*Mann & Gurpide* 1966):

$$\varrho_{AB} = \frac{({}^{3H}/{}^{14C})_{Bt}}{(\alpha_A/\alpha_B)\ ({}^{3H}/{}^{14C})\ \text{perfused.}} \tag{5}$$

Not only isotopic ratios but also concentrations of the labelled compounds in tissue are measured in these experiments. The ratio of the concentration of the labelled compound in tissue to its concentration in the perfusion medium is a value frequently measured in *in vivo* and *in vitro* studies. It is considered to indicate the »uptake« of the compound by the tissue. It should be noted, however, that ratio of isotopic concentrations does not necessarily correspond to concentration ratios of the compounds since the labelled compounds in tissue may be diluted by contributions from precursors supplied in the medium or produced endogenously.

By prolonging the perfusion until a steady state is reached the perfused labelled compounds replace the corresponding unlabelled compounds originally present in the tissue if there are no other endogenous sources for these compounds. Under these circumstances the concentration of the compounds in the tissue can be calculated from isotopic data. For instance, if [³H] A and [¹⁴C] B are perfused (Fig. 1) it follows that at the steady state,

$$c_{At} = \frac{c^{3H}_{At}}{\text{sp. act. of A perfused}} + \frac{c^{14C}_{At}}{\text{sp. act. of B perfused}}. \tag{6}$$

The values calculated from Equation 6 can be submitted to experimental verification by direct measurement of the compounds in the tissue at the end of the perfusion.

Calculation of rates

From the concentration values and the values of the α's, β's, γ's and ϱ's, actual rates of entry, metabolism, and release (Fig. 1) can be calculated as follows.

The rate of entry of A is given by the expression $v_{oA} = \varphi c_A \alpha_A$ and the rate of release of A is

$$v_{A\bar{p}} = \varphi c_A \beta_A + \varphi c_B \gamma_{BA}, \tag{7}$$

since A leaving the tissue may originate from both perfused A and B.

To calculate v_{AB} and v_{BA} the definition (*Mann & Gurpide* 1966) of ϱ_{AB} and ϱ_{BA} can be used, *i. e.*

$$\varrho_{AB} = v_{AB} / (v_{oA} + v_{BA}); \quad \varrho_{BA} = v_{BA} / (v_{oB} + v_{AB}). \tag{8}$$

Then a system of 2 simultaneous equations with v_{AB} and v_{BA} as unknowns can be written and solved to yield

$$v_{AB} = \frac{\varrho_{AB} (v_{oB} + \varrho_{BA} v_{oB})}{1 - \varrho_{AB}\, \varrho_{BA}}. \tag{9}$$

Material balance at the steady state requires that

$$v_{Ax} = v_{oA} + v_{BA} - v_{AB} - v_{A\bar{p}}. \tag{10}$$

Obviously, similar formulae result for v_{oB}, $v_{B\bar{p}}$, v_{BA} and v_{Bx}, as is evident from the symmetry of the model in Fig. 1.

Thus, this experimental design is capable of yielding values for steady state rates at which biochemical events occur. Therefore, kinetic studies usually performed in cell-free systems can be attempted with whole cells.

By similarity with the term used in *in vivo* studies, the »production rate« of the compound in the tissue can be defined as the rate at which it appears intracellularly *de novo, i. e.* entering from the constantly renewed medium or formed from intracellular precursors. The production rate of A solely derived from A and B in the medium, therefore, is given by the following expression:

$$PR_A = v_{oA} + \varrho_{BA} v_{oB}. \tag{11}$$

Since the specific activity of the intracellular compound at the steady state is given by the ratio of the amounts of labelled to unlabelled compound entering *de novo* into the tissue, it follows that

$$a_{A_t}^{^3H} = c_{A_t}^{^3H} / c_{At} = \varphi \alpha_A c_A^{^3H} / PR_A \quad \text{or} \quad PR_A = \frac{\varphi \alpha_A c_A^{^3H}}{c_{At}^{^3H} / c_{At}}. \tag{12}$$

It is also convenient to introduce the concept of intracellular clearance (IC) of the hormone, defined as the ratio of the production rate per gram of tissue to the concentration of the compound in the tissue, *i. e.*

$$IC_A = \frac{PR_A}{W c_{At}} = \frac{\varphi \alpha_A}{W} \cdot \frac{c_A^{^3H}}{c_{At}^{^3H}}, \tag{13}$$

where W represents the weight of tissue perfused.

Other relationships

There are many other relationships that can be established among the parameters defined so far. A list of some of the relationships which have been found useful in interpreting the isotopic data are shown below. These formulae will be used for the discussion of the results in the sections to follow.

Assuming that both compound A entering the tissue from the perfusion medium and A formed intracellularly from B have the same metabolic fate, it follows that

$$\beta_A / \alpha_A = \gamma_{BA} / \alpha_{B \varrho BA}. \tag{14}$$

Therefore, since $v_{A\bar{p}} = \varphi (c_A \beta_A + c_B \gamma_{BA})$ and $PR_A = \varphi (c_A \alpha_A + c_B \alpha_{B \varrho BA})$ (Equations 7 and 11) it follows that $\beta_A / \alpha_A = v_{A\bar{p}} / PR_A$. \tag{15}

Assuming that entry and exit of the compound into and out of cells can be described by simple diffusion it is apparent that $v_{oA} = P x A x c_A$ and $v_{A\bar{p}} = P' x A x d_A c_A$ where P and P' are permeability coefficients. A is the area available for exchange and d_A is the fraction of the intracellular compound available in a diffusible form. Therefore, if $P = P', v_{A\bar{p}} = \varphi \alpha_A d_A c_A$ and, from Eq 12,

$$\beta_A / \alpha_A = v_{A\bar{p}} / PR_A = d_A c_{At}^{^3H} / c_A^{^3H} \tag{16}$$

or

$$d_A = \frac{\beta_A}{\alpha_A} \frac{c_A^{^3H}}{c_{At}^{^3H}} \tag{17}$$

254

By defining a fractional rate $k_{A\bar{p}}$ under steady state conditions as $k_{A\bar{p}} = v_{A\bar{p}} / Wc_{At}$ it follows from Equation 15 that $k_{A\bar{p}} = \beta_A\, IC_A/\alpha_A$. When chase experiments indicate an apparent first order kinetics for the release of the labelled hormones, the half-life corresponding to this process is given by the expression

$$(t_{1/2})_A = \frac{\ln 2}{k_{A\bar{p}}} = \frac{0.693}{IC_A}\frac{\alpha_A}{\beta_A}. \tag{18}$$

Expressions for the ratio of concentrations of the labelled compound can be obtained. Thus, from Equations 16, 13 and 12 it follows that

$$\frac{c_{At}^{^3H}}{c_A^{^3H}} = \frac{\beta_A}{d_A\alpha_A} = \frac{\varphi\alpha_A c_{At}}{PR_A} = \frac{\varphi\alpha_A}{W}\cdot\frac{1}{IC_A}. \tag{19}$$

The ratio between concentrations of 2 labelled compounds in tissue is given by the expression

$$\frac{c_{At}^{^3H}}{c_{Bt}^{^3H}} = \frac{IC_B}{\varrho_{AB}IC_A}, \tag{20}$$

as can be verified by substituting each factor in the right side of the equation by their corresponding expression in terms of isotopic data (Equations 5 and 13).

RESULTS

Due to space limitations, we have chosen to present diagrams (Figs. 2 to 10) describing typical results obtained with some of the tissues and compounds tested and to leave out experimental details and raw isotopic data. Several experiments of each type have been run with satisfactory reproducibility of patterns.

The results will be discussed by considering the information made available by these experiments in the following order: 1) entry of hormones into cells, 2) metabolism of the hormones and 3) release of the hormones from the tissue.

Entry of Hormones into Cells

The fraction of a perfused compound that enters cells depends not only on permeability factors but also on variables such as amount of tissue, thickness

255

Human Endometrium

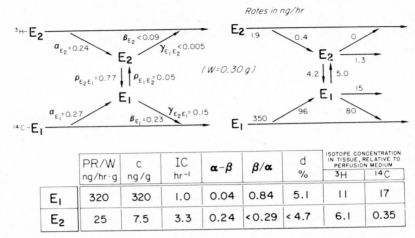

	PR/W ng/hr·g	c ng/g	IC hr⁻¹	α−β	β/α	d %	ISOTOPE CONCENTRATION IN TISSUE, RELATIVE TO PERFUSION MEDIUM	
							³H	¹⁴C
E_1	320	320	1.0	0.04	0.84	5.1	11	17
E_2	25	7.5	3.3	0.24	<0.29	<4.7	6.1	0.35

Fig. 2.

Normal proliferative endometrium from a 34 year old subject.

Human Endometrium

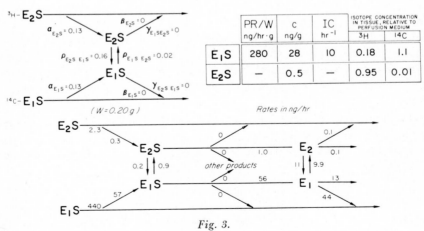

Fig. 3.

Normal secretory endometrium from a 20 year old subject.

Human Endometrium

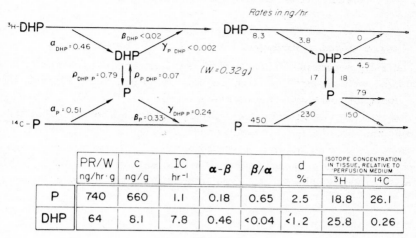

	PR/W ng/hr·g	c ng/g	IC hr⁻¹	α–β	β/α	d %	ISOTOPE CONCENTRATION IN TISSUE, RELATIVE TO PERFUSION MEDIUM	
							³H	¹⁴C
P	740	660	1.1	0.18	0.65	2.5	18.8	26.1
DHP	64	8.1	7.8	0.46	<0.04	<1.2	25.8	0.26

Fig. 4.
Normal secretory endometrium from a 40 year old subject.

of the slices, geometry of the perfusion chamber and rate of flow of the medium. Therefore, when studying the relative entry of various compounds into tissues an effort was made to obtain comparable results. This was achieved by perfusing compounds as a mixture (*e. g.*, oestrogens and androgens, oestrogens and progesterone); or, when studying the influence of additions to the medium on the entry of hormones into tissues, by perfusing identical portions of tissue simultaneously.

The data shown in Figs. 2 to 10 and unreported experimental results together with data already published (*Gurpide & Welch* 1969) allow us to present the following general conclusions.

E_1, E_2, P, T, and Δ enter human endometrium slices from a buffer solution with equal facility, *i. e.*, when various mixtures of these compounds were perfused their α values were similar. In some cases, however, the entry of E_1 was significantly higher than the entry of E_2, but no pattern can be established at this point to relate this behaviour to the origin of the tissue. No consistent differences in the entry of the steroids to specimens taken at different times of the menstrual cycle were observed.

The entry of E_1 was consistently equal to the entry of E_2 into tissue in all perfusions of placenta, foetal membranes, and choriocarcinoma cells Be/Wo.

Uridine and cytidine enter equally well into slices of human endometrium and more easily than do oestrogens perfused simultaneously.

257

Similarly, no differences were noted in the fractions of perfused cortisol (F) and cortisone (E) entering into slices of rabbit liver.

Free versus sulphated oestrogens

The entry of oestrone sulphate (E_1S) and oestradiol-3-sulphate (E_2S) was compared with the entry of E_1 and E_2 into endometrium, endometrial adenocarcinoma, placenta and choriocarcinoma cells (Be/Wo). The entry of sulphated oestrogens into these tissues was surprisingly high. Although the utilization by placenta of sulphated steroids and the biological activity of conjugated oestrogens are well known, the permeability of cell membranes to ionized organic compounds is generally considered to be low (*Davis* 1958). Table 2 shows the relative values of the α's for sulphated and unconjugated oestrogens.

Unesterified versus phosphorylated uridine

The relative entry of uridine and uridine-5′-monophosphate (UMP) was studied by Dr. John Tseng using rat liver slices and suspension of hepatocytes. In line with the results obtained with esterified oestrogens, phosphorylation did not prevent the entry of uridine in spite of the strong ionic character of UMP.

Table 2.
Relative Entry of Sulphated and Unconjugated Oestrogens.

Tissue (human)	$\dfrac{\alpha E_1S}{\alpha E_1}$	$\dfrac{\alpha E_2S}{\alpha E_2}$	$\dfrac{\alpha E_2S}{\alpha E_1S}$	$\dfrac{\alpha E_2}{\alpha E_1}$
Endometrium				
Secretory	0.49	0.56	1.03	0.90
Postmenopausal	0.78	0.82	0.69	0.66
Adenocarcinoma	0.45	0.57	0.37	0.47
Placenta				
Term	0.83	0.80	0.91	0.94
Early (12–18 wks.)	0.90	0.87	0.96	0.99
Choriocarcinoma cells (Be/Wo)	0.42	0.34	0.81	1.01

Human Placenta

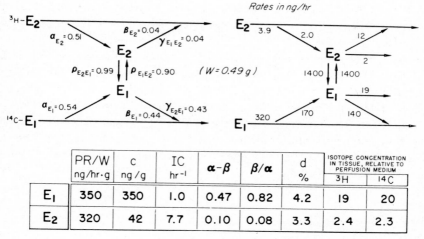

Rates in ng/hr

(W = 0.49 g)

	PR/W ng/hr·g	c ng/g	IC hr⁻¹	$\alpha-\beta$	β/α	d %	ISOTOPE CONCENTRATION IN TISSUE, RELATIVE TO PERFUSION MEDIUM	
							³H	¹⁴C
E_1	350	350	1.0	0.47	0.82	4.2	19	20
E_2	320	42	7.7	0.10	0.08	3.3	2.4	2.3

Fig. 5.

Normal human term placenta.

Influence of concentration

Most of the perfusion experiments were conducted using the minimum amounts of ³H and ¹⁴C labelled tracers necessary for adequate counting in the final products. Since even the carrier-free specific activity of ¹⁴C tracers is relatively low (approximately 300 cpm/ng, for steroids) rather high concentrations of these tracers (approximately 20 ng/ml) were needed. The ³H labelled tracers can be perfused at about 1/100th of these concentrations because they are available in a higher specific activity. Changes in concentrations were achieved by changing the label of the perfused compounds (for instance perfusing [¹⁴C] A and [³H] B instead of [³H] A and [¹⁴C] B, or by adding unlabelled compounds to the medium. In some runs the tissue slices were separated into two identical portions and each was perfused with only tritiated tracers, *e. g.* [³H] A for one and [³H] B for the other. The data from each perfusion were then combined to calculate the dynamic parameters at the lowest possible oestrogen concentrations.

It was found that the fraction of perfused oestrogens entering endometrium was not reduced by increases in concentration from 0.2 to 5000 ng per ml of buffer.

Such behaviour can be explained by assuming entry from buffer by simple diffusion, described by the expression $v_{oA} = Kc_A$ (so that $\alpha_A = v_{oA} / \varphi c_A =$

259

$K / \varphi = $ constant). However, it can also be explained by assuming the presence of a carrier mechanism characterized by the kinetic expression $v_{oA} = c_A V_{max} / (K' + c_A)$ (*Stein* 1967) with a value for K' much larger than the concentrations tested. In such a case, c_A can be neglected with respect to K' and again $v_{oA} = Kc_A$.

Kinetic studies on the entry of E_2 into placental slices were performed by perfusing simultaneously 4 identical portions of the same tissue with different concentrations of E_2. A *Lineweaver & Burk* (1934) plot of the data indicated a V_{max} of 140 μg/h per g of tissue and K_M of approximately 15×10^{-6} M calculated assuming that the small concentration of E_1 present in the medium (20 ng/ml) had negligible influence on the entry of E_2 at the levels tested. It is worth noting that in these experiments an increase in concentrations of E_2 reduced the entry of E_1.

Effect of hormones and drugs

Increases in the concentration of E_2 in the medium to 5 μg/ml resulted in a significant decrease of the entry of P into human endometrium (Table 3) without noticeably affecting the entry of E_1 and E_2.

Midterm Placenta

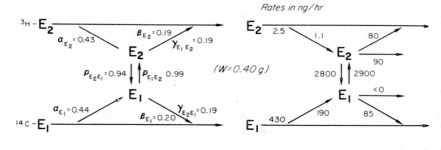

	PR/W ng/hr·g	c ng/g	IC hr⁻¹	$\alpha-\beta$	β/α	d %	ISOTOPE CONCENTRATION IN TISSUE, RELATIVE TO PERFUSION MEDIUM 3H	14C
E_1	470	140	3.4	0.24	0.46	7.8	5.4	5.8
E_2	470	120	4.0	0.24	0.43	9.0	4.8	4.8

Fig. 6.
Normal 18 week human placenta.

Table 3.
Effect of Additions to Medium on Entry of Steroids into Human Endometrium.

Type of Tissue	Concentration of compound added to buffer (μg/ml)					Entry relative to control		
	E_2	Ethynyl Oestradiol	Mestranol	PGE_2	$PGF_{2\alpha}$	E_1	E_2	P
Proliferative	5 μg/ml	—	—	—	—	1.00	1.17	0.55
Proliferative	5 μg/ml	—	—	—	—	0.82	1.02	0.55
	—	5 μg/ml	—	—	—	0.70	0.59	0.58
Secretory	—	5 μg/ml	—	—	—	0.79	0.53	0.48
Postmenopausal hyperplastic	—	—	5 μg/ml	—	—	0.85	0.80	0.78
Decidua	—	—	5 μg/ml	—	—	0.74	0.69	0.65
Secretory	—	—	—	5 μg/ml	—	1.03	1.06	1.06
Secretory	—	—	—	—	5 μg/ml	1.10	1.03	0.97

Ethynyl oestradiol (and mestranol to a lesser extent) also reduced significantly the entry of P and oestrogens.

Addition of prostaglandins, PGE_2, and $PGF_{2\alpha}$, at concentrations of 5 µg/ml did not affect the entry of oestrogens or P into endometrium.

Cortisol added to the medium (5µg/ml) was found to increase by about 20 % the entry of uridine and UMP into rat liver slices, an effect already noted for orotic acid by *Yu & Feigelson* (1969). The effect of oestrogens on the entry of these nucleic acid precursors into human endometrium is under study. The data of *Billing et al.* (1969) indicate that an increase in the entry is to be expected. As pointed out by *Hamilton* (1968), such phenomena are relevant to the interpretation of experiments in which hormonal action on RNA synthesis is measured by the incorporation of radioactive precursors added to the medium.

Effect of plasma binding proteins on entry of oestrogens into endometrium

It was found that human serum albumin reduces the entry of both E_1 and E_2 into endometrium. However, when a partially purified preparation of human gonadal steroid binding globulin [*i. e.* a β globulin in human plasma that binds E_2 and T (*Rosner et al.* 1969)] shown to be completely free of

Human Chorion Laeve Cells

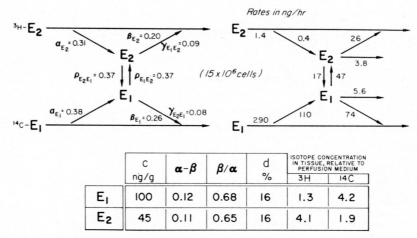

	c ng/g	α-β	β/α	d %	ISOTOPE CONCENTRATION IN TISSUE, RELATIVE TO PERFUSION MEDIUM	
					3H	14C
E_1	100	0.12	0.68	16	1.3	4.2
E_2	45	0.11	0.65	16	4.1	1.9

Fig. 7.

Cell suspension prepared by trypsinization of normal human chorionic membranes after normal delivery.

Choriocarcinoma Cells   Be / Wo

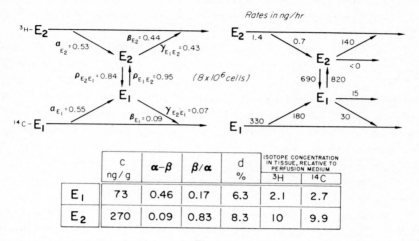

Fig. 8.
Choriocarcinoma cells (Be/Wo) scraped from walls of culture bottle.

albumin was added to the medium a different result was obtained. At concentrations adjusted to produce approximately the same per cent binding as the albumin solution previously used (about 50 %, as determined by equilibrium dialysis), the entry of oestrogens into endometrium was either unchanged or increased with respect to the entry of the oestrogens from buffer alone. Addition of heparinized human plasma to the buffer resulted in a drastic reduction in the entry of the oestrogens. This work is conducted in collaboration with Dr. W. Rosner from the Roosevelt Hospital, New York. We feel that we should obtain further confirmatory evidence before drawing a definite conclusion from these experiments. Studies in progress involve perfusions with highly purified binding proteins from plasma and examination of radioactivity in nuclei.

Metabolism

Interconversion between perfused compounds

Rates corresponding to a variety of metabolic reactions involving 11β-, 17β- and 20α-hydroxysteroid dehydrogenases, arylsulphatase, aromatase, $5'$-nucleotidase and uridine kinase, have been measured.

There are several ways to evaluate the extent of the metabolic reactions between two perfused labelled compounds. Since different manners of evaluation can lead to discrepant interpretations, it is important to consider all of them.

One way of evaluating a metabolic conversion is to measure the intracellular isotope ratio in the product at the steady state, *viz*, to examine the ϱ value (Equation 5). It should be noted, however, that this parameter indicates the relative quantitative importance of the conversion with respect to all other metabolic processes (Equation 9) rather than the magnitude of the conversion. For instance, ϱ_{AB} and ϱ_{BA} may be quite different even when the actual rates of the two opposing reactions are approximately equal (Fig. 2).

Comparison of actual rates of metabolism calculated from data obtained in these tracer perfusion experiments is a more direct way of evaluating metabolic processes.

Still another manner of analyzing the results is to examine the fractional rate (k) for the process, *i. e.* the ratio of the rate to the amount of substrate in the tissue. Even if v_{AB} were approximately equal to v_{BA}, k_{AB} might be larger than k_{BA} if the concentration of A in the tissue were smaller than the concentration of B.

The relative concentration of the two related compounds *in vivo* or during incubations has also been used for the evaluation of the »preferred direction«

Rabbit Liver

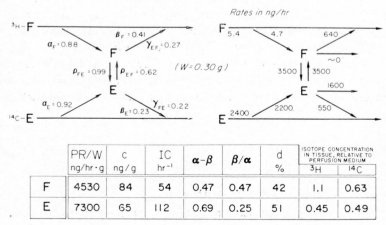

	PR/W ng/hr·g	c ng/g	IC hr⁻¹	α−β	β/α	d %	ISOTOPE CONCENTRATION IN TISSUE, RELATIVE TO PERFUSION MEDIUM	
							³H	¹⁴C
F	4530	84	54	0.47	0.47	42	1.1	0.63
E	7300	65	112	0.69	0.25	51	0.45	0.49

Fig. 9.
Slices of rabbit liver.

Rat Liver

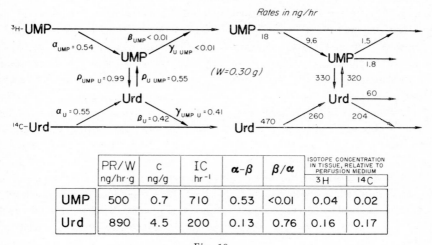

Fig. 10.
Slices of rat liver.

	PR/W ng/hr·g	c ng/g	IC hr⁻¹	$\alpha-\beta$	β/α	ISOTOPE CONCENTRATION IN TISSUE, RELATIVE TO PERFUSION MEDIUM	
						^3H	^{14}C
UMP	500	0.7	710	0.53	<0.01	0.04	0.02
Urd	890	4.5	200	0.13	0.76	0.16	0.17

of reversible reactions even though the concentrations of the two related compounds depend on many factors.

It might then be senseless to use any one of these measurements to determine which of the two opposing reactions is favoured in the system. It is possible to have a situation in which $\varrho_{AB} > \varrho_{BA}$ and $k_{AB} < k_{BA}$ even when $v_{AB} = v_{BA}$ and $c_A > c_B$. Thus, a complete picture of rates and concentrations, such as that provided by perfusion tracer experiments, may be necessary to describe the system.

The data in Figs. 2 to 10 lead to the following conclusions about the interconversion between perfused compounds.

Oestrone and oestradiol

As previously reported it can be stated in general terms that extensive interconversion between E_1 and E_2 occurs in human endometrium and trophoblastic tissue (*Lucis* 1965; *Ryan & Engel* 1953). Under experimental conditions in which very low concentrations of E_1 and E_2 were used, it was always found with slices of human endometrium (Fig. 2) that $\varrho E_2 E_1 > \varrho E_1 E_2$. However, when the data are expressed in terms of rates, it is found that the amounts converted are approximately equal although the fractional rate for the oxidative reaction is larger.

Addition of E_2 to the medium used to perfuse endometrium resulted in a decrease in the value of $\varrho E_2 E_1$, presumably as a result of the increase in the release of E_2 to the medium. Surprisingly, $\varrho E_1 E_2$ increased when more E_2 was fed into the system. This finding could be explained either by invoking a limited exit of E_1 from the cells or by considering that the conversion of E_1 to E_2 is accelerated by changes in the concentrations of reduced cofactors brought about specifically by E_2 acting on the transhydrogenase system (*Engel* 1970).

Ethynyl oestradiol reduced the interconversion between E_1 and E_2, as suggested by the diminution of the ϱ's and the fractional rates of conversion. The inhibitory effect of the drug on the E_2 17β-dehydrogenase has been reported by *Jarabak & Sack* (1969).

In the term placenta the interconversion between E_1 and E_2 appears to be the predominant metabolic reaction in which these compounds participate since the ϱ values in both directions are very large (Fig. 5). The extensive recycling of material between the two oestrogens results in relatively high values for the rates of interconversion.

At low levels of perfused oestrogens the concentration of E_1 in placenta is much larger than the concentration of E_2. Even at loads of E_2 of 5 $\mu g/ml$ of buffer, the concentration of E_1 is larger than that of E_2.

By changing the concentration of E_2 in simultaneous perfusions with identical amounts of placental slices, a kinetic study of the dehydrogenase reaction was conducted. A high value for V_{max} (250 $\mu g/h$ per g of tissue) was estimated for the conversion of E_2 to E_1. It was interesting to note that the addition of T to the medium in concentrations of 10 $\mu g/ml$ did not reduce significantly the conversion of E_2 to E_1, in agreement with the results reported by *Langer et al.* (1959) and *Jarabak & Sack* (1969). At this concentration the aromatization of T was small (0.4 %) while at concentrations of about 1 ng/ml, 47 % of the hormone was aromatized, indicating a lower capacity of the aromatase in comparison to the E_2 17β-dehydrogenase system.

Chorionic membrane and cells (Fig. 7), amnion and choriocarcinoma cells (Be/Wo line) (Fig. 8) also showed high 17β-dehydrogenase activity.

As previously reported (*Gurpide & Welch* 1969), the interconversion between E_1 and E_2 by skeletal muscle is negligible in comparison to endometrium or trophoblastic tissue.

Testosterone and androstenedione

Data already published indicate a striking similarity in the ϱ values for the interconversion by human endometrium of T and $\varDelta$ and E_1 and E_2 when perfused as a mixture. It is worth noting, however, that a load of T in the medium

266

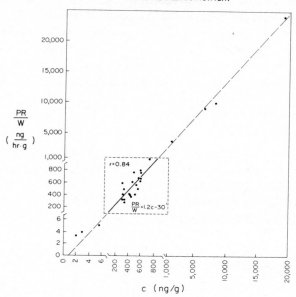

Fig. 11.

Correlation between production rates per gram of tissue and intracellular concentrations of E_1 in human endometrium. Three different scales are used to cover various ranges of concentrations. Data in box were used to calculate regression and correlation coefficients shown in the figure.

did not change the value of $\varrho \Delta T$, in contrast to the effect of E_2 on $\varrho E_1 E_2$ and $\varrho \Delta T$, again suggesting a specific effect of E_2 on the transhydrogenase.

Oestrogen sulphates

E_1S and E_2S are interconverted in endometrial and trophoblastic tissue only to a small extent, probably due to the predominance of sulphatase activity in these tissues. Practically all of the oestrogen sulphates entering the tissue could be accounted for by the release into the medium of unconjugated oestrogens.

Progesterone and 20α-dihydroprogesterone

Similarly to the observations of *Zander* (1965) with placenta and to those

267

of *Bryson & Sweat* (1967), extensive conversion by human endometrium of 20αDHP to P was noted (Fig. 4). The extent of the reverse reaction was small and in some instances the failure of P to introduce enough ^{14}C into 20αDHP precluded the calculation of rates of interconversion between these two compounds.

Addition to the medium of E_2 or ethynyl oestradiol at concentrations of 5 μg/ml markedly reduced the conversion of 20αDHP to P.

Nucleosides and nucleotides

Uridine and cytidine were extensively interconverted by slices of human endometrium, ρ's and rates of conversion of cytidine to uridine being larger than those corresponding to the reverse reaction.

Uridine and UMP were interconverted by slices of rat liver (Fig. 10). UMP entering the tissue was almost completely converted to uridine.

Cortisol and cortisone

The interconversion of these two compounds in rabbit liver slices was very extensive, as shown in Fig. 9.

Intracellular clearance

By analogy with studies of hormone levels in blood in *in vivo* experiments, we attempted to correlate the production rate of the hormone per gram of tissue (PR/W) with its intracellular concentration. The ratio of these two values represents a »clearance« (IC in h^{-1}), expressed as the amount of tissue containing the quantity of hormone which is irreversibly removed per unit of time.

The concentration of the hormone in tissue was calculated from the isotopic data by using Equation 6 which assumes a complete replacement of the endogenous oestrogen by the perfused labelled compound. In a few samples of placental slices the values calculated in this indirect manner were tested by measuring specific activities of the hormone in tissue using radioimmunoassays. A very good agreement was found.

Intracellular clearance can also be directly calculated from Equation 19.

Data on clearance of E_1 by human endometrial slices are shown in Fig. 11. It is evident from the data that the PR/W ratio is remarkably constant in a range of production rates from 4 to 24 000 ng/h. These extremes corresponded to concentrations of 4 to 19 000 ng/g. Linear regression analysis of the data indicates that the clearance for oestrone is equal to approximately 1.2 h^{-1}.

One may question whether or not this value applies to physiological conditions. To investigate this point we measured the concentration of the hormone in human endometrium immediately after curetting. The levels found for E_1 were 30–240 ng/g of tissue, values which fall within the range of concentrations resulting from the perfusions. Therefore, we consider that the clearance for E_1 of 1.2 h^{-1} might be of physiological relevance. Of course, the value for the intracellular clearance of the hormone depends on rates of metabolic reaction which might be different *in vivo* and *in vitro*. *In vitro* perfusions will help to evaluate the dependence of this parameter upon changes in metabolism.

The data corresponding to intracellular clearance of E_2 in endometrium have been more difficult to evaluate since a large range of values was found. We think that such variability might be due, at least in part, to imprecision in measurements. Nevertheless, the intracellular clearance for E_2 was estimated to be similar to that of E_1, although higher values for IC_{E2} were noted.

No significant differences in the clearance of oestrogens were found among the various types of endometrium tested, *e. g.* proliferative, secretory, hyperplastic, or post menopausal.

Clearance of E_1 and E_2 from human endometrium was not significantly reduced by the addition of as much as 5 μg/ml of E_2 or mestranol. On the other hand, ethynyl oestradiol at 5 μg/ml reduced considerably the intracellular clearance of E_2, most likely by slowing its irreversible removal via E_1 as a consequence of the previously mentioned inhibitory effect on the oestrogen 17β-dehydrogenase.

Intracellular clearances in human endometrium of E_1, P, and Δ were similar but those of uridine and cytidine were much larger. Liver clearances for uridine, UMP, F and E were also large.

Values for intracellular clearance of E_1 in placenta were approximately 1.7 h^{-1}. Placental intracellular clearances for E_2 were found to be larger than those for E_1.

Ratios of concentrations of labelled compounds in tissues

Fig. 2 indicates that the concentration of labelled E_2 was more than 6 times higher in tissue than in perfusion medium ($c_{E2t}^{3H} / c_{E2}^{3H} = 6.1$) while the tracer of E_1 was concentrated 17-fold with respect to the medium ($c_{E1t}^{14C} / c_{E1}^{14C} = 17$). These results are typical for endometrium. As indicated by Equation 19 and found experimentally for oestrogens in human endometrium, such ratios do not depend on the amount of compound perfused if permeability and intracellular clearance remain constant.

However, in 2 perfusions performed with proliferative endometrium and much lower concentrations of tritiated E_1 or E_2 (about 0.1 ng/ml), there was an unusually high tissue-to-medium ratio for E_2 (but not for E_1). Furthermore, in these experiments the ratio of concentrations of labelled E_1 and E_2 after perfusion of tritiated E_1 ($c_{E1t}^{3H} / c_{E2t}^{3H}$) was lower than the corresponding ratio obtained when higher oestrogen concentrations were used. These results indicate that the retention of E_2 at very low intracellular concentration of the hormone (about 2 ng/g of tissue) is relatively greater than its retention at higher levels, thus providing evidence for the existence of systems saturable by the hormone. This observation corresponds to the findings of *Alberga & Baulieu* (1968) and *Rochefort & Baulieu* (1969), who used endometrium and whole uterus from castrated rats and to the *in vivo* results obtained by *Jensen et al.* (1967) with immature rats.

Endogenous concentrations of E_1 plus E_2 in human endometrium were estimated to be larger than 50 ng/g and the lowest level found was 13 ng/g for E_2. Therefore, physiologically, the specific binding systems for oestrogen in human endometrium may be saturated.

The ratio of the concentrations of perfused labelled P in human endometrium and perfused medium ($c_{Pt}^{14C} / c_{P}^{14C}$) is large, 26 in the example given in Fig. 4. This result is in agreement with the findings of other authors (*Edwards & Brush* 1970).

Neither oestrogen sulphates (Fig. 3) nor T (*Gurpide & Welch* 1969) seem to be concentrated by human endometrium.

Slices of skeletal muscle did not concentrate E_1, E_2, T or Δ with respect to the medium. The highest ratio for labelled hormone in tissue and medium, shown by E_1, was 0.3.

Release of Hormones from Perfused Tissue

It was reported previously that a large fraction of perfused E_1 and Δ entering the slices of human endometrium is released back into the medium after participating in reversible reactions while practically no E_2 or T leaves this tissue.

The new data presented in Figs. 2 to 10 confirmed and extended the observation that some compounds transit through tissue with limited net uptake while others are taken up extensively and leave it almost entirely as metabolites.

We look at the ratio β/α as indicative of the fraction of the intracellular compound released to the medium. As shown by Equation 15, β/α describes the fraction of the hormone appearing *de novo* in the cell that is transferred to the medium.

It is apparent from the data for E_1 and E_2 in human endometrium and placenta (Figs. 2 and 5) that the preferential release to the medium of the oestrogens as E_1 rather than E_2 is not the result of a small conversion of E_1 to E_2 or to the high concentrations of E_1 perfused since $\beta_{E_2}/\alpha_{E_2} < \beta_{E_1}/\alpha_{E_1}$ even when $v_{E_1E_2} = v_{E_2E_1}$ and $PR_{E_2} = PR_{E_1}$.

As follows from Equation 19, the quotient of the ratios β/α for 2 compounds perfused as a mixture is given by the expression

$$\frac{\beta_A/\alpha_A}{\beta_B/\alpha_B} = \frac{\alpha_A d_A/IC_A}{\alpha_B d_B/IC_B}. \tag{21}$$

The values for the diffusible fraction (d) and the intracellular clearance (IC) which appear in Equation 21 are determined by many factors, among them reactivity, binding and intracellular distribution of the hormones. There is a scarcity of data on concentration, protein binding and localization of hormones in human endometrium, in contrast to the intensive work done with E_2 in uteri of animals.

Data reported by *Korenman* (1963) indicate that E_1 competes with E_2 for binding to cytosol from uteri of mature rabbits but no comparable information is available for human endometrium. *Noteboom & Gorski* (1965) have found that about 50 % of the total radioactivity present in immature rat uteri is localized in the nuclei following the *in vivo* administration of [^{3}H] E_2. *Brush et al.* (1967) reported that nuclei from human endometrium contained a large fraction of the intracellular radioactivity after injection of labelled E_2 before hysterectomy. However, a large part of the radioactivity found in nuclei may be loosely and even unspecifically associated with these organelles, as can be surmised from the data of *Clark & Gorski* (1969).

In order to test for compartmentalization of E_2, approximately 500 mg of proliferative human endometrium was subjected to a short incubation with 1 ng of [^{3}H] E_2 followed by an exposure to 1000 ng of [^{14}C] E_2. After rapid rinsing the tissue was placed in the chamber and perfused with a buffer solution containing unlabelled E_1 and E_2. Eluate and tissue were analyzed for their content of labelled E_1 and E_2. Tritium disappeared more slowly from the tissue than ^{14}C. The ^{3}H/^{14}C ratio of the material remaining in the tissue was higher than the original, mainly due to the high ^{3}H/^{14}C ratio in the residual E_2. Evidently there was no fast and complete mixing of intracellular E_2 since otherwise no differences in isotope ratios would have been observed. These findings can be explained by assuming that [^{3}H] E_2, incubated in amounts which might not greatly exceed the capacity of specific receptors

271

GLOSSARY

Perfusion medium: solution flowing into chamber containing tissue

Perfusate: solution leaving the chamber

$c_A^{^3H}$ = concentration of tritiated compound A in the perfusion medium (cpm/ml)

$c_{At}^{^3H}$ = concentration of tritiated compound A in tissue (cpm/g)

$c_{A\bar{p}}^{^3H}$ = concentration of tritiated A in perfusate (cpm/ml)

$a_{At}^{^3H}$ = specific activity of A in tissue with respect to ^3H at the steady state (cpm/ng)

$(^3H/^{14}C)_{At}$ = isotope ratio in A in tissue

c_A = concentration of A in perfusion medium (ng/ml)

$c_{A\bar{p}}$ = concentration of A in perfusate (ng/ml)

c_{At} = concentrations of A in tissue (ng/g)

d_A = fraction of A in tissue present in a diffusible form

Rates = described in Fig. 1

$\alpha, \beta, \gamma, \varrho$, PR, IC = see text for definitions

φ = flow rate of perfusion medium (ml/h)

W = weight of tissue perfused (g)

ACKNOWLEDGMENTS

We are grateful to Mr. Luis Escarcena for the oxygen measurements.

This work was supported by Grant No. M70-7-C from the Population Council, New York, Grant No. AM-HD-14554 from the National Institutes of Health and an Institutional Research Grant from the American Cancer Society.

REFERENCES

Alberga A. & Baulieu E. E.: Mol. Pharmacol. *4* (1968) 311.
Billing R. J., Barbiroli B. & Smellie R. M. S.: Biochem. J. *114* (1969) 37P.
Brush M. C., Taylor R. W. & King R. J. B.: J. endocr. *39* (1967) 599.
Bryson M. J. & Sweat M. L.: Endocrinology *81* (1967) 729.
Clark J. H. & Gorski J.: Biochim. biophys. Acta (Amst.) *192* (1969) 508.

Davis B. D.: Arch. Biochem. Biophys. *78* (1958) 497.

Duncan I. B. R. & Bell E. J.: Brit. med. J. *2* (1961) 863.

Edwards R. & Brush M. G.: Excerpta med. (Amst.) *210* (1970) 153.

Engel L. L.: Endocrinology *87* (1970) 827.

Giorgi E. P., Grant J. K., Scott L. S. & Stewart J. C.: Excerpta med. (Amst.) *210* (1970) 280.

Gurpide E. & Welch M.: J. biol. Chem. *244* (1969) 5159.

Hamilton T. H.: Science *161* (1968) 649.

Huibergtse W. H. & Ungar F.: Life Sci. *9* (1970) 349.

Jarabak J. & Sack G. H. Jr.: Biochemistry *8* (1968) 2203.

Jensen E. V., DeSombre E. R., Hurst D. J., Kawashima T. & Jungblot P. W.: Arch. D'Anat. Microscop. *56* (Suppl.) (1967) 547.

Korenman S. G.: J. clin. Endocr. *28* (1968) 127.

Langer L. J., Alexander J. A. & Engel L. L.: J. biol. Chem. *234* (1959) 2609.

Lineweaver H. & Burke D.: J. Amer. chem. Soc. *56* (1934) 658.

Lucis O. J.: Steroids *5* (1965) 163.

Mann J. & Gurpide E.: J. clin. Endocr. *26* (1966) 1346.

Merchant D. J., Kahn V. H. & Murphy W. H.: Handbook of Cell and Organ Culture, Burgess Publ. Co., Minneapolis (1964).

Noteboom W. D. & Gorski J.: Arch. Biochem. Biophys. *111* (1965) 559.

Orti E., Baker R. K., Lanman J. T. & Brasch H.: Lab. & Clin. Med. *66* (1965) 973.

Pattillo R. A. & Gey G. O.: Cancer Res. *28* (1968) 1231.

Rappaport C. & Howze G. B.: Proc. Soc. exp. Biol. Med. *121* (1966) 1010.

Rochefort H. & Baulieu E. E.: Endocrinology *84* (1969) 108.

Rosner W., Christy N. P. & Kelly W. G.: Biochemistry *8* (1969) 3100.

Ryan K. J. & Engel L. L.: Endocrinology *52* (1953) 287.

Saffran M., Ford P., Matthews E. K., Kraml M. & Garbaczewska L.: Canad. J. Biochem. *45* (1967) 1901.

Stein W. D.: The Movement of Molecules Across Cell Membranes, Academic Press, New York (1967).

Tait S. A. S., Tait J. F., Flood C. & Okamoto M.: Endocrinology *81* (1967) 1213.

Tait S .A. S., Schulster D., Okamoto M., Flood C. & Tait J. F.: Endocrinology *86* (1970) 360.

Ungar F., Turnipseed M. R. & McCoy K. E.: Excerpta med. (Amst.) *210* (1970) 478.

Yu F. L. & Feigelson P.: Arch. Biochem. Biophys. *129* (1969) 152.

Zander J.: Excerpta med. (Amst.) *83* (1965) 715.

DISCUSSION

Robel: The kinetic studies you are doing are very important for physiological purposes. Personally I think there is a pitfall in your data, which probably is related to the state of pyridine nucleotide cofactors. I wonder if their state in the perfusions you are using is the same as in the normally responsive tissue? If that could be controlled, the rate of oestradiol, for example, coming out of the tissue may be strikingly changed. What happens in your model when there is a tissue compartmentalization of compounds? Secondly, what calculations can be done when you have only conversion in one direction, from A to B?

275

Gurpide: I do not believe that the values for intracellular interconversion which we obtained *in vitro* are those which prevail *in vivo*. It is of interest, however, to determine *in vitro* how rates of interconversion are influenced by factors such as oxygen concentration, substrate levels. and addition of hormones and drugs to the medium. Kinetic parameters of the enzymatic reactions involved in these conversions can also be studied *in vitro*. I would like to emphasize that the values of the rates of entry of compounds into the cell do not depend on the extent of interconversion. The release of oestrone rather than oestradiol from human endometrium *in vitro* is not the result of poor conversion of oestrone to oestradiol. Even in cases when such conversion was high, the same pattern prevailed.

We consider that there is compartmentalization of the steroids in the cells, particularly for oestradiol in nuclei and cytoplasm in human endometrium. However, there is no information available at the moment on either the kinetics of exchange of the steroids between these compartments or on the concentration dependence of their relative size. We are at present studying these problems. We have found that the $^3H/^{14}C$ ratio of a compound is the same in nuclei and cytoplasm at the end of the perfusion. Therefore, compartmentalization does not affect the calculations of α's and β's in our studies. It might, however, produce erroneous results in the amount of steroid content of the cells as calculated indirectly from measurements of radioactivity assuming complete replacement of endogenous material by the perfused compounds.

Concerning your last question, the values of α and β corresponding to compound A can still be calculated when the conversion of B to A is irreversible.

Wira: In your presentation, you spoke of entry into the cells or cell fractions. I was wondering what evidence you have from your perfusion studies that oestrone is inside the cell, rather than binding to cell surfaces?

Gurpide: In the first place I would like to emphasize that oestrone is strongly concentrated by human endometrium and must be considered an important hormone for this tissue. *MacDonald et al.* (1969) indicated that oestrone might have different physiological effects than oestradiol in human endometrium, particularly as observed in postmenopausal women.

We determine that oestrone and oestradiol measured in tissues is not contaminated with extracellular labelled compounds in the following experiments. After removing the slices from the chamber at the end of the perfusion, we wash them with buffer containing unlabelled oestrone and oestradiol, collecting samples of the wash every 10 seconds during the first minutes. We observe that the $^3H/^{14}C$ ratio in each compound becomes constant in less than 2 min and is identical to the ratio of the compound in tissue after prolonged washing. If we have perfused [^3H] OE_2 and [^{14}C] OE_1, the washes will show a very high but declining $^3H/^{14}C$ ratio in OE_2 during the first minute, but this ratio becomes constant after two minutes. Similarly, washed oestrone has a very low ratio, which increases and becomes constant in less than two minutes. All the data in tissue are obtained from slices thoroughly washed.

Baulieu: Concerning the problem of the entry of steroids into the tissue, if I understood correctly your evidence, the answer was that you have just a diffusion. You didn't find any limiting step or saturable mechanism?

Gurpide: We have not observed any saturable transport mechanism for oestrogen in human endometrium at concentrations of oestrogen as high as 5 $\mu g/ml$. We were able, however, to determine a V_{max} for the entry of oestradiol into human placental slices, as mentioned in the paper.

276

Baulieu: Now, there is something in your paper which you didn't have the time to discuss and which concerns an oestrogen sulphate. You find that its entry into tissue is »free«, if I may say that, and I wonder if we could argue that in this *in vitro* perfusion system you may have damaged some system which limitates the entry of hormones into the tissues. One way to see if these *in vitro* perfusion studies are pertinent to the *in vivo* situation would be to look *in vivo* for the entry of double labelled oestrogen sulphate into the uterus.

Your point about the plasma protein is extremely interesting. If what you say is correct, one possibility for explaining the effect with the relatively specific fraction you used, which is not albumin, could be the entry of the specific transport protein into the tissue. This eventually could fit with the intracellular presence of transcortin in the uterus, which was demonstrated by our group. Actually, experiments should now be feasible with the rat, because *C. Mercier-Bodard* and *J. P. Raynaud* found recently that there is a plasma protein in the rat which binds oestradiol, is different from albumin and, contrary to the human, does not bind testosterone. This is a high affinity oestrogen binding protein, which you find in the rat and which could be used for studies with rat uterus.

Gurpide: Your suggestion of an *in vivo* experiment with double labelled oestrogen sulphates is an interesting one. However, I doubt that we would be able to obtain by these means measurable counts of oestrogen sulphates in human endometrium because of the rapid hydrolysis by the sulphatase in the tissue.

Stumpf: Regarding the significance of the rapidity of diffusion *in vivo*, we have done *in vivo* studies in the rat. Dr. *A. Tchernitchin* in our laboratory injected a single dose of $[^3H]$ oestradiol intravenously and removed pieces of uterine tissue at different time intervals. Already one and a half minute after the injection, there are indications of nuclear concentration of radioactivity in the autoradiograms. From these *in vivo* experiments, there is indication that the hormone rapidly enters the tissue. This would agree with your results.

Baulieu: I don't understand what you mean. The rate of entry does not mean that there is not an active process which has been damaged here. Your experiments are neither for nor against my feeling.

Stumpf: I thought you considered that there was a breakdown of barriers, or so, in the *in vitro* situation, which would not be relevant *in vivo*.

Baulieu: Not necessarily a barrier, an active transport system.

Stumpf: – which is broken down –

Baulieu: May be broken down in the tissue studied *in vitro*.

Gurpide: We find in endometrium, when studying progesterone entry, that there are things that cut the entry to half, and really the progesterone entry goes on, so there is something that seems to react to that exogeneously.

Ferin: Did you see any difference beween proliferative and secretory endometrium?

Gurpide: No, we did not.

Diczfalusy: Dr. Gurpide, you might study the entry of oestrogen sulphates using mid-gestation human foetal tissues, where the aryl sulphatase activity is very little, if any (e. g. *Schwers et al.* 1965). That may be a useful preparation.

I have a very naive question, and I am sure you have given consideration to this, but we ourselves find that we can never reach accurate figures in isolating radioactive material, unless we use an internal standard and crystallize the material to constant specific activity. I think it would be useful for our readers if you could give us a little more information about how the tissue concentrations are estimated in your own studies.

Gurpide: Thank you for your suggestion to use foetal tissues. We tested for radiochemical purity of the isolated oestrogens by acetylation and chromatography of the acetates; $^3H/^{14}C$ ratios and specific activities remained constant. The radiochemical purity of the progesterone isolated from tissue and perfusate was ascertained by crystallization after addition of carriers. Experimental details on the isolation procedures are described in a previous publication (*Gurpide & Welch* 1969).

References:

MacDonald P. C., Grodin J. M. & Siiteri P. K. In: Gual C., Ed. Progress in Endocrinology, Excerpta Medica Found. (Amst.) (1969) 70.
Gurpide E. & Welch M.: J. biol. Chem. *244* (1969) 5159.
Schwers J., Govaerts-Videtsky M., Wiqvist N. & Diczfalusy E.: Acta endocr. (Kbh.) *50* (1965) 597.

Unité de Recherches sur le Métabolisme Moléculaire
et la Physio-Pathologie des Stéroides de l'Institut National de la Santé
et de la Recherche Médicale, Département de Chimie Biologique,
Faculté de Médecine de Paris-Sud, 78 Avenue du Gnénéral Leclerc – 94 Bicêtre

STEROID HORMONE METABOLISM IN RESPONSIVE TISSUES IN VITRO*

By

Paul Robel

ABSTRACT

Of the information available on steroid hormone metabolism in responsive tissues, only that relating hormone metabolism to physiological activity is reviewed, *i. e.* metabolite activity in isolated *in vitro* systems, binding of metabolites to target tissue *receptors*, specific steroid hormone metabolizing enzymes and relationship of hormone metabolism to target organ physiological state.

Further, evidence is presented in the androgen field, demonstrating 5α-reduced metabolites, formed inside the target cells, as active compounds. This has led to a consideration of testosterone as a »prehormone«. The possibility that similar events take place in tissues responding to progesterone is discussed.

Finally, the role of hormone metabolism in the regulation of hormone availability and/or renewal in target cells is discussed. In this context, reference is made to the potential role of plasma binding proteins and cytosol *receptors*.

Steroid hormone metabolism is not restricted to classical metabolic organs such as the liver or the intestine (the splanchnic system). Studies of steroid dyna-

---

* This presentation is based on the concepts reported by E. E. Baulieu, A. Alberga, I. Jung, M. C. Lebeau, C. Mercier-Bodard, E. Milgrom, J. P. Raynaud, C. Raynaud-Jammet, H. Rochefort, H. Truong-Richard-Foy and P. Robel (Recent Progress in Hormone Research, 1971, in press). The definitions of *receptor*, »neo-nuclear«, will be found in this paper.

mics *in vivo* gave several rough estimations of steroid hormone metabolism in extra splanchnic organs (*Tait & Burstein* 1964). Incubation of a variety of target and non-target tissues *in vitro*, using whole tissue, slices, homogenates and tissue subfractions, gave direct information on the enzymes present in peripheral tissues. A great number of publications appeared in the past decade, so that a comprehensive review seems unfeasible. Such *in vitro* studies, particularly when various cofactors are added, although they show the metabolic potentialities of the tissues studied, give no information on the pattern of metabolism existing *in vivo*, since they introduce artifacts due to the absence of blood supply, changes in tissue permeability, ill defined exposure of structure bound enzymes and arbitrary supply of cofactors. The use of tissue superfusion, however, can give some valid information on steroid hormone disposition, metabolite formation and excretion in an isolated tissue (*Gurpide* 1969). However, even in this case, one cannot be sure that the metabolism of steroid hormone observed approaches the *in vivo* situation, since it is not known if the metabolism observed occurred in a situation where the tissue was still responsive to hormone action.

This presentation will therefore be mainly restricted to the significance of target organ metabolism for hormone action (Fig. 1). In the simplest situation, formation of metabolites is minimal or particular to some animal species. One can be sure that the steroid hormone is active by itself. When hormone metabolites are formed to a quantitatively significant extent, various possibilities

HORMONES
AND
TARGET TISSUE METABOLITES

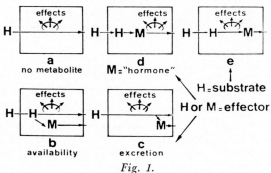

Fig. 1.

Hormones and target tissue metabolites.

may be considered (*Baulieu* 1967). 1) The process of hormone metabolism may be coupled to another important metabolic mechanism of the cell, as suggested by *Talalay & Williams-Ashman* (1960). 2) Inactive by themselves, the metabolites could regulate the amount of hormone available to receptors and/or favour its renewal. The eventual roles of plasma and intracellular proteins in such hormone turnover will be discussed. 3) Conversely the formation of active metabolite(s) might lead to a concept of the conventional »hormone« as a »prehormone« which is converted inside the target tissue to the directly active compounds. One major difficulty lies in the assessment of steroid metabolite activity. Most of the bioassays used the *in vivo* administration of compounds tested and measurement of the response of target organs. In this case the chemical form and amount of each metabolite reaching the organ studied is unknown. Topical administration does not circumvent completely these difficulties. *In vitro* study of hormone action is restricted to organ and eventually cell culture systems, which, at the present time, seem to be the only ones to meet the following requirements: 1) isolated *in vitro* system approaching physiological steady state conditions, 2) simultaneous demonstration of hormone metabolism and action (*Baulieu & Robel* 1970). However, since steroid hormone action follows its interaction with a target cell protein, studies of steroid hormone metabolites retention and binding, using a variety of *in vitro* procedures can also serve as a guideline to the problem of metabolite activity.

ENZYMES OF STEROID HORMONE METABOLISM IN RESPONSIVE TISSUES

A widespread occurrence of Δ^4-3-oxo-steroid-5α-reductase, NAD/NADP dependent 3α- and 3β-hydroxysteroid dehydrogenases, 11β-hydroxysteroid dehydrogenase, 17β-hydroxysteroid dehydrogenase and 20α-hydroxysteroid dehydrogenase was found in many tissues of several mammalian species. Such enzyme activities are well documented for testosterone and androstenedione (*Kochakian* 1959; *Ofner* 1968), for progesterone (*Wiest* 1963; *Bryson & Sweat* 1967), for cortisol (*Burton* 1965) and oestrogens (*Jutting et al.* 1967; *MacCartney & Thomas* 1969). However, no distinct relationship of the enzyme distribution to tissue responsiveness was demonstrated, since the same enzymes were found in peripheral target and non-target organs. The absence of desmolase activity and the absolute preponderance (or exclusive occurrence) of 5α-reduced metabolites is a striking feature shared by all peripheral organs such as the skin, kidneys, bone, muscle... Moreover, steroid hormone metabolism is not restricted to its own target organs, for example progesterone or oestradiol are also metabolized in the prostate (*Acevedo & Goldzieher* 1965*a,b*). Finally, occurrence in small amounts of polar metabolites bearing one hydroxyl group in position 6β, 16α or 2β was also reported.

THE SIMPLEST CASE: NO OR LITTLE HORMONE METABOLISM

Oestradiol

In the immature or castrated rat, no metabolism of oestradiol is observed in the uterus (*Jensen et al.* 1966). The fact that no oestrone can be detected in the target tissue does not necessarily preclude the possibility that reversible oxidation and reduction of 17-oxygen function takes place. However, the use of [17α-³H] oestradiol conclusively demonstrated that rat uterus has no ability to oxidize oestradiol to oestrone meanwhile hormone effect is observed. 17β-hydroxysteroid dehydrogenase activity can be observed in other species and in other experimental conditions. An oestrogen inducible 17β-hydroxysteroid NAD(P) oxydoreductase was described in rabbit uterus (*Jutting et al.* 1967; *MacCartney & Thomas* 1969). However, oxidation of oestradiol is not favoured at physiological pH unless there is an appropriate supply of NADP. Despite variations between mammalian species, oestrogen metabolism does not seem to play a significant role in oestradiol action and appears as a secondary phenomenon in highly stimulated tissues. The necessary integrity of the 17β-hydroxyl radical for oestrogen high affinity binding to uterine receptors also points out that oestradiol is the active compound (*Baulieu et al.* 1967).

Glucocorticoids

Schaumburg & Bojesen (1968) demonstrated that corticosterone is not metabolized by rat thymocytes *in vitro*. Similar results were obtained for cortisol by *Munck & Brinck-Johnsen* (1969). Analysis of radioactive steroids in cell-bound and supernatant fractions from 40 min incubation of [³H] cortisol showed that more than 80 % of the ³H labelled steroid firmly bound to cells was unaltered cortisol, whereas more metabolites were found in the incubation medium. Moreover a cortisol metabolite such as tetrahydrocortisol did not compete for cortisol binding and did not inhibit glucose uptake by thymus cells.

Rat hepatoma cell cultures do not metabolize dexamethasone. With cortisol at 5 nM physiological concentration, most of the radioactivity from nuclear extracts was unchanged cortisol, while less than 20 per cent migrated with di- and tetrahydrocortisol (*Baxter & Tomkins* 1970). Cell cytoplasma contained also a small amount of metabolites whereas the incubation medium contained only unchanged cortisol.

282

Aldosterone

During *in vitro* studies of aldosterone action on isolated toad urinary bladder, hormone metabolism was not observed (*Crabbe* 1963; *Sharp et al.* 1966).

Aldosterone is likely to be converted to reduced metabolites by the kidney, although no quantitative information on its metabolism *in vitro* is available. In any case, metabolites are not specifically bound to renal nuclear *receptors* as is aldosterone (*Fanestil & Edelman* 1966).

STEROID HORMONES AND THE ENZYMATIC TRANSFER OF HYDROGEN

Villee & Hagerman (1959) initiated a series of investigations, starting from an *in vitro* effect of 17β-oestradiol to stimulate substrate oxidation in human endometrium and placenta, which formed the basis for what may be called the *transhydrogenase theory of oestrogen action*. *Talalay & Williams-Ashman* (1960) subsequently found that the effect of oestrogen in this placental system was to activate a transhydrogenase system which transfers hydrogen from NADPH to NAD; indeed the possibility was advanced that such transfer of hydrogen (protons and electrons) from one pyridine nucleotide to another might ultimately prove to be the molecular basis of the action of steroid hormones. Since then, many data were accumulated which seemed incompatible with the general thesis advanced. Among other arguments, the studies of *Jensen et al.* (1966) eliminated dehydrogenation of oestradiol in rat uterus; the physiological effective dose of oestrogen is well below the 10^{-7} to 10^{-8} M level which operates the »transhydrogenase effect«; oestradiol does not stimulate oxygen consumption in rat uterus; synthetic oestrogens cannot serve as cofactors of such transhydrogenase; oestrogens are inactive *in vitro* despite their action on transhydrogenation. Finally occurrence of the transhydrogenase system seems to appear in tissues which have been subjected to high levels of oestrogen for prolonged periods, so that transhydrogenase may represent an induced enzyme which may not have any primary relationship to the mechanism of oestrogen action.

FORMATION OF ACTIVE METABOLITES AT TARGET LEVEL

Androgens

Testosterone metabolism

Testosterone is extensively metabolized in various tissues other than classical metabolic organs such as the liver.

was formed, demonstrating the one-way activity of 3β-hydroxysteroid dehydrogenase. Some *epi*androsterone was found, especially in the nuclei. Consequently, there is evidence for the formation of two categories of metabolites from testosterone (Fig. 2), androstanolone and 3α-androstanediol being representative of one series, the metabolism of which is actually similar to that of testosterone and leads to preferential nuclear accumulation of androstanolone; and 3β-androstanediol typical of the second category, which does not give androstanolone thus sustaining the consideration of testosterone action being dually mediated by two kinds of metabolites, androstanolone controlling tissue growth and 3β-androstanediol controlling secretion (Fig. 3).

Metabolic pattern can lead to a prediction of androgen activity in tissue culture. Thus, androstenedione metabolism having shown a metabolic pattern very similar to that of testosterone, subsequent study of activity in organ culture did show that androstenedione was as potent as testosterone itself (*Roy & Robel,* unpublished observation).

In conclusion, parallel studies of androgen metabolism and histological action strongly suggest that testosterone action on the ventral prostate is related to the formation of an active metabolite. The discovery of prostatic binding proteins, which could intervene in separate types of action (*Baulieu et al.* 1971), also emphasizes the importance of metabolites in hormone action, as depicted in Fig. 4. However, there is still no conclusive evidence that testosterone is inactive by itself, or even that formation of metabolites is really necessary for hormone action.

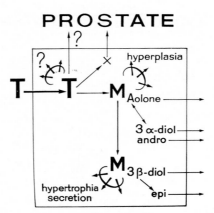

Fig. 3.

Testosterone metabolism and action in rat ventral prostate culture: *a model.*
× stands for unknown metabolites. Arrows going out of the frame indicate
exit of steroids from prostatic cell.

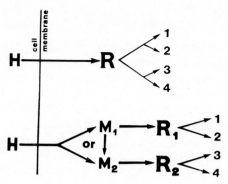

Fig. 4.

Steroid hormone or steroid hormone metabolite RECEPTOR(S). a) There is one RECEPTOR, source of all effects 1,2,3,4 (upper part). b) There are different RECEP-TORS consequently to the metabolic differential of the hormone H into metabolites M_1 and M_2 (lower part).

Steroid induction of porphyrin synthesis in liver cell culture

A number of steroid metabolites strongly stimulate porphyrin biosynthesis in chick embryo liver cells growing in primary culture (*Granick & Kappas* 1967). These metabolites are of the *5β*-H type; they are derived from the biotrans-formation of C 19 and C 21 hormones, such as testosterone, progesterone and 17α-hydroxy progesterone, and they are active in inducing porphyrinogenesis in concentration at least as low as 10^{-6} to 10^{-8} M. Typical inducing steroids are *5β*-androsterone, *5β*-pregnane-3α,20α-diol, *3α*-hydroxy-*5β*-pregnane-11,20-dione, and *5β*-pregnane-3α,17,20α-triol. Steroid hormones themselves are either inactive or have a weak activiy, as do metabolites of the *5α*-H type. These porphyrogenic steroids also stimulate heme synthesis in chick blastoderm erythoid cells, and they may normally play a role in the control of heme bio-synthesis in all cells through regulation of the formation of δ-aminolevulinic acid synthetase, the initial and rate-limiting enzyme in the heme bioassay pathway.

Progesterone

The first detailed report on progesterone metabolism *in vitro* by a target tissue was that of *Wiest* (1963). It was shown that a small metabolic activity was present in rat uterus, greater in the decidua than in residual myo-metrium. The main metabolite observed was 3α-hydroxy-5α-pregnane-20-one. 5α-Pregnane-3,20-dione was also observed. Activities of 3α-hydroxysteroid de-hydrogenase and Δ^4-5α-reductase were most pronounced in uterine segments

287

obtained during oestrus and were least pronounced (or absent) during pseudo-pregnancy.

Wichmann (1967) added more information to progesterone metabolism in the pregnant rat uterus. 5α-reductase was the main enzyme activity found, together with 3α-hydroxysteroid dehydrogenase and 20α-hydroxysteroid dehydrogenase (an activity which was not found in non-pregnant rats by Wiest). Moreover it was found that 20α-hydroxysteroid dehydrogenase was located in the supernatant while 5α-reductase and 3α-hydroxysteroid dehydrogenase activities were observed mainly in the nuclear-myofibrillar fraction.

Bryson & Sweat (1967, 1969) have studied progesterone metabolism by human uterus *in vitro*. As in the rat, a proliferative endometrium was much more active than the myometrium. The main enzymatic activities were 5α-reductase and 20α-hydroxysteroid dehydrogenase, but a small amount of 5β-reductase and 6β-hydroxylase were also observed, whereas no 3α-hydroxysteroid dehydrogenase activity could be demonstrated.

Extensive metabolism of progesterone was observed during chick oviduct mince incubation, since after one hour of incubation only 35 % of the radioactivity chromatographed as progesterone (*O'Malley et al.* 1969). Finally, the conversion of progesterone to allopregnanedione was shown to take place in magnum nuclei (*Morgan & Wilson* 1970), and retention of this metabolite was shown to take place only in the magnum and shell gland of the oviduct, the comb and the brain. Similar observation was made by *Armstrong* (1970) for rat uterus nuclei with the addition that nuclear 5α-reductase activity is increased under conditions in which the biological activity of progesterone is enhanced.

Despite the demonstration that progesterone metabolism takes place in the target organs of several species, relevance of such findings to progesterone action is not clear. 1) 5α-reduced metabolites such as 5α-pregnane-3,20-dione or 3α-hydroxy-5α-pregnane-20-one are inactive in a mouse intrauterine test (*Hooker & Forbes* 1949a,b). 2) The intrauterine concentration of progesterone appears to relate directly to biological events associated with hormonal function (*Wiest* 1970). 3) The major part of tissue radioactivity in experiments with tissue slices (30 min incubation) remains unchanged progesterone (*Milgrom & Baulieu* 1970). 4) 5α-pregnane-3,20-dione has a smaller affinity for the guinea pig cytosol *receptor* than progesterone (*Milgrom & Baulieu* 1970; *Rao & Wiest* 1970). However, Wilson's finding of 5α-pregnanedione retention in chick oviduct nuclei could reopen the discussion of biological activity of progesterone metabolites.

288

STEROID HORMONE METABOLISM AS A LOCAL
REGULATION OF HORMONE TURNOVER

Theoretically, steroid hormone metabolism inside the target cell may display a regulatory function, either by a final control of the intracellular hormone concentration or by formation of metabolites which may compete for hormone binding to plasma and cell proteins. With the use of tracers in continuous flow incubation of tissue slices, it might be possible to investigate the renewal of steroid hormone in a target tissue and to evaluate the modification of kinetic parameters by addition of metabolites to the superfusion medium (*Gurpide* 1969). In absence of direct evidence of this kind, only speculations are possible.

Progesterone

In rat uterus, a progesterone binding protein has been described, identical in all respects to rat plasma CBG (*Milgrom & Baulieu* 1970*a*). When rat uterine cytosol was incubated with equimolar concentrations of cortisol and progesterone, cortisol was slightly more bound. However, when whole uterus incubations were performed and cytosol binding tested afterwards, it was found that progesterone was readily bound to the CBG like proteins whereas cortisol was not (*Milgrom & Baulieu* 1970*b*). This was explained by two findings: the incorporation of radioactivity into the tissue was much higher after progesterone incubation than after cortisol incubation, and whereas unchanged progesterone represented 70 % of the tissue radioactivity, there was very little unchanged cortisol. These differences in incorporation and metabolism resulted in both relatively high tissue concentration of progesterone and low concentration of cortisol. The same process was shown to operate also *in vivo* to select the bound hormone, active in the organ studied.

Testosterone

The binding of testosterone and its metabolites to prostate cytosol and to plasma sex hormone binding protein (SBP) were compared (*Baulieu & Robel* 1970).

Androstanolone is more strongly bound than testosterone but both steroids are equally bound to the rat prostate cytosol *receptor* and to human SBP. Conversely the 5α-androstane-3α and 3β,17β-diols are not bound to the rat ventral prostate cytosol androstanolone *receptor* (and likewise to the human one), whereas they have at least the same affinity for SBP as testosterone itself (*Kato & Horton* 1968).

Therefore a hypothetical regulatory system may be considered (Fig. 5). Testosterone is converted to metabolites such as androstanolone or 3β-androstanediol, which may be responsible for hormonal activity. Moreover metabolites like the androstanediols, which are not bound to cytosol, could

289

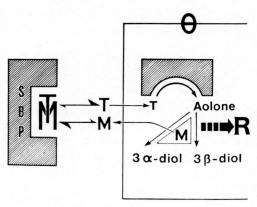

Fig. 5.

Plasma binding protein; possible role in testosterone (T) and metabolite (M) turnover.
SBP = sex hormone binding protein.

easily come out of the cell, in particular because they have a high affinity
for SBP; competition of androstanediols and testosterone for SBP binding
sites could in turn favour the entry of testosterone into the cell. Such a
mechanism could provide a specific supply of hormone bound to plasma
proteins to cells containing at the same time *receptors* for hormone and
enzymes able to produce metabolites which compete for hormone binding to
plasma proteins.

ACKNOWLEDGMENTS

Experiments reported in this review have been partially supported by the CNRS, the
DARST, the Fondation pour la Recherche Médicale Française, the Ford Foundation
and Roussel-UCLAF.

REFERENCES

Acevedo H. F. & Goldzieher J. W.: Biochim. biophys. Acta (Amst.) *97* (1965*a*) 571.
Acevedo H. F. & Goldzieher J. W.: Biochim. biophys. Acta (Amst.) *111* (1965*b*) 294.
Anderson K. D. & Liao S.: Nature (Lond.) *219* (1968) 277.
Armstrong D. T. & King E. R.: Fed. Proc. *29* (1970) 250.
Baulieu E. E.: Excerpta med. (Amst.) Internat. Congr. Ser. *132* (1967) 37.
Baulieu E. E. & Robel P. In: Griffiths K., Ed. Some aspects of the aetiology and bio-
chemistry of prostatic cancer. Cardiff (1970) in press.

Baulieu E. E., Alberga A. & Jung I.: C. R. Acad. Sci. (Paris) 265 (1967) 501.

Baulieu E. E., Lasnitzki I. & Robel P.: Nature (Lond.) 219 (1968) 1155.

Baulieu E. E., Jung I., Blondeau J. P. & Robel P. In: Schering Workshop on Steroid Hormone Receptors. Berlin, Pergamon Press (1971) in press.

Baxter J. D. & Tomkins G. M.: Proc. Nat. Acad. Sci. U. S. A. 65 (1970) 709.

Bruchovsky N. & Wilson J. D.: J. biol. Chem. 243 (1968) 2012.

Bryson M. J. & Sweat M. L.: Endocrinology 81 (1967) 729.

Bryson M. J. & Sweat M. L.: Endocrinology 84 (1969) 1071.

Burton A. F.: Endocrinology 77 (1965) 325.

Chamberlain J., Jagarinec N. & Ofner P.: Biochem. J. 99 (1966) 610.

Crabbe J. In: The sodium retaining action of aldosterone, Arscia, Brussels (1963) 1.

Fanestil D. D. & Edelman I. S.: Proc. Nat. Acad. Sci. U. S. A. 56 (1966) 872.

Fang S., Anderson K. M. & Liao S.: J. biol. Chem. 244 (1969) 6584.

Farnsworth W. E.: American Endocrine Soc. 47th Meeting, New York (1965) 54.

Farnsworth W. E. & Brown J. R.: J. Amer. med. Ass. 83 (1963) 431.

Gloyna R. E. & Wilson J. D.: J. clin. Endocr. Metab. 29 (1969) 970.

Granick S. & Kappas A.: J. biol. Chem. 242 (1967) 4587.

Gurpide E.: Excerpta med. (Amst.) Internat. Congr. Ser. 184 (1969) 837.

Hooker C. W. & Forbes T. R.: Endocrinology 44 (1949a) 61.

Hooker C. W. & Forbes T. R.: Endocrinology 45 (1949b) 71.

Jaffe R. B.: Steroids 14 (1969) 483.

Jensen E. V., Jacobson H. I., Flesher J. W., Saha N. N., Gupta G. M., Smith S., Colucci V., Shiplacoff D., Newmann H. G., DeSombre E. R. & Jungblut P. W. In: Pincus G., Nakao T. and Tait J. F., Eds. Steroid Dynamics, Academic Press, New York (1966) 133.

Jutting G., Thun K. J. & Kuss E.: European J. Biochem. 2 (1967) 146.

Kato T. & Horton R.: J. clin. Endocr. Metab. 28 (1968) 1160.

Kochakian C. D. In: Mosettig E., Ed. Proc. 4th Internat. Congr. Biochemistry, Vol. 4. Pergamon Press, London (1959) 196.

Kowarski A., Shalf J. & Migeon C. J.: J. biol. Chem. 244 (1969) 5269.

Lasnitzki I.: J. Nat. Cancer Inst. 35 (1965) 339 and 1001.

MacCartney J. C. & Thomas G. H.: J. Endocr. 43 (1969) 247.

Mainwaring W. I. P. In: Griffiths K.. Ed. Some aspects of the aetiology and biochemistry of prostatic cancer. Cardiff (1970) in press.

Milgrom E. & Baulieu E. E.: Endocrinology 87 (1970a) 276.

Milgrom E. & Baulieu E. E.: Biochem. Biophys. Res. Comm. 40 (1970b) 723.

Milgrom E., Atger M. & Baulieu E. E.: Steroids 16 (1970c) 741.

Morgan M. D. & Wilson J. D.: J. biol. Chem. 245 (1970) 3781.

Munck A. & Brinck-Johnsen T.: J. biol. Chem. 243 (1969) 5556.

Ofner P.: Vitam. and Horm. 26 (1968) 237.

O'Malley B., McGuire W. L., Kohler P. O. & Korenman S. G.: Recent Progr. Hormone Res. 25 (1969) 105.

Rao B. R. & Wiest W. G.: Excerpta med. (Amst.) Internat. Congr. Ser. 210 (1970) Abstr. No. 314.

Robel P., Lasnitzki I. & Baulieu E. E.: Biochimie (Paris) (1971) in press.

Schaumburg B. P. & Bojesen E.: Biochim. biophys. Acta (Amst.) 170 (1968) 172.

Sharp G. W., Komack C. L. & Leaf A.: J. clin. Invest. 45 (1966) 450.

Shimizaki J., Kurihara H., Ito Y. & Shida K.: Gunma J. Med. Sci. 14 (1965) 326.

Sholiton L. J. & Werk E. E.: Acta endocr. (Kbh.) 61 (1969) 641.

Siiteri P. K. & Wilson J. D.: J. clin. Invest. 49 (1970) 1737.

Tait J. F. & Burstein S. In: Pincus G., Thimann K. V. & Astwood E. B., Eds. The Hormones, Vol. 5 (1964) 441. Academic Press, New York.

Talalay P. & Williams-Ashman H. G.: Recent Progr. Hormone Res. *16* (1960) 1.

Villee C. A. & Hagerman D. D.: J. biol. Chem. *234* (1959) 2031.

Wichmann K.: Acta endocr. (Kbh.) Suppl. *116* (1967).

Wiest W. G.: Endocrinology *73* (1963) 310.

Wiest W. G.: Endocrinology *87* (1970) 43.

DISCUSSION

Ryan: You were saying that the *3β* compound was bound to the so called microsomal fraction. Could you define this in operational terms? Is is bound to ribosomes? Did you subfractionate the microsomes?

Robel: Not yet.

Ryan: How did you prepare it?

Robel: The microsomal fraction was prepared by classical centrifugation procedures (*Robel et al.* 1971), then rehomogenized in buffer containing the radioactive compound and incubated for two hours at 0°C. Then the microsomes were sedimented again and the radioactivity in the pellet measured. Sephadex G 25 column chromatography was done to insure that all the radioactivity in the microsomal pellet was indeed bound.

Lerner: Do you have any data concerning the steroid content of the calf serum you used? Was it from a female or a male? Finally, if there are any steroids, how do you get rid of them?

Robel: Unfortunately, that calf serum was from a commercial source, and I cannot tell you if it was from male or female; in a few experiments, the serum of an old mare was used, and we didn't find any significant differences between the two. Moreover – and this fits well with what Dr. Gurpide told us – we have found that using testosterone concentration in a very wide range (from 10^{-5} to 10^{-10} M) does not change significantly the metabolic pattern of testosterone after 24 hours culture. So, we don't think that the presence of steroids in the serum plays a significant role in metabolic studies. Moreover, in morphological studies, we had to use very high concentrations of hormone, much above the physiological range, which shows that the culture system is not completely satisfactory, for many reasons. Thus, the presence of normal amounts of testosterone in calf serum does not play an important role in our opinion.

Nakane: Concerning 3β-diol, how did you determine the dose? Is this the minimum dose that will give the response of hypersecretion, or is it way beyond the minimum level?

Robel: The doses were the same for all three compounds; they were chosen according to Lasnitzki's previous experiments with testosterone. These are not exactly the minimal effective doses, since the smallest one we currently use is 1 μg of steroid for 1 ml of culture medium, and we can also obtain a clear response with 0.5 μg, but the minimal effective dose – we checked that also – was not different from one compound to another. Moreover, we have tried to compare the results with those of *in vivo* experiments *in situ*. For that purpose, a solution of testosterone or of a metabolite was injected inside the lumen of a seminal vesicle completely regressed 2 to 3 weeks after castration. Here, again, we found that dihydrotestosterone was slightly more active than testosterone, and that the 3β-diol compared very well with testosterone as regards the height of the epithelium and the secretion. The minimal effective dose was about 0.1 μg of steroid, when the morphological effect was studied two days after a single injection.

Nakane: The reason why I asked the question was that I was wondering if it was a toxic dose. It has been found in many tissues that when a sublethal dose of the toxic material is given, the tissues usually respond rather quickly by acute hypersecretion shortly after the exposure. This has been shown in plasma cells with X days, and in synthesis of basement membranes with physical as well as chemical agents (*Pierce & Nakane* 1969).

Robel: With the highest dose of 3β-diol used, only 80 % of the alveoli showed secretion, so 20 % did not hypersecrete and the »toxic« effect was not a general one. However, if the concentration of steroid is raised to, let's say 5 times the highest dose reported, clear toxic effects and even necrosis of the culture may occur.

Lunenfeld: Could one speculate on a correlation between an observed response and the cellular site of the target receptor?

Robel: Thank you for your question. If I could answer it, I would be glad. But in fact, that is what we try to study further.

Martini: Is there any known effect of the 3β-diol compound on the central nervous system? We have found that the brain is able to transform testosterone into dihydrotestosterone and into the 3β-hydroxy compound. But I do not know of any effect of this compound on sexual behaviour, feedback mechanisms, etc.

Robel: The 3β-androstanediol is almost inactive in most *in vivo* experiments, at least in the classical androgenic bioassays. This can be explained by the results of *in vivo* experiments carried out in man by *Mauvais-Jarvis* and coworkers (1970) with radioactive 3β-diol, which show that this compound is readily converted to other compounds, including conjugates. So it may not get easily to target tissues. However, *Nikkari* (personal communication) has done some *in vivo* experiments concerning serum production in rat, and in that test it seems that 3β-diol is a very active compound.

Martini: The reason why I was asking was because also the anterior pituitary is secreting something.

Robel: I am speaking of external secretion.

Sato: Do you have any idea as to why dispersed cultures do not work? Are the reductases missing?

Robel: Steroid metabolism should occur. There is no reason to doubt it. But not even dihydrotestosterone is active in the few attempts that have been done to study the isolated cell responsiveness.

Ryan: Dr. Robel, I would like to ask a question about terminology, because you have included the word »prehormone« in your paper. Emmens described a prehormone as a substance which was inactive locally in contrast to a hormone which was active locally. In his classical experiments, the prehormones were active only at doses in which they were active systemically, while the true hormones were active locally. I am afraid that we are going to have our terminology confused if you start calling testosterone a prehormone.

Robel: Yes, you are right, we have not demonstrated that testosterone is inactive. We must find conditions where testosterone is no longer metabolized by responsive tissue, where dihydrotestosterone is still active, and then check testosterone activity.

References:

Mauvais-Jarvis P., Guillemant S., Corvol P., Floch H. H. & Bardou L.: Steroids *16* (1970) 173.
Pierce G. B. & Nakane P. K.: Lab. Invest. *21* (1969) 27.
Robel P., Lasnitzki I. & Baulieu E. E.: Biochimie (1971) in press.

Department of Animal Science and Division of Biological Sciences,
Cornell University, Ithaca, New York, U. S. A.

SURVIVAL AND GONADOTROPHIN RESPONSIVENESS
OF LUTEAL CELLS IN VITRO

By

William Hansel

ABSTRACT

Simplified methods for incubating luteal tissues have been developed.
Progesterone biosynthesis in washed, minced bovine luteal tissue is
stimulated by added bovine LH. The response is linear in the range
2–200 ng added LH per ml of medium. The use of covariance analysis
to correct for differences in time elapsing between mincing the tissue
and the beginning of incubation reduces the standard error of the mean
and results in marked improvement in the indices of precision. Progesterone biosynthesis in washed, minced bovine luteal tissues appears
specific for LH; no other pituitary hormones give a response, and the
response is completely negated by adding anti-bovine LH serum to the
incubation medium. Prior treatment of cattle from which the incubated
corpora lutea are obtained with various levels of human chorionic
gonadotrophin, results in greatly increased luteal tissue weights. However, this tissue has a markedly reduced sensitivity to LH added *in vitro*.
No conclusive evidence was found for a feedback inhibition of progesterone on its own synthesis in this system. The incubation system developed
is sensitive enough to serve as a bioassay for LH in biological tissues and
fluids. Preliminary data suggest that a simplified protein binding assay
can be successfully used to measure the progestins synthesized by minced,
washed bovine luteal tissue in response to added bovine LH.

Suarez Soto & Legault Démare demonstrated in 1960 that incubated slices of
rat ovarian tissue were able to synthesize progesterone, and that this synthesis
could be stimulated by addition of pregnant mare serum (PMS) to the in-

cubation medium. *Duncan et al.* also showed in 1960 that porcine luteal tissue slices synthesized progesterone *in vitro*, and these reports were soon followed by similar ones for species in which luteal tissue is readily separable from the remainder of the ovary. These include, among others, the cow (*Savard et al.* 1965; *Seifart & Hansel* 1965; *Armstrong & Black* 1966), the rabbit (*Armstrong* 1966), human (*Rice et al.* 1964) and opossum (*Cook & Nalbandov* 1968). The system has been used to investigate steroidogenic pathways in several species (*Hellig & Savard* 1966; *Wilks et al.* 1970), to study the site and mode of action of luteinizing hormone (LH) in several species (*Savard et al.* 1969; *Armstrong* 1968), to study the influence of endometrial tissue on luteal steroidogenesis (*Duncan et al.* 1961), and as a possible basis for a LH bioassay (*Moody & Hansel* 1969). The method continues to attract attention, perhaps because of its simplicity and relatively high repeatability when the techniques are satisfactorily established within a laboratory.

It is important, at the outset, to establish certain definitions. The term »total progesterone«, as used here, refers to the mean mass of progesterone as determined spectrophotometrically, or by other methods, in both the tissue and medium in any treatment group. »Basal progesterone biosynthesis« is the difference between the means of the incubated control and unincubated control groups. »Net progesterone biosynthesis« represents the difference between the means of any treatment group and the unincubated control group. »LH stimulated progesterone biosynthesis« is the difference between the means of an incubated luteinizing hormone treated group and the incubated control group.

METHODS

Basic incubation techniques

Since most incubation work has been done with bovine luteal tissue, the basic techniques used in our laboratory for bovine tissue will be described in some detail, and adaptations for tissues from other species will be described as appropriate.

1) *Collection of luteal tissue for incubation*

Corpora lutea are removed manually from the ovaries of normally cycling cattle on days 10–12 of the oestrous cycle (day 0 = oestrus) through an incision in the anterior wall of the vagina dorsolateral to the cervix, as described by *Casida* (1963). Care should be taken to avoid damaging the corpus luteum by exerting too much pressure on it in dislodging it from the ovary. This technique is rapid, simple, and ensures a degree of uniformity of the tissues

296

being studied. Corpora lutea collected at this stage of the cycle usually weigh 4 to 6 g. Corpora lutea with central cysts larger than 1 cm are discarded. Animals may be used repeatedly, although normally at least one normal oestrous cycle is allowed to intervene between successive collections of luteal tissue from the same animal.

Luteal tissue collected from pregnant animals, or animals at other stages of the cycle may be used, but the amount of tissue obtainable and its limited response to LH are limiting factors at earlier stages of the cycle, and the tissue loses its ability to respond to exogenous gonadotrophin by day 18 or 19 of the cycle (*Armstrong & Black* 1966).

Some investigators have used tissue obtained from slaughtered animals, and such tissue can prove satisfactory if it is quickly removed from the slaughtered animal. *Bowerman & Melampy* (1962) have shown that considerable conversion of progesterone to 20β-hydroxypregn-4-en-3-one (20β-ol) occurs in tissue left in the carcasses of slaughtered cattle for periods of 30 minutes or more; conversion is less rapid in luteal tissue removed from the animal and allowed to stand in Krebs-Ringer bicarbonate buffer in the laboratory at room temperature for similar periods of time. *Armstrong & Black* (1966) showed that there is a great reduction in synthetic capacity if the tissue is maintained anaerobically at body temperature for 30 minutes.

Obviously, the risks involved in collecting material from commercial abattoirs are great, since many cattle are slaughtered because of infertility, and the time required to remove the tissue to a suitable laboratory for incubation is often longer than desirable. When it is necessary to use slaughterhouse material it is probably advisable to obtain luteal tissue from pregnant animals. The stage of pregnancy can be accurately dated by crown-rump measurements of the foetus as described by *Gjesdal* (1969).

2) *Preparation and incubation of minced luteal tissue*

After collection, the corpus luteum is rinsed three times with chilled physiological saline to remove blood. After removal to a nearby laboratory, it is carefully trimmed of extraneous tissue and as much of the connective tissue as possible. This procedure requires 2–5 minutes. The corpus luteum is then quartered, placed on a sheet of dental wax and minced with a new single edge razor blade until particles less than 1 mm in diameter are obtained (*Moody & Hansel* 1969). The minced tissue is swirled in a 300 ml beaker containing 200 ml chilled saline, allowed to settle and the supernatant poured off. This process is repeated 4 additional times to ensure removal of substances released from the minced tissue that inhibit LH-stimulated progesterone synthesis. The supernatant saline should appear clear at the end of the washing process. Mincing effectively reduces the variation due to tissue sampling and allows the use of smaller amounts of tissue in each incubation flask. The tissue is kept in chilled saline, except during the actual mincing process, which is carried out as quickly as possible.

The minced tissue is quickly weighed on a Roller-Smith balance and weights per sample flask are adjusted to within a 10 mg range. The minced tissue samples (usually in the weight range of 75–200 mg) are placed in 25 ml Erlenmeyer flasks containing 5 ml Krebs-Ringer bicarbonate buffer. Routinely, the buffer contains 2 mg glucose/ml and 30 m moles nicotinamide, and has a pH between 7.15 and 7.55 (*Seifart & Hansel* 1968). Amounts of LH, usually ranging from 1 to 200 ng/ml, are added to appropriate sample flasks. Each flask is flushed for 10 seconds with a stream of 95 % O_2 : 5 % CO_2, stoppered, placed in a Dubnoff metabolic shaker, and the time recorded. The entire process, from removal of the corpus luteum from the animal to the beginning of incubation should be carried out in less than 1 h. A typical experimental outline is shown in Table 1. Each sample is incubated its own 2 h period at 37.5°C; at the end of this period the incubation is terminated by placing the samples on dry ice. Samples are stored at –20°C until analyzed for progesterone.

3) *Preparation and incubation of sliced tissue*

Sliced luteal tissues from rats, rabbits, cattle, sheep, humans, pigs and opossums (see *Moody & Hansel* 1969) have been studied. We normally produce heavily luteinized rat ovaries for slicing by giving intact, immature female rats single sc injections of pregnant mare serum (50 IU, Ayerst) at 29 days of age, followed 60 h later by single sc injections of human chorionic gonadotrophin (25 IU, Ayerst). The rats are sacrificed at 36 days of age and the ovaries sliced as described below for incubation studies.

Table 1.

Basic experimental design of *in vitro* luteal tissue progesterone biosynthesis experiments.

Treatment	n	Description
		No *in vitro* treatment. Represents initial
Unincubated control	3	progesterone content of the corpus luteum
Incubated control	5	Incubated in buffer
LH Standard I (8 ng)	5	Incubated in buffer with low level LH
LH standard II (80 ng)	5	Incubated in buffer with high level LH
Unknown (Serum X)		
Level I	5	0.5 ml serum plus 4.5 ml buffer
Level II	5	Undiluted serum (5 ml)

We normally utilize Dutch Belted rabbits sacrificed on day 11 of pseudo-pregnancy as a source of rabbit luteal tissue. The rabbit corpora lutea are dissected from the ovary before use. Where necessary, luteal tissue from several rabbits are pooled before random distribution into incubation flasks; this is not necessary in the case of ewe, cow or pig corpora lutea since these glands are relatively large and easily removed from the remainder of the ovary.

In earlier studies tissue was sliced with a Stadie-Riggs hand microtome shimmed with aluminum foil to give slices approximately 50 μm thick. These slices were incubated under continuous gas flow (*Seifart & Hansel* 1968). However, the slicing technique described by *Armstrong & Greep* (1962) is simpler and faster, and it is unnecessary to maintain continuous gas flow.

The corpus luteum is sliced into 4 sections resembling segments of an orange. Each segment is then sliced laterally beginning at one end. The tissue is held against a sheet of dental wax beneath a thick microscope slide and sliced along the edge of the slide with a stainless steel razor blade. Slices approximately 50 μm thick are randomized and placed in 20 ml beakers containing 10 ml of chilled saline. The beakers are numbered one more than needed for the samples in any experiment; the tissue in the extra beaker is used to adjust each sample to within a 10 mg weight range. The randomized tissue samples are then removed from the beaker, blotted dry on filter paper, quickly weighed and placed in 25 ml Erlenmeyer flasks containing 5 ml Krebs-Ringer bicarbonate buffer. The flasks are then flushed for 10 s with 95 %/0 O_2 : 5 %/0 CO_2, stoppered, put on a Dubnoff metabolic shaker and the time recorded. Each flask is then incubated for exactly 2 h at 37.5°C.

4) Addition of precursors, stimulatory hormones and blocking agents

An almost infinite variety of experiments testing the effects of compounds that block steroidogenesis at various levels both *in vitro* and *in vivo,* the effects of gonadotrophins, cyclic 3'5' AMP and other stimulatory compounds, and the effects of adding various labelled steroid precursors have been carried out. Normally, these compounds are added to the complete incubation medium prior to addition of the minced or sliced tissue.

A concentrated bovine LH (NIH-LH-B5) solution (25 μg LH/ml) in saline is prepared. Three ml aliquots of this solution are placed in individual vials and frozen at −20°C. These vials are thawed and the necessary dilutions for LH standards made on the day each incubation is carried out. Normally, these frozen aliquots are not retained for longer than 3 months.

Steroids are added to the incubation medium by first adsorbing them to bovine serum albumin as described by *Fuller & Hansel* (1970). The required amount of steroid is dissolved in ethanol, which is adsorbed on filter paper. The filter paper is then dried and immersed overnight at room temperature in a 0.5 % bovine serum albumin solution. The steroid is adsorbed almost quantitatively (97 %) by the albumin, which is then added to the incubation medium in the required amounts. Water soluble compounds such as acetate, mevalonate (the Na-salt of D,L mevalonic acid) and inhibitors, such as amino-glutethimide phosphate, are added directly to the Krebs-Ringer bicarbonate incubation medium. Some authors (see *Savard et al.* 1969) have used proteins, such as albumin, and detergents, such as Tween 80, to increase the solubility of cholesterol in the incubation medium.

5) *Progesterone analysis*

[4-^{14}C] Progesterone (0.002 μCi) is added to each incubation flask prior to thawing and to three counting vials. The radioactivity of each sample is later compared with the mean activity in the three counting vials, and the progesterone measured is corrected for 100 % recovery. The thawed contents of each incubation flask are poured into 250 ml round bottom flasks and refluxed with 50 ml 95 % ethanol for 45 minutes, followed by a second refluxing with 30 ml 95 % ethanol for 30 minutes. Care is taken to rinse the incubation flasks and reflux with ethanol. The ethanol extracts are filtered through Whatman No. 1 filter paper and dried with the aid of a vacuum rotor in a water bath at 60°C. The dried extracts are transferred to centrifuge tubes with three rinses of 3 ml ethyl ether. The ether is dried under a stream of nitrogen in a warm sand bath and the extract is concentrated on the bottom of each tube by successive rinses, and evaporations of 1.0, 1.0, and 0.5 ml ethyl ether.

Thin layer chromatography (TLC) is carried out in two single dimensional systems. In the first of these, 20 $\times$ 20 cm glass chromatography plates are coated with a 0.5 mm slurry of silica gel G, containing 2.5 mg fluorescent zinc silicate per g of silica gel. The plates are air dried, heated to 120–125°C for 45 min, and stored in a double doored oven at 37°C until used. Four samples and a standard are spotted in separate lanes on each plate. The plate is chromatographed in hexane:ethyl acetate (5:2). This solvent system carries most of the pigments to the top of the plate, while moving the progesterone less than 2 cm from the origin. These plates are then dried and placed in a tank containing benzene:ethyl acetate (3:1). This system moves the progesterone 1/3 to 1/2 way up the plate. These plates are then viewed under ultra-violet light and the progesterone spots are identified, marked and scraped onto weighing paper. The silica gel is then transferred to a centrifuge tube and the progesterone extracted from it by adding 3 ml of ether, shaking, centrifuging the silica gel, and decanting into a clean test tube three times. The ether extract is taken to dryness and concentrated as described above.

The sample is then spotted on a second chromatography plate on which the silica gel is spread at a thickness of 0.25 mm. Again, 4 samples and one standard are spotted on each plate which is developed in a tank of isopropyl ether:ethyl acetate (5:2). The spots are again observed under ultraviolet light, marked, scraped from the plate, and weighed. Silica gel blanks for the samples are taken from the same R_F as the progesterone spots, and the weight of the silica gel is adjusted to equal that of the samples, so as to nullify any ultra-violet absorbance eluted from the silica gel itself.

The samples are taken up in 0.3 to 0.5 ml of benzene:methylene chloride (1:1) for spotting on the first (thick) silica gel plate. Since the sample at this point contains considerable pigmented material, the spots are allowed to dif-fuse to about 2.5–3 cm in diameter. Each sample tube is carefully rinsed with about 0.2 ml of benzene:ethylene chloride, which is transferred to the plate. The samples for the second (0.25 mm) silica gel plate are taken up in benzene:methylene chloride (1:1) in amounts of 0.2, 0.1 and 0.1 ml; in this case, care is taken that the spots are kept smaller than 1 cm in diameter.

Progesterone is quantitated by ultraviolet absorption with a Beckman DB spectrophotometer, or an instrument of similar capabilities. Equal volumes of redistilled absolute ethanol are added to the sample and its blank. Both are shaken on a vortex mixer, and centrifuged for 2 min. The supernatant is transferred to 1 ml cuvettes, and ultraviolet absorbance recorded for the dif-ference between blank and sample at 225, 230, 240, 250 and 255 mμ. The sample is transferred again to the original test tube which is sealed with para-film to prevent evaporation.

A 0.5 ml aliquot of the sample, pipetted into a counting vial, is evaporated to dryness, and 10 ml of counting fluid (4 g PPO + 0.1 g POPOP/1000 ml toluene) is added. Radioactivity is measured on an appropriate liquid scintilla-tion spectrometer.

To minimize the influence of ultraviolet absorbancy by non-specific conta-minants, an Allen factor (*Allen* 1950) is calculated by:

$$O.D._{240} - \frac{O.D._{225} + O.D._{255}}{2}.$$

The concentration of progesterone/ml in each sample is then determined from a standard curve established for pure progesterone. The progesterone sample is corrected for dilution, and expressed as progesterone per sample. The progesterone value is then corrected by use of the recovery factor determined by liquid scintillation counting and expressed as corrected progesterone/sample, and, finally as corrected micrograms progesterone/g of luteal tissue.

Occasionally, it is desirable to measure the progesterone in small aliquots of either the medium or the extract of the medium and tissue. Since ultraviolet absorption techniques usually lack the necessary sensitivity for these measure-ments, it is necessary to use gas liquid chromatography (GLC) techniques such as described by *Kazama & Hansel* (1970), or *Lukaszewska & Hansel* (1970).

301

When GLC measurements are to be made it is advisable to carry out the second TLC step outlined above in benzene and ethyl acetate (3:2).

6) *Statistical analysis of incubation data*

Most incubation experiments have been carried out according to the design shown in Table 1, or some modification of it. Statistical analysis of the standard curve, bioassay data, potency estimates and confidence limits are calculated according to *Finney* (1964). Lambda values are calculated by the method of *Gaddum* (cited by *Bliss* 1952).

It has been found that the elapsed time from completion of the mincing until the samples are put on the incubator is of critical importance (*Moody & Hansel* 1969). The last samples put on the incubator synthesize considerably less progesterone than the first samples. Therefore, it is necessary to correct the data for this time effect by covariance analysis, as outlined by *Steel & Torrey* (1960). An example of this is shown in Table 2.

Table 2.

Total progesterone concentration after two-hour incubation of a washed mince preparation (data are corrected for the time effect by covariance analysis).

Sample no.	ng LH/ml medium	Time incubation started	Progesterone μg/g tissue			
			Before time correction	Mean	Covariance corrected	Mean
1	0	11:02	92		92	
2		11:10	96		100	
3		11:17	83		90	
4		11:27	85		97	
5		11:35	77	87 ± 3.4	93	94 ± 1.8
6	1.6	11:04	98		99	
7		11:11	100		106	
8		11:19	92		103	
9		11:29	87		104	
10		11:38	78	91 ± 4.0	100	102 ± 1.3
11	16	11:06	137		141	
12		11:13	135		147	
13		11:20	130		149	
14		11:30	121		151	
15		11:41	99	124 ± 6.9	141	146 ± 2.1
16	160	11:07	181		190	
17		11:14	157		178	
18		11:23	138		174	
19		11:33	127		180	
20		11:44	115	144 ± 11.6	187	182 ± 3.0

Determination of »progestin« biosynthesis by protein binding assay

Luteal tissue is collected, prepared and incubated in 22 ml vials, as described above for minced tissue, and frozen on dry ice. The incubation vials are allowed to thaw overnight in a refrigerator. The vials are then brought to room temperature and homogenized in a Ten Broeck tissue grinder. The contents of the tissue grinder are then transferred back to the incubation vials, using 1.0 ml of distilled water to rinse and transfer. Ten ml of hexane, or petroleum ether (30–60°C), as described by *Johansson* (1970) are added to each vial, which is shaken on a horizontal shaker for 30 min. Aliquots of the solvent (approx. 50–200 μl, depending on amount of tissue used in the incubation) are transferred to protein binding assay (PBA) tubes, using a Hamilton syringe. The tubes are allowed to dry overnight and PBA assays are carried out as described by *Johansson* (1970). The »total progestin« values obtained are corrected for time by covariance analysis as described above.

RESULTS AND DISCUSSION

Factors affecting LH stimulated progesterone biosynthesis in incubated luteal tissue

Early studies by *Savard and co-workers* (1965) and *Seifart & Hansel* (1968), among others, established the basic conditions necessary for successful incubation of bovine luteal tissue. It is clear from these studies that incubations carried out over a 4 hour period have few advantages over 2 hour incubations. The effect of time of incubation on progesterone synthesis is shown in Fig. 1. Progesterone synthesis does not plateau at the end of two hours, but the index of precision is decreased in longer incubations due to increased within group variation, a reduced slope, or a combination of these factors. However, there is some indication that longer incubation times may make it possible to distinguish the effects of lower levels of added LH because of the increased progesterone synthesis with time.

These studies clearly indicate that the addition of nicotinamide to the incubation medium increases progesterone synthesis, probably by maintaining the integrity of the pyridine nucleotides. All workers are also in agreement that the addition of NADPH$_2$ to the incubation medium results in a consistent stimulation of progesterone synthesis, even in tissue that is already maximally stimulated with LH. In our experience, good progesterone synthesis has usually not been obtained in the experiments in which more than one hour elapses between the time the luteal tissue is removed from the animal and the time it is placed in incubation.

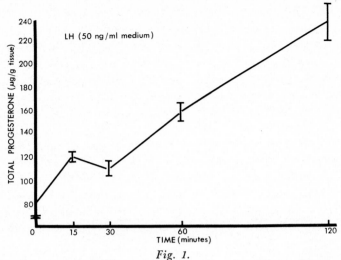

Fig. 1.

Effect of time on LH stimulated luteal tissue progesterone biosynthesis.

Our work (*Hansel & Seifart* 1967) also indicates that progesterone synthesis by bovine luteal tissue represents a specific response to bovine LH. Evidence for this statement may be found in Fig. 2, from which it may be seen that FSH, TSH, ACTH, STH and prolactin failed to evoke a significant response, and that the response obtained by adding all six anterior pituitary hormones was not different from that resulting from the addition of LH alone. The addition of higher levels of TSH gave a response in some experiments but this was probably due to the LH present as a contaminant in the TSH preparation used. Table 3 (*Snook,* unpublished data) shows that as little as 0.0025 ml of an anti-LH serum prepared in mares against bovine LH effectively overcomes the stimulatory effect of 0.5 μg of bovine LH when both are included in the incubation medium. This result provides further evidence of the specificity of the response.

The studies of *Seifart & Hansel* (1968) indicated that differences in initial progesterone content of the individual luteal tissue slices accounted for approximately 45 % of the total variation observed in the response. Thus, it became important to reduce the variability resulting from tissue inhomogeneity. The findings of *Moody & Hansel* (1969) that minced tissue can be used if it is thoroughly washed, resulted in a considerable reduction in the error variance of the response. The additional finding of the beneficial effects of correction for time effects by covariance analysis further reduced the within-group variation in the data, and made it possible to carry out incubations in which

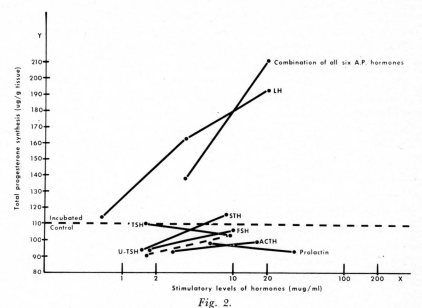

Fig. 2.

Influence of anterior pituitary hormones individually and in combination
on progesterone synthesis *in vitro*.

Table 3.

The effect of antibovine LH on the stimulation of *in vitro* progesterone synthesis by
bovine LH in bovine corpus luteum slices[1].

Treatment	Number of Replicates	Dose of LH (μg)	Dose of Antiserum (ml)	Progesterone synthesized μg/g tissue
Non-incubated Controls	2	None	None	56.74 ± 0.21
Incubated Controls	5	None	None	125.51 ± 7.82
NIH-LH-B3	5	0.5 μg	None	164.96 ± 3.73[2]
Antibovine LH + NIH-LH-B3	5	0.5 μg	.005	123.98 ± 9.89[3]
Antibovine LH + NIH-LH-B3	5	0.5 μg	.0025	129.15 ± 6.99[3]

[1] The antiserum was incubated with the LH for one hour at 37°C and then allowed
to stand overnight in the cold room. The antiserum and LH, or LH alone were incubated as described in the text.

[2] Significantly different from incubated controls. $P < 0.01$.

[3] Not significantly different from incubated controls.

305

the index of precision (λ) was greatly improved. In some trials, this correction reduced λ values from about 0.65 to about 0.15. Covariance analysis is also useful in removing within group variation from data obtained with sliced preparations (see Table 4).

These procedures made it possible to conduct incubations with smaller tissue weights per flask. However, it was felt desirable to study the possibility of increasing the amount of luteal tissue available from each animal by stimulating corpus luteum growth by treatment with human chorionic gonadotrophin (HCG). This is desirable since more tissue can be used per flask to reduce the error due to sampling, and more samples can be obtained from one corpus luteum. However, a series of experiments (*Moody* 1968) in which levels of HCG ranging from 5 to 15 000 IU were administered to Holstein heifers at various times during the first 9 days of the oestrous cycle (see Table 5) illustrated that, although corpora lutea weighing as much as 16.4 g could be produced in this way, the tissue lost a great deal of its sensitivity to LH added *in vitro*. An example of the response obtained with luteal tissue from HCG treated animals is shown in Table 6, from which it may be seen that the tissue did not respond at all to the 10 ng/ml level of LH, and only minimally to the 100 ng level. The lowered sensitivity and the relatively flat dose response curve obtained with tissue from HCG treated animals may result from depletion of the steroidogenic precursors necessary for LH stimulated progesterone biosynthesis. Several observations suggest that luteal progesterone synthesis *in vitro* is closely related to endogenous substrate and variations in the pool size of immediate precursors for steroid hormone formation. If it is assumed that only the immediate precursors, perhaps some reactive form of cholesterol, are susceptible to LH, then the degree of stimulation and the amount of variability seen in progesterone synthesis are dictated by the size of these precursor pools.

Table 4.

Correction for time effect in a luteal tissue slice preparation by covariance analysis.

ng LH/ml medium	Total Progesterone μg/g Tissue	
	Uncorrected	Covariance corrected
1.6	169 ± 4.8	181 ± 2.4
16.0	206 ± 8.8	235 ± 1.0
160.0	270 ± 8.0	292 ± 5.1
	= 0.343	= 0.128

Table 5.

Schedule of *in vivo* pretreatments of heifers with HCG, HCG plus oestradiol, or oestradiol alone.

Experiment	Day of Oestrous Cycle												Corpora lutea weights g
	0	1	2	3	4	5	6	7	8	9	10	11[1]	
					HCG 10³ IU								
P22	0	1	1	1	2	2	2	2	0	0	0	0	7.2
P24	0	1	1	1	2	3	3	4	0	0	0	0	16.4
P25	0	1	2	3	3	2	1	1	0	0	0	0	10.8
P27	0	1	1	1	2	4	1	1	0	0	0	0	6.2
P29	0	0	0	1	2	2	3	2	1	0	0	E[2]	7.1
P36	0	0	0	0	0	0	0	0	5	0	0	0	7.1
P37	0	0	0	0	0	0	0	0	0	5	0	0	8.1
P41	0	0	0	0	0	0	5	0	0	0	0	E[2]	12.1

[1] All corpora were removed on day 11 except in experiment P29 in which the corpus was removed on day 12.

[2] Oestradiol (3 mg) was given 9 hours before removal of the corpus luteum. In experiment P41, the 3 mg oestradiol treatment was replaced with 2 mg.

We have not been able to find good evidence that progesterone exerts an end product inhibition on its own synthesis in this system. *Seifart & Hansel* (1968) attempted to elucidate this question by calculating an intraclass correlation coefficient between tissue weight and progesterone synthesized per gram of tissue within several levels of LH treatment. One hundred and sixty

Table 6.

Total progesterone after two-hour incubation of luteal tissue slices from heifer pretreated with 15 000 IU HCG.

ng LH/ml medium	n	Total Progesterone μg/g tissue
0 (unincubated control)	5	84
0 (incubated control)	5	196
1	5	192
10	5	180
100	5	213

six pairs of observations from 12 individual experiments were allotted to 15 different levels of LH ranging from 0.6 to 150 ng/ml. Progesterone values were expressed as net synthesis to eliminate between experiment variation. The correlation between the two parameters was calculated within levels for the entire population. If a feedback existed, it should have been reflected in a negative correlation between weight of tissue and steroid synthesized per gram of tissue. The calculated correlation coefficient, however, was found to be –0.15, which is statistically non-significant. Thus, feedback inhibition of progesterone did not seem to play an important role in the experiments studied. However, in one more recent experiment (*Moody & Hansel* 1969) in which washed minced tissue was used and the data corrected for time effect by covariance analysis, it was possible to show that more progesterone was synthesized by a low tissue weight group (75 mg) than by a high tissue weight group (185 mg) when each was treated with 160 ng of LH (see Table 7). This

Table 7.

Washed minced luteal tissue progesterone biosynthesis with two tissue weights and two levels of LH (data corrected for time effect by covariance analysis).

ng LH/ml medium	Average tissue weight (mg)	n	Progesterone μg/g tissue		
			Total	Net	LH stimulated
0 (unincubated control)	187	2	103	–	–
0 (incubated control)	184	5	213	110	–
16	184	5	271	168	58
160	186	5	326	223	113
0 (unincubated control)	74	2	100	–	–
0 (incubated control)	75	5	203	103	–
16	76	5	275	175	72
160	74	5	380	380	177[a]

	Regression analysis		
	F value for regression	Regression coefficient	Index of precision (λ)
Tissue weight (185)	40.04***	55.6	0.282
Tissue weight (75)	77.20***	105.2	0.198

*** $P < 0.005$.

[a] Synthesized more progesterone than the corresponding high tissue weight group ($P < 0.005$).

result suggests the possibility of a feedback inhibition. It should also be pointed out that *Ichii et al.* (1963) demonstrated an inhibition of side chain cleavage reaction of cholesterol when progesterone was added to incubations of acetone extracts of extranuclear fractions from bovine corpora lutea. However, data obtained from cell-free preparations such as this, are probably not transferable to conditions in the intact cell.

If end product inhibition is, indeed an important factor limiting progesterone synthesis in these preparations, the use of superfusion techniques such as those described by *Tait et al.* (1970) might have a distinct advantage. However, preliminary work in our laboratory suggests that the progesterone produced in washed minced bovine luteal tissue preparations undergoing superfusion is not markedly greater than that obtained by the incubation techniques described (see Addendum).

Attempts to use in vitro progesterone synthesis as a bioassay for LH

It has long been the goal of those working with luteal tissue incubations to develop a bioassay for LH sufficiently sensitive to accurately measure the levels of LH in peripheral blood and in other biological tissues and fluids. We have been particularly interested in this prospect, since it would enable us to measure blood levels of bovine LH with a preparation utilizing bovine tissues. The development of successful immunoassays for LH have only served to heighten our interest in developing a bioassay, so that values obtained by the two methods may be compared.

The initial studies (*Seifart* 1968) showed clearly the applicability of the *in vitro* bioassay for biological materials. Table 8 shows the results obtained in a bioassay of anterior pituitary glands from cows killed at different stages of the oestrous cycle. The potency estimates of the glands taken at the various stages of the cycle are shown in Table 9. Analysis of the data by the methods of *Finney* (1964) for parallel line assays showed that the regression of all four pituitary extracts and the standards were highly significant and linear. Moreover, all five regression lines were parallel, indicating that no interactions existed. The mean index of precision of the combined assay was 0.50. These values agree well with those which have been obtained in our laboratory, and others for LH potencies of bovine pituitaries at these stages of the cycle.

The data in Table 3 show that the addition of as little as 0.0025 ml of LH antiserum completely inhibits the stimulation of progesterone synthesis by exogenous LH, and results in values not significantly different from those obtained with LH free Krebs-Ringer buffer. Thus, the conclusion appears justified that Krebs-Ringer buffer can be used as a zero level control medium.

Several attempts have been made to apply the improved techniques of tissue mincing and incubation to actual measurements of LH in serum in peripheral blood obtained from cattle. The results of one such attempt are shown in

309

Table 8.

Experimental design and results of bioassay of anterior pituitary glands from heifers at different stages of the oestrous cycle.

	Final dilution factor in pituitary extracts assayed	Volume of extract employed for assay (ml)	Total progesterone (μg/g tissue)
Incubated control:			139.6
Standards:			
1 mμg LH/ml			154.7
5 mμg LH/ml			200.3
25 mμg LH/ml			220.5
125 mμg LH/ml			233.2
Pituitaries:			
Oestrus	2.84×10^4	1	161.4
		5	185.6
Day 8	8.03×10^5	1	147.6
		5	183.6
Day 16	4.24×10^5	1	146.5
		5	185.9
Day 19	4.20×10^5	1	202.0
		5	250.2

Table 10. Serum from a bull calf was assayed for LH concentration by a parallel line bioassay technique. Analyses of variance and potency estimations calculated as outlined by *Finney* (1964) are shown in Table 10. The analysis gave a highly significant regression and showed no evidence of lack of parallelism. The potency was estimated at 27.3 ng LH/ml of serum (95 % confidence limits = 12.4–59.2). An unsuccessful attempt at hypophysectomy

Table 9.

Potency estimates of bovine pituitary glands from different stages of the oestrous cycle expressed as μg NIH-LH-B2/mg dried tissue.

Day of cycle	Potency	Standard error
0	10.65	± 2.17
7	3.07	± 2.21
16	3.41	± 1.93
19	4.20	± 2.03

Table 10.

Experimental design and results of *in vitro* bioassay of serum from
a hypophysectomized bull calf.

	n	Total progesterone Uncorrected for time (μg/g tissue)	Covariance corrected for time (μg/g tissue)
Controls: (KR)			
Unincubated	2	96	–
Incubated	5	139	–
Standards: (KR)			
1.6 ng/ml medium	5	159	189
160 ng/ml medium	5	239	268
Serum: (Hypophysectomized calf)			
5 ml serum	5	216	237
1 ml serum + 4 ml KR	5	189	–
0.5 ml serum + 4.5 ml KR	5	174	200

of this calf had been made. When its blood was concentrated by an ethanol
acetone precipitation procedure and assayed for LH by the ovarian ascorbic
acid depletion (OAAD) technique of *Parlow* (1958), an estimate of 40 ng of
LH/ml of plasma was obtained (*Varian et al.* 1967).

These results and others, not specifically cited, indicate that the method
may have sufficient sensitivity, specificity and precision to serve as a bioassay
for bovine LH. The system has the added advantage that it is based upon a
normal physiological function of the bovine corpus luteum, *i. e.*, synthesis of
progesterone and its induction by LH.

However, the methodology involved, especially the methods for isolating
and measuring the progesterone synthesized, are time consuming and limit the
number of assays that can be carried out. Application of the rapid protein
binding assay techniques to measure the »progestins« produced, as outlined
above, may eliminate this problem. The incubations themselves are rather
simple to carry out. *Concannon,* working in our laboratory (unpublished data)
has carried out several experiments to test this possibility and it appears
(Fig. 3) that a linear dose response curve can be obtained by simply measuring
the »progestins« synthesized in the incubation by a protein binding assay carried out on whole extracts of the incubated tissue and medium. Further studies
to test this possibility are being carried out.

Table 11.
Analysis of variance and potency estimation for serum from a partially hypophysectomized bull calf (*Finney* 1952).

Adjustment for mean		99,045		
Nature of variation	df	Sum of sqs.	Mean square	F
Preparation	1	541	541	2.98
Regression	1	18,896	18,896	104.14**
Parallelism	1	9	9	0.05
Between doses	3	19,408		
Error (within dose)	16	2,903	181.44	
Total	19	22,311		

ACKNOWLEDGMENTS

The author gratefully acknowledges the help of Mr. Raymond Saatman in developing the techniques described and in carrying them out. E. L. Moody, K. H. Seifart, P. W. Concannon, R. B. Snook, J. W. Wilks and G. B. Fuller have all helped to collect the data cited and their cooperation is gratefully acknowledged.

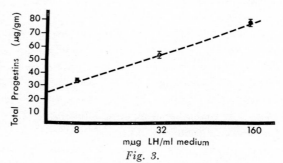

Fig. 3.
Log-dose response curve for »total progestins« as determined by the rapid protein binding assay of a hexane extract of minced bovine luteal tissue incubated with several levels of LH.

Table 12.

Progestin synthesis in superfused minced bovine luteal tissues in response to
two levels of LH added to the perfusate.

	Progestin »secreted« into the medium (μg/g/h)		
Min of incubation	Control buffer	100 ng/LH/ml	1 μg LH/ml
10	6.0	6.6	5.5
20	6.6	6.3	7.0
30	5.1	5.6	6.9
LH added			
40	4.6	6.1	7.0
50	4.6	6.1	6.2
60	4.9	6.4	7.6
78	4.5	5.4	7.8
80	4.1	5.4	7.6
90	4.1	6.1	8.0
100	4.1	6.4	8.3
110	4.1	6.5	8.7
120	4.2	6.7	8.9
130	4.1	7.0	9.6
140	4.1	7.5	9.4
150	4.1	9.2	11.0
160	4.1	7.8	10.1
170	4.1	8.1	9.5
180	4.2	7.8	10.9
190	4.2	8.1	10.3
200	4.2	8.1	10.4
210	4.1	8.1	10.6
220	4.1	8.8	11.4
230	4.1	8.8	11.9
240	4.1	8.8	12.6

REFERENCES

Allen W. M.: J. clin. Endocr. *10* (1950) 71.
Armstrong D. T.: J. Reprod. Fertil. Suppl. *1* (1966) 101.
Armstrong D. T.: Recent Progr. Hormone Res. *24* (1968) 255.
Armstrong D. T. & Greep R. O.: Endocrinology *70* (1962) 701.
Armstrong D. T. & Black D. L.: Endocrinology *78* (1966) 937.
Bliss C. I.: The Statistics of Bioassay, Academic Press Inc., New York (1952).
Bowerman A. M. & Melampy R. M.: Proc. Soc. exp. Biol. Med. *109* (1962) 45.
Casida L. E.: Techniques and Procedures in Animal Production Research, American
Society of Animal Science, 1963, p. 108.

Cook B. & Nalbandov A. V.: J. Reprod. Fertil. *15* (1968) 267.
Duncan G. W., Bowerman A. M., Hearn W. R. & Melampy R. M.: Proc. Soc. exp. Biol. Med. *104* (1960) 17.
Duncan G. W., Bowerman A. M., Anderson L. L., Hearn W. R. & Melampy R. M.: Endocrinology *68* (1961) 199.
Finney D. J.: 2nd Ed. Statistical Methods in Biological Assay, Hafner Publishing Co., New York (1964).
Fuller G. B. & Hansel W.: Proc. Soc. exp. Biol. Med. (in press) 1971.
Gjesdal F.: Acta vet. scand. *10* (1969) 197.
Hansel W. & Seifart K.: J. Dairy Sci. *50* (1967) 1948.
Hellig H. R. & Savard K.: Biochemistry (Wash.) *5* (1966) 2944.
Ichii S., Forchielli E. & Dorfman R. I.: Steroids *2* (1963) 631.
Johansson E. D. R.: Acta endocr. (Kbh.) Suppl. *147* (1970) 188.
Kazama D. T. & Hansel W.: Endocrinology *86* (1970) 1252.
Legault Démare, Mauleon J. P. & Suarez Soto M.: Acta endocr. (Kbh.) *34* (1960) 163.
Lukaszewska J. & Hansel W.: Endocrinology *86* (1970) 261.
Moody E. L.: An *In Vitro* Bioassay for Luteinizing Hormone Based on Progesterone Biosynthesis by Bovine Luteal Tissue Slices, Cornell University Thesis (1968).
Moody E. L. & Hansel W.: Endocrinology *84* (1969) 451.
Parlow A. E.: Fed. Proc. *17* (1958) 402.
Rice B. F., Hammerstein J. & Savard K.: J. clin. Endocr. *24* (1964) 606.
Savard K., Marsh J. M. & Rice B. F.: Recent Progr. Hormone Res. *21* (1965) 285.
Savard K., LeMaire W. & Kumari L.: McKerns K. W., Ed. The Gonads, Meredith Corp., New York (1969) 119.
Seifart K. H.: An Attempt to Develop an *In Vitro* Bioassay for Pituitary Luteinizing Hormone, Cornell University Thesis (1968).
Seifart K. H. & Hansel W.: Fed. Proc. *24* (1965) 320.
Seifart K. H. & Hansel W.: Endocrinology *82* (1968) 232.
Steel R. G. P. & Torrey J. H.: Principles and Procedures of Statistics. McGraw-Hill Book Co. Inc., New York (1960).
Suarez Soto J. & Legault Démare J.: Acta endocr. (Kbh.) *33* (1960) 444.
Tait S. A. S., Schulster D., Okaimoto M., Flood C. & Tait J. F.: Endocrinology *86* (1970) 360.
Varian N. B., Henricks D. M. & Melampy R. M.: J. Animal Sci. *26* (1967) 1496.
Wilks J. W., Fuller G. B. & Hansel W.: Endocrinology *87* (1970) 581.

ADDENDUM

In further studies with superfusion techniques, the progestins »secreted« per unit of time into the perfusion medium by luteal tissue subjected to several treatments have been measured by the rapid protein binding assay method. In the technique we have developed, Krebs-Ringer bicarbonate buffer, prepared and gassed as previously described, is pumped through cylindrical glass chambers containing the washed minced bovine luteal tissue at a rate of 0.25 ml/min. Sixteen samples are superfused simultaneously by using a multichannel peristaltic pump (Harvard Apparatus Model 1203). Perfusates are collected at 10 min intervals, frozen and later analyzed for progesterone.

The stimulatory effect of two levels of LH in this system is illustrated in Table 12. The LH was added to the superfusion medium after incubation for 30 minutes in the control buffer. Each figure in Table 12 represents the mean of duplicate determinations. LH was removed from the perfusion fluid supplying one member of each pair during the interval 60–120 min. Interestingly, the response was not diminished by removing LH during this period of time. As a very rough approximation, the »secretion« shown in Table 12 represents about 10 per cent of the normal *in vivo* progesterone secretion rate for a cow at the 10th day of the oestrous cycle.

DISCUSSION

Diczfalusy: Did I understand correctly, Dr. Hansel, that you find that your estimates of LH, using the *in vitro* assay with progesterone formation as the endpoint, give lower estimates of LH than the immunoassays, or *vice versa?*

Hansel: No, the reverse seems to be the case. However, these results must be viewed with caution, since relatively few bioassays have been done, in contrast to immunoassays which are being done routinely. For example, data in the slide I passed over rather quickly showed a level of 27 ng/ml of plasma in a young bull. A comparable figure measured by immunoassay might be in the range of 2 to 10 ng/ml. LH levels in bulls seem to fluctuate quite a bit from day to day. Cows have very high plasma LH levels at the beginning of oestrus. These peaks, which last only about 5 hours, may be as high as 50 ng/ml. Progesterone apparently feeds back to inhibit LH secretion in the cow, and rising levels of oestrogen may trigger the LH peak seen at oestrus.

Diczfalusy: Is the same standard used in both assays?

Hansel: Yes.

Hamberger: I should like to add some information concerning the metabolic effects in the superovulated rat corpus luteum, where we did not get a very pronounced dose response effect following the addition of LH. We have made similar experiments, using the same type of buffer and the same range of LH concentrations, and we get effects *in vitro* on both glucose uptake and lactic acid production. Even there we find that the slope of the dose response curve is not very steep. We also performed experiments in which we hypophysectomized animals after pretreatment with PMS and HCG, because we got the idea that we might increase the response in that way, but we were not successful. We got exactly the same results when the hypophysectomies were performed 5–7 days after the HCG injection.

My second point concerns TSH. I think it was reported by *Major & Armstrong* (1968) that they got a remarkable increase in glucose uptake and lactate production in prepubertal rat ovaries by TSH *in vitro* and we get it too. If we compare with the OAAD tests, we get about ten times as pronounced a response as you would expect from these tests, using the NIH preparations. We have also treated these preparations with urea, and we cannot get rid of the effect. So, maybe the effect by TSH, which is showing the same type of slope as that of LH, is not just due to a contamination, but to an effect of TSH itself on these parameters.

Hansel: I think our results are similar as far as the performance of luteal tissue from HCG treated animals is concerned. Turning to the TSH data, I think we must be a bit careful in interpreting the effects of urea treatment, since it may not inactivate all of the LH in a given TSH preparation.

Hamberger: According to Armstrong's data and to ours, it is exactly ten times higher contamination, and we get exactly the same increase compared with the OAAD tests with the TSH preparation, so it fits nicely.

Martini: A good way out would probably be to neutralize the LH with an antiserum against LH and to see whether the effect is still there afterwards. Can you not neutralize the effect with an anti-LH antiserum?

Hansel: One of the slides showed that anti-LH (0.0025 ml of antiserum) completely neutralized the effect of 0.5 μg of LH. However, we have not studied the effect of adding anti-LH to any of the TSH preparations.

Kohler: I wonder if you have tried any modifications of the LH in this system, such as the removal of the carbohydrate. Here is a bioassay system where the metabolic clearance differs from the situation *in vivo.* We have set up *Channing*'s granulosa cell system to look at this problem with HCG (*Channing* 1970). Perhaps your method would be better.

Hansel: I think this is a very good suggestion. We have not used any of the subunits of LH, but this is certainly something we hope to do, particularly now that these are pretty well characterized. I would like to comment on Channing's system, which you mentioned. It is important to remember that, in her system, we are dealing with granulosa cells that have developed in culture into something like luteal cells, and which produces progesterone.

Kohler: Channing calls the change in the granulosa cells »luteinization«. Since there is an induction of progesterone synthesis by LH or HCG, I would not characterize this as dedifferentiation.

Eshkol: On page 297 of your page, it is stated that you wash your minced tissue five times in saline, and you state that this is to »ensure removal of substances released from the minced tissue that inhibit LH-stimulated progesterone synthesis.« Could you tell us what you mean by this? What are the inhibiting substances in that tissue?

Secondly, how well do your two progesterone methods compare with each other? If we compare some of your Tables with Fig. 3, it seems as if there would be some discrepancy in the progesterone levels. An example is in Table 7, where you get with 16 ng LH per ml of medium total progesterone of about 270 ng per gram tissue, and by the protein binding assay, in Fig. 3, even with much higher concentrations of LH, you did not get the same amounts of progesterone. Could you comment on this?

Hansel: I can try. Let me take the first question. What do we mean when we say that we wash out »inhibitory substances«? We don't know the nature of these »inhibitory substances«. All we know is that if we wash until the saline is no longer cloudy, the tissue will synthesize progesterone.

Eshkol: Do you really find that you have an inhibition if you do not wash the tissue?

Hansel: Yes, they do not synthesize.

Now, how do the progesterone methods compare? As a general statement, results with gas liquid chromatography and thin layer isolation followed by spectrophotometry compare very well. Results with the protein binding method are more erratic. Concerning the relatively large differences in Figure 3 and Table 7 that you pointed out, most of the variation in the response resides in the initial progesterone content of the tissue. Even under the best of conditions the response is somewhat variable, and that is why it is important to have incubated control tissues in all experiments. It should also be noted that the values in Figure 3 are based on rapid protein binding method.

Eshkol: Did you by any chance compare the various methods for progesterone, using the same pool of tissue, so as to find out what the correlation between the two methods is?

Hansel: I can't give you a correlation figure, but agreement is fairly good between gas liquid chromatography and spectrophotometry. It is not so good between gas liquid chromatography and protein binding methods when used for progesterone in bovine blood.

Lunenfeld: Did you ever try any other protein binding methods, besides the rapid Johansson method, such as using thin layer chromatography or any other additional purification steps?

Hansel: I suspect we have tried them all. However, the data I have reported are all based on the quick method which involves no thin layer chromatography.

Lunenfeld: Did you get a better correlation when you used more specific methods?

Hansel: Generally, we did not.

Ferin: Did you add some progestational drugs to the culture medium to see if you get an inhibitory effect on the synthesis of progesterone?

Hansel: We have not used progestational drugs, but have added aminoglutethimide (an inhibitor of 20-hydroxylation of cholesterol) to rat, rabbit and bovine luteal tissue incubations (*Wilks et al.* 1970).

We are also adding fractions of a luteolytic material extracted from bovine endometrial tissues (*Lukaszewska & Hansel* 1970) to these incubations of bovine luteal tissue.

Lunenfeld: When you said »LH bound« to corpus luteum, did you mean to say that you have some evidence that LH is actually bound to corpus luteum?

Hansel: We have no direct evidence of an LH receptor in bovine luteal tissue.

References:

Channing C. P.: Recent Progr. Hormone Res. *26* (1970) 589.
Lukaszewska J. & Hansel W.: Endocrinology *86* (1970) 261.
Major P. & Armstrong D. T.: J. Endocr. *48* (1968) 73.
Wilks J. W., Fuller G. B. & Hansel W.: Endocrinology *87* (1970) 581.

Department of Obstetrics & Gynecology, Physiology, Medicine and Biochemistry,
Vanderbilt University Medical School, Nashville,
Tennessee, U. S. A. 37203

ASSESSMENT OF SEX STEROID ACTION IN VITRO

By

Anthony R. Means and Bert W. O'Malley

ABSTRACT

This review summarizes the present knowledge concerning *in vitro* effects of sex steroid hormones. Moreover, methods are described which may allow the assessment of oestrogen action on chick oviduct *in vivo* by assaying the cell free synthesis of a tissue specific protein (ovalbumin) *in vitro*.

Studies on the mechanism of action of the sex steroid hormones have become one of the most popular areas of research in both endocrinology and regulatory biology of higher organisms during the past few years. The central problem here is to define in chemically precise terms the sequence of events which are initiated by a steroid hormone upon entry into the cells of their respective target organs. This goal would be rendered considerably more accessible if *in vitro* systems were available which enabled study of the direct interaction of hormones with target cells. Unfortunately, this method of approach to the problem of steroid hormone action has met with only limited success. In the following sections we briefly review the literature concerning sex steroid action *in vitro* and finally offer data from our laboratories which were obtained utilizing *in vitro* methodology to assess the molecular action of oestrogens.

Androgen deprivation results in a marked atrophy of the male accessory genital glands. Treatment of androgen-deficient animals with testosterone results in complete restoration with regard to structure and function. In the case of the prostate, growth which follows treatment of castrate animals with androgen is the net result of hypertrophy and hyperplasia of the epithelial cells as well as formation and retention of secretory products in the glandular acini (*Williams-Ashman & Shimazaki* 1969). Available information points towards a primary nuclear site of action for testosterone following the complexing of the steroid to a cytoplasmic »receptor« protein. Interaction of the hormone-receptor complex with the genome precipitates an increase in the synthesis of RNA which in turn codes for the translation of new protein necessary for the subsequent return to normal physiological function. Much of the data supporting this sequence of events is derived from *in vivo* studies. Indeed, attempts to duplicate *in vitro* many of the known biosynthetic events occurring in the prostate in response to testosterone have been futile.

The only known function of the male accessory glands is to secrete the fluids that comprise the seminal plasma (*Mann* 1970). Citric acid is the major contribution of the ventral prostate to seminal fluid and, indeed, this organic acid has been reported to represent a sensitive and reliable indication of prostatic activity. *Farnsworth* (1967) has taken advantage of this fact in order to study some effects of testosterone *in vitro* using minces of rat ventral prostate. Incubation of the tissue with 10^{-7} M testosterone was observed to stimulate the biosynthesis of citrate from radio-labelled sodium acetate. Similarly testosterone *in vitro* enhanced the production of free fatty acids and lactate production, whereas a decrease was noted in the $[^{14}C]$ O_2 production from acetate. It was also reported that 10^{-7} M testosterone accelerated the incorporation of radioactive amino acids into proteins. These data were interpreted in a manner which suggested that increased biosynthetic activity in response to testosterone was a consequence of the facilitated removal of citric acid. Depletion of citrate would then promote a compensatory increase in the mobilization or precursors of acetyl coenzyme A to restore the normal citrate concentration. Energy derived from the increased rate of glycolysis would then be available for synthesis of lipids, proteins and nucleic acids.

Further experimentation using the system described above revealed that testosterone increased the cellular uptake of K^+ (*Farnsworth* 1968). Moreover incubation of prostate microsomes with testosterone was reported by *Farnsworth* (1968) to enhance the activity of $Na^+ - K^+$ dependent ATPase. Thus this author suggested that the androgenic regulation of prostatic growth and function might be due to metabolic pace-setting of the sodium pump. On the other hand, *Ahmed & Williams-Ashman* (1969) were unable to demonstrate an effect of testosterone *in vitro* on Na^+-K^+ ATPase activity of prostatic microsomes. Several experimental conditions were reported to have been utilized including the system of Farnsworth, but all to no avail. Injection of testosterone to orchiectomized rats, however, was effective in restoring prostatic ATPase activity to the level found in intact males. These contrasting data do not lend support to a primary action of testosterone on the Na^+-K^+-stimulated ATPase system and suggest that caution must be exercised in the interpretation of *in vivo* effects of androgen on this enzyme component of the endoplasmic reticulum of ventral prostate.

Increased production of citrate in response to testosterone *in vitro* was also demonstrated using mouse ventral prostate maintained in organ culture (*Lostroh* 1968). However, it was also shown that insulin facilitated this response to testosterone and in fact, insulin alone could maintain the level of citrate secretion for several days. Moreover insulin was required to realize a net increase in the synthesis of protein by prostate tissue. These data then raise the possibility of a permissive role for insulin in the action of androgen on prostate tissue *in vitro* and raise the question as to whether citrate synthesis is a valid criterion for assessing the action of androgenic substances *in vitro*.

Baulieu et al. (1968) have suggested that testosterone is rapidly metabolized to DHT by rat prostate tissue maintained in organ culture. Moreover it was demonstrated that both testosterone and DHT were active with regard to increasing height, secretory activity and hyperplasia of the epithelial cells. These results would indicate that further, more definitive studies concerning the mechanism of testosterone action on prostate in culture may be rewarding.

A completely different approach to the problem of *in vitro* effects on testosterone has been taken by *Sluyser* (1966*a,b*). DNA was isolated from rat tissues as was the lysine-rich histone fraction (*Sluyser* 1966*a*). DNA-histone complexes were then reconstituted and it was reported that addition of testosterone lowered the T_m of prostate histone-DNA complexes but not of combinations containing histones from other tissues (*i. e.* liver, spleen or thymus). Additional experiments revealed that the lysine-rich histones from prostate were capable of binding [3H] testosterone (*Sluyser* 1966*b*). It was suggested that prostate histones have receptor sites for testosterone. At present the significance of these observations remains unclear. Histones are known to exhibit homogeneity between organs from the same animals and even between different organisms (*Hnilica* 1967; *Delange et al.* 1969). Furthermore it is difficult to rule out the presence of some acidic nuclear protein and/or »chromosomal« RNA in the histone preparations. Again this approach does not appear to lend particular promise to the study of hormone effects *in vitro*.

Since testosterone and DHT have been demonstrated to stimulate nuclear RNA synthesis when injected *in vivo*, *Bashirelahi & Villee* (1970) investigated the effects of these androgens on RNA synthesis by nuclei isolated from prostate of orchiectomized rats. Incubation for 30 minutes in the presence of DHT resulted in an increase in the incorporation of uridine. On the other hand, testosterone had no stimulatory activity. DHT effect was demonstrable with nuclei from both immature and mature castrate rats. The authors suggested that this evidence supported the view that DHT is the active form of the hormone in prostate nuclei. Since most data indicate that testosterone (or DHT) must be bound to a cytoplasmic receptor before entering the nucleus, it is difficult to evaluate the physiological significance of a direct action of a steroid on the nucleus. Clearly more experiments of this type are in order.

PROGESTERONE

Progesterone has been demonstrated to be required for the preparation of the uterine endometrium prior to implantation of the blastocyst and is the most important steroid mediator of pregnancy (*Corner* 1947). Moreover in some species a role for progesterone has been established for alveolar development in breast tissue (*Folley & Malpress* 1948). Finally this steroid provides the specific stimulus for the production of the egg white protein, avidin, by chick oviduct (*O'Malley et al.* 1969). As was the case for androgen action the bulk of available data on actions of progestational steroids has been obtained from *in vivo* studies.

One of the few reports dealing with the *in vitro* effects of progesterone on uterine endometrium comes from the laboratory of *Nordqvist* (1970). Biopsies of human endometrium were incubated in Medium 199, and synthesis of DNA and RNA was monitored by the incorporation of [^{3}H] thymidine and [^{14}C]-uridine respectively. Addition to the medium of progesterone resulted in rapid and pronounced inhibition of both DNA and RNA synthesis. Moreover the magnitude of the steroid-induced suppression varied in endometria obtained from different stages of the menstrual cycle. Thus addition of progesterone had much less effect in tissue from uteri in the midsecretory phase of the cycle and therefore already under a strong influence of progesterone *in vivo*. Finally these responses were considered to be specific for progesterone since both oestradiol and pregnenolone were without effect.

Progesterone has also been demonstrated to exert an effect on explants of mouse mammary tissue maintained in organ culture (*Turkington & Hill* 1969). Synthesis of α lactalbumin (a whey protein) is repressed by progesterone when this steroid is added in explants of mammary glands obtained from mid-pregnancy mice. It is possible, therefore, that progesterone acts to inhibit lactose synthesis *in vivo* during pregnancy and that only at parturition when

321

plasma progesterone levels fall precipitously, can the rate of lactose synthesis increase.

To a large extent data concerning the regulation of protein synthesis by progesterone *in vivo* have been garnered utilizing the chick oviduct. Whereas oestrogen administration to immature chicks results in a marked growth and differentiation of the oviduct, a single injection of progesterone results in the induction of synthesis of the specific oviduct protein, avidin. Moreover the oviduct is a remarkably versatile model in that progesterone will not only induce production of avidin *in vivo* but is also effective in minces of oviduct and in monolayer cell culture. A typical induction curve for avidin synthesis *in vitro* is shown in Table 1. Avidin synthesis was first noted in oviduct minces at 6 h and reached a maximum between 48 and 72 h. On the other hand no demonstrable synthesis of this egg white protein was noted in cell culture until 12 h following addition of progesterone. Again maximum synthesis was observed at about 48 h.

Other oviduct proteins such as ovalbumin and lysozyme are not induced by progesterone *in vitro*. Similarly there is no stimulation of total protein synthesis as measured by the incorporation of radioactive amino acids into protein. On the other hand, avidin induction is blocked by inhibition of RNA and protein synthesis but continued DNA synthesis is apparently not required (*O'Malley* 1969). These data argue that changes in nuclear RNA metabolism may precede the synthesis and accumulation of avidin molecules *in vitro*. However, although a prior stimulation of new species of nuclear RNA has clearly been established to be the case *in vivo* following progesterone administration to immature chicks it has been very difficult to obtain similar data *in vitro*.

Table 1.
Avidin synthesis: induction by progesterone *in vitro**.

Time after addition of progesterone (h)	Oviduct mince (μg avidin/g oviduct)	Oviduct cell culture (μg avidin/culture)
0	0	0
6	0.4	0
12	1.0	0.05
24	4.0	0.50
48	5.5	0.63
72	6.0	0.69

* Avidin was measured in a 105 000 *g* supernatant fluid by the [^{14}C] biotin binding assay of *Korenman & O'Malley* (1967).

Nevertheless the induction of avidin synthesis by progesterone *in vitro* may offer a method by which to assess progestational activity. Of a wide variety of steroids tested, only those compounds with progestational activity (*i. e.* endometrial proliferation) are effective in stimulating avidin synthesis (Table 2). Furthermore the degree of progestational activity appears to be proportional to the effectiveness of a steroid to stimulate avidin production. Thus the more potent progestins such as 17-ethynyl-19-nortestosterone were more stimulatory than progesterone with respect to avidin production, whereas steroids with less progestational potency than progesterone (19-norprogesterone) were also less effective inducers of avidin (*O'Malley et al.* 1969).

OESTROGENS

As for androgens and progestins, relatively few studies have been reported which deal with *in vitro* effects of oestrogen. Most data obtained *in vitro* concerning the rat uterine model for oestrogen action have involved studies of nuclear events. *Libby* (1968) has investigated histone acetylation in a rat uterine homogenate. Addition of 17β-oestradiol at 10^{-9} M was reported to

Table 2.
Steroid specificity of the induction of avidin synthesis in oviduct mince*.

Compound	Avidin (μg/g oviduct)
None	0.00
Progesterone	1.00
17-Ethynyl-19-Nortestosterone	1.46
17-Methyl Nortestosterone	1.03
19-Norprogesterone	0.62
20α-Hydroxy-Δ^4-pregnen-3-one	0.48
Deoxycorticosterone	0.33
Testosterone	0.25
Cortisol	0.00
Dehydro*epi*androsterone	0.00
Androsterone	0.00
Pregnenolone	0.00
Oestriol	0.00
17β-Oestradiol	0.00

* Tissue was analyzed for avidin 12 h after addition of steroid. Compounds were added at a concentration of 5 μg/ml.

stimulate the incorporation of acetate into arginine-rich but not lysine-rich histone fractions. This author suggests that enhanced acetylation of histones leads to an increased template activity of uterine chromatin. Whereas such a conclusion cannot be logically supported by the above data, *Barker & Warren* (1967) have incubated oestradiol with uterine chromatin and demonstrated a stimulation in the rate of incorporation of AMP into RNA. 17α-Oestradiol was without effect and no oestrogen stimulation was noted when lung chromatin was utilized. A problem here was that a 12 h incubation was required in order to demonstrate an effect and during this time template activity of control chromatin increased 2-fold.

Another report from Warren's laboratory dealt with the effect of oestrone on RNA synthesis by isolated uterine nuclei (*Seshadri & Warren* 1969). Incubation of rat uterine nuclei with 10^{-8} to 10^{-6} M oestrone for 100 min resulted in a stimulation of the incorporation of [^{3}H]guanosine into RNA. Other substrates such as GMP, GTP or UTP did not show this response. Likewise 17β-oestradiol did not exert a stimulatory effect and tissue specificity was demonstrated by the failure of oestrone to enhance RNA synthesis by lung nuclei.

A somewhat different approach to the problem of *in vitro* effects of oestrogen was taken by *Raynaud-Jammet & Baulieu* (1969). When 17β-oestradiol was present during the preparation of calf uterine nuclei and then the nuclei were assayed for RNA polymerase activity, more RNA was synthesized than from nuclei isolated in the absence of added steroid. Moreover a stimulation of RNA synthesis was also obtained by preincubating 17β-oestradiol with uterine cytosol, then adding isolated nuclei and assaying for RNA polymerase activity. Preincubation of the oestrogen with cytosol was an absolute necessity in order to demonstrate a stimulation. Whereas these experiments were somewhat preliminary in nature, they have prompted a resurgence of studies concerned with sex steroid action *in vitro*. Modifications of such procedures may reveal valuable information in the near future.

The chick oviduct offers another model in which to study the mechanism of action of the female sex steroids. Oestrogen administration to the immature chick results in massive hypertrophy of the oviduct which is accompanied by cytodifferentiation and hyperplasia as well as by biochemical specialization (*O'Malley et al.* 1969). Studies with monolayer cell cultures of oviduct have demonstrated that addition of oestrogen *in vitro* results in some of the same changes as seen *in vivo* (*Kohler & O'Malley* 1967). Thus within 2–3 days following addition of oestrogen to the culture medium the predominant cell-type began to change from fibroblastic to epitheloid. This change was associated with increased DNA synthesis and the induction of ovalbumin production.

Chemical induction of growth in several cell types has been associated with a marked and rapid enhancement of ornithine decarboxylase activity and the subsequent intracellular accumulation of polyamines. Slices of oviduct from 6 day old chicks were placed in tissue medium and incubated for 3.5 h in the presence or absence of oestrogen (*Cohen et al.* 1970). Presence of diethylstilboestrol resulted in a 15-fold stimulation of ornithine decarboxylase activity (Table 3). Moreover cycloheximide abolished the response suggesting that protein synthesis was required for the hormone-mediated stimulation of enzyme activity. These data represent one of the few instances of an effect of oestrogen *in vitro* on synthesis of a specific protein.

Thus far we have reviewed *in vitro* effects of sex steroid hormones and it is clear that much more work needs to be directed towards this very important problem. We now turn our attention to the use of *in vitro* methods for the assessment of steroid hormone action. The ultimate demonstration of a physiologic response to a steroid hormone would be the cell-free synthesis of a specific protein in a reconstituted chemically defined system. The chick oviduct emerges as a likely candidate for such a demonstration since oestrogen treatment results in the synthesis of large quantities of the tissue-specific protein, ovalbumin.

Administration of oestrogen to the immature chick not only induces synthesis of specific proteins such as ovalbumin and lysozyme but also promotes an overall increase in oviduct protein synthesis. This increase has been demonstrated to be manifest both quantitatively (incorporation of amino acid into protein) and qualitatively (changes in the population of soluble proteins analyzed by polyacrylamide gel electrophoresis) (*O'Malley & Means* 1970).

Table 3.

Stimulation of oviduct ornithine decarboxylase by oestrogen (DES) *in vitro*.

Experimental Conditions	Enzyme Activity p moles $^{14}CO_2$/30 min/ 0.1 mg protein
Control	18
Oestrogen	329
Cycloheximide	1
Oestrogen + Cycloheximide	2

Oviducts were obtained and incubated in Medium 199 at 37°C for 3.5 h. Oestrogen (diethylstilboestrol) when present was added at the beginning of the incubation to a final concentration of 5 μg/ml. Cycloheximide was added at a final concentration of 25 μg/ml. Ornithine decarboxylase activity was measured as the release of $[^{14}C]$ CO_2 from $[^{14}C]$ ornithine as described by *Stastny & Cohen* (1970).

Moreover oestrogen brings about an increase in the synthesis of oviduct ribosomes within one day following administration to the immature chick. For at least 7 days of hormone treatment the oviduct content of ribosomes continues to increase but by 10 days has begun to decline. Concomitant with the increased synthesis of ribosomes are oestrogen-induced changes in the distribution of ribosomes and polysomes analyzed by sucrose gradient centrifugation. A large proportion of particles exist as monomers in the unstimulated oviduct. On the other hand, after 4 days treatment with DES more than 90 % of the cytoplasmic RNA particles exist as aggregates of 2 or more ribosomes.

Ribonucleoprotein preparations were tested for their ability to synthesize protein in a cell-free system. Oestrogen administration results in a doubling of incorporation activity within 24 hours. By 4 days of hormone treatment polysomal protein synthesis assayed *in vitro* reaches a maximum before beginning to decline at 7 days of oestrogen. The marked stimulation of incorporation activity at 4 days is in keeping with the striking increases in ribosome synthesis and conversion of monomers to polysomes noted at the same time. Again the decline in protein synthesis *in vitro* occurs coordinately with a decreased synthesis of ribosomes and a further shift in the polysome pattern.

Since major changes occur in the population of soluble proteins in the oviduct after oestrogen administration and since all proteins are made on cell polysomes, experiments were undertaken to determine whether qualitatively different peptides were synthesized by isolated polysomes in the cell-free system. This was accomplished by analyzing the products translated *in vitro* by polyacrylamide gel electrophoresis. Polyribosomes were incubated in the cell-free protein synthesizing system. Reactions were terminated by centrifuging the incubates at $105\,000 \times g$ in order to remove ribosomes. The resulting supernatant fluid containing newly synthesized peptides was dialyzed overnight against 2 changes of 0.1 M $NaHCO_3$ (pH 7.4). Samples were concentrated by dialysis against 75 % sucrose and applied to polyacrylamide gels. In order to minimize difference due to technique, the peptides were double-labelled, that is polyribosomes from unstimulated oviducts were incubated with [³H] valine whereas those from chicks treated for 4 days with oestrogen were labelled with [¹⁴C] valine. Following incubation these preparations were pooled and carried through the remaining procedures together. Electrophoresis was carried out for 2.3 h and gels were then fractionated and radioactivity determined by liquid scintillation spectrometry. Differences were apparent between 0 and 4 days of DES when corrected cpm were plotted (Fig. 1 A). In order to clarify differences, the ratio of corrected ³H cpm to ¹⁴C cpm was plotted and these data can be seen in Fig. 1 B. The ratio of ³H to ¹⁴C at various points on the gels varies considerably thus demonstrating that striking changes occur in the population of peptides synthesized *in vitro* before and after

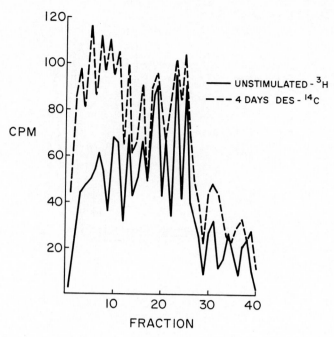

Fig. 1 A.

Electrophoretograms of peptides synthesized by oviduct polysomes *in vitro* at 0 and 4 days of DES treatment. Peptides were double labelled as follows: polyribosomes from unstimulated chicks were incubated in the complete cell-free system (*Means et al.* 1969) with [³H] valine and those from 4 day DES-treated animals were incubated with [¹⁴C] valine. Following incubation at 37°C for 30 min the samples were pooled and carried through the remaining procedures together as described in the text. Samples were analyzed on 10 % polyacrylamide gels at a running pH of 10.2. Gels were fractionated and radioactivity of each fraction was determined by liquid scintillation spectrometry under optimal conditions for double-labelling. Counting efficiencies were 26 % for ³H and 46 % for ¹⁴C with no ³H contribution to the ¹⁴C channel but with a ¹⁴C spillover of 23 % into the ³H channel. Radioactivity values were appropriately corrected before plotting. ———— ³H (unstimulated); ––––– ¹⁴C (4 days DES).

oestrogen treatment. Moreover similar differences in the peptides synthesized by unstimulated and DES-treated polysomes were observed when the isotopes were reversed. That is, when [¹⁴C] valine was used with polysomes from un-stimulated oviducts and 4 day DES-treated polysomes were labelled with [³H] valine.

In order to demonstrate the reliability of the interpretation of the data presented in Fig. 1, a similar double label experiment was performed utilizing only polysomes from 4-day treated chicks (labelling one batch with ¹⁴C and

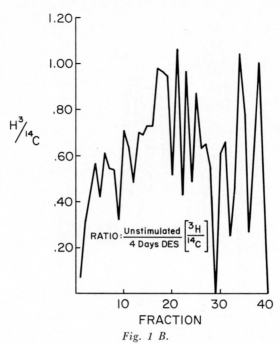

Fig. 1 B.

Ratio ³H/¹⁴C for each fraction of the electrophoretogram presented in Fig. 1 A.

one with ³H). Fig. 2 shows that in this case the ratio of ³H to ¹⁴C is nearly constant varying only between 0.69 and 0.73. Furthermore concomitant measurements of protease and ribonuclease activity before and after oestrogen treatment revealed no demonstrable changes. Therefore we attribute these changes in the peptides synthesized *in vitro* to reflect earlier changes in hormone-induced synthesis of new populations of target tissue messenger RNA.

Only about 25–35 % of the acid-insoluble radioactivity was released from the ribosomes following incubation in the cell-free system. In order to demonstrate that the soluble radioactivity was present as completed tissue proteins, it was necessary to determine the nature of these peptides. Ovalbumin comprises approximately 60 % of the total oviduct protein in chicks treated for 15 days with oestrogen. A specific antibody for ovalbumin was prepared in rabbits and reacted with dialyzed supernatant fluid obtained from the cell-free system. Table 4 shows that a time-dependent increase in antibody precipitable radioactivity accounted for 25 % of the total acid-insoluble counts present in the ribosome-free supernate. On the other hand no radioactive material precipitated with antiovalbumin if the cell-free reaction included

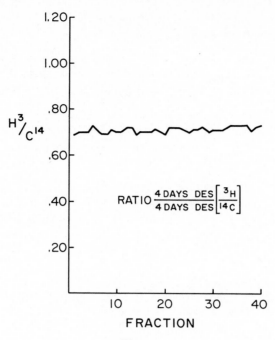

Fig. 2.

Ratio of ^{3}H/^{14}C of an experiment performed exactly as described in Fig. 1 except that both groups of polysomes (labelled with [^{14}C] valine and [^{3}H] valine) were from oviduct of 4 day DES-treated chicks.

polysomes from unstimulated oviducts. These data suggest that it is possible to demonstrate the synthesis of an oviduct-specific protein in a polysomal cell-free system. Although immunological competence cannot be taken as conclusive evidence for identity it is strongly suggestive. Furthermore, the fact that the polysomes from unstimulated oviduct fail to synthesize antibody-reacting material *in vitro* strengthens the argument since the oviduct of the unstimulated chick does not produce ovalbumin *in vivo*.

Data concerning ovalbumin synthesis reported in Table 4 do not answer the question of whether the proteins are initiated and completed *in vitro*. It is entirely possible that several partially completed ovalbumin molecules exist on the polysomes and addition of only a few amino acids are required for completion and release of the protein. In order to demonstrate the presence of an intact messenger RNA it is necessary to synthesize a specific protein *de novo*. We have therefore begun to further define the cell-free system using chick oviduct ribosomes. When polysomes from chick oviduct are resuspended in a

Table 4.
Synthesis of ovalbumin by isolated oviduct polysomes *in vitro*.

Source of polysomes	Time of incubation	Total acid-insoluble peptide released (cpm/tube)	Released peptide precipitable by antiovalbumin (cpm/tube)
15 days DES	0	0	0
	15	1465	370
	30	3035	760
	45	4470	1120
	60	6070	1500
	90	7900	1950
Unstimulated	60	2860	0
	90	3725	0

Polysomes were isolated from oviducts of unstimulated or 15 days DES-treated immature chicks and were incubated in a cell-free protein-synthesizing system as previously described (*Means et al.* 1969). Each tube contained 400 μg polysomes (as protein) and 250 μg of a pH 5 enzyme fraction. Reaction was carried out at 37°C. Following incubation samples were centrifuged at 105 000 g for 1 h to pellet ribosomes. Antiovalbumin (100 μl) was added to an aliquot (100 μl) of the resulting 105 000 g supernatant fluid as described in the text. Authentic ovalbumin (25 μg) was added as a carrier. Tubes were allowed to stand at 4°C overnight, then were centrifuged at 1000 g for 10 min. Pellets were washed twice with phosphate-buffered saline (.01 M phosphate; 0.14 M NaCl pH 7.4) and finally dissolved in 0.5 ml of NCS solubilizer (Nuclear Chicago Co.). Radioactivity was determined by liquid scintillation spectrometry at a ^{14}C counting efficiency of 88 %.

medium containing 0.24 M sucrose, 0.0001 M EDTA and 0.0001 M dithiothrietol (standard sucrose) and then made 0.5 M with respect to KCl, they lose a large part of their ability to incorporate amino acid into peptide in the complete cell-free system developed for regular polysomes. Analysis of the ribosomes on sucrose gradients reveals that by far the prevalent species is the monomer. This is illustrated in Fig. 3 where the top panel (A) represents the regular preparation of polysomes. Resuspension of polysomes in standard sucrose (Fig. 3 B) results in no demonstrable difference in relation to regular polysomes. On the other hand the addition of KCl results in a marked breakdown of the polysomes into single ribosomes (Fig. 3 C).

Three protein factors, M1, M2 and M3 have been isolated from the 0.5 M KCl wash of reticulocyte ribosomes (*Prichard et al.* 1970). These proteins have been demonstrated to be required for the initiation of globin synthesis on the

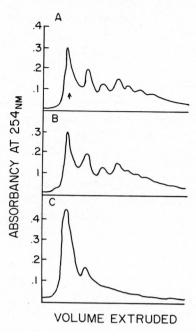

Fig. 3.

Sucrose gradient profiles of oviduct polysomes isolated from chicks treated for 15 days with DES. Polysomes were isolated by the procedure of *Means et al.* (1969). Ten A_{254nm} units of the polysomal suspensions was applied to each gradient of 12 ml (0.3–1.0 M sucrose). Centrifugation was performed for 1 h in the SW 40 Ti rotor of the Spinco L2-65B at a temperature of 2°C. Gradients were analyzed by fractionation on an ISCO Model D Gradient Fractionator which monitors continually the A_{254nm}. Direction of sedimentation is from left to right (top to bottom of the gradient) and the first peak (designated by the arrow in panel A) in panels A, B and C represents the single ribosome peak. A) Polysomes resuspended in Medium X (0.25 M sucrose, 0.035 M Tris-HCl, 0.025 M KCl, 0.005 M Cl_2, pH 7.6); B) Polysomes resuspended in Standard Sucrose; C) Polysomes resuspended in Standard Sucrose and made 0.5 M with respect to KCl.

ribosomes. Moreover in the presence of these factors the synthesis of authentic α and β globin chains have been established *in vitro*. Investigations were thus begun to show whether such factors also existed in the oviduct. As mentioned above the KCl-washed ribosomes were much less active than regular polysomes when assayed in the complete cell-free system. As can be seen from Table 5 only 400 cpm of [14C] phenylalanine were incorporated during a 20 min incubation in the presence of saturating levels of transferases and synthetases required for protein synthesis. On the other hand addition of KCl-wash to the complete system resulted in more than an 8-fold stimulation of incorporation activity (*i. e.* to 3400 cpm).

One of the peculiarities of the regular oviduct polysome system is that the addition of synthetic messenger such as polyuridylic acid failed to enhance amino acid incorporation. This observation was interpreted to mean that the polysomes were already saturated with messenger and that incubation did not result in the release of functional ribosomes, or that oviduct ribosomes were unable to bind poly U. As can be seen from Table 5 this situation does not hold for the KCl-washed ribosomes. Addition of poly U results in an increase in protein synthesis by salt washed ribosomes (*i. e.* 400 to 3000 cpm). Moreover the presence of the salt wash results in an order of magnitude in the poly U directed incorporation of [^{14}C] phe (*i. e.* 3000 to 29 000 cpm). These data show that 1) the KCl-washed ribosomes are messenger-deficient and 2) that factors present in the KCl-wash are capable of effecting a striking increase in protein synthesis.

Table 5.

Protein synthesis on salt-washed ribosomes from oviduct.

Incubation conditions	Natural message system (cpm [^{14}C] phe/mg protein)	Polyuridylic acid system (cpm [^{14}C] phe/mg protein)
Complete	400	3100
Complete + KCl-wash	3400	29 300

Polysomes were isolated from oviducts of chicks treated for 15 days with DES (*Means et al.* 1970) and resuspended in standard sucrose (0.25 M sucrose, 0.001 M dithiothrietol, 0.0001 M EDTA) to a concentration of 120 A$_{260nm}$ per ml. KCl was then added to a final concentration of 0.5 M and samples were centrifuged at 150 000 $\times$ g for 1 h. The salt-wash was decanted and stored at –120°C in 200 μl aliquots. Pellets were resuspended in standard sucrose to a final concentration of 120 A$_{260nm}$ per ml. Ribosomes (125 μg protein; 0.2 A$_{260nm}$) were incubated in the complete cell-free system for 30 min at 37°C. Concentrations of constituents in a final vol of 0.1 ml were as follows: ATP, 1.0 mM; GTP, 0.5 mM; PEP, 7.5 mM; pyruvate kinase, 1.5 IU; Mg^{+2}, 6.0 mM; K$^+$. 100 mM; thioglycerol, 10 mM; TRIS-HCl, 30 mM (pH 7.2); 19 unlabelled amino acids; 0.02 mM each; [^{14}C] phenylalanine, 0.02 mM (0.1 μCi); and pH 5 enzyme fraction, 40 μg protein. Polyuridylic acid and KCl-wash when added were present in amounts of 20 μg and 70 μg of protein respectively. Incubation was continued for 20 min at 37°C. Following the incubation period reactions were terminated by addition of 1.0 ml of 10 % trichloroacetic acid and prepared for determination of radioactivity as previously described (*Means et al.* 1969).

At present the precise nature of the stimulatory factors is unknown. Activity requires a high ionic strength (0.3–0.5 M KCl), the presence of a sulphhydral protecting agent, destroyed by heating and pronase but not by ribonuclease We are now in the process of isolating the stimulatory substances in order to determine if they are similar to the initiation factors previously reported for the reticulocyte system. Furthermore the messenger-deficient system affords us the opportunity of adding a natural messenger RNA and synthesizing an authentic tissue specific protein such as ovalbumin *in vitro*. Studies are presently underway directed towards the isolation of ovalbumin message from oviduct polysomes and identification and characterization of the protein products synthesized *in vitro* on KCl-washed ribosomes. By utilizing such a cell-free system to study protein synthesis, we may now directly examine the effects of steroid hormones on specific cellular mRNA's. Moreover we can also determine the extent of steroid-mediated regulation of translation.

ACKNOWLEDGMENTS

These investigations were supported in part by the following research grants: P-576 from American Cancer Society; HD-04473 from N. I. H. C. D.; and 630-0141A from the Ford Foundation.

REFERENCES

Ahmed K. & Williams-Ashman H. G.: Biochem. J. *113* (1969) 829.
Barker K. L. & Warren J. C.: Endocrinology *80* (1967) 536.
Bashirelaki N. & Villee C. A.: Biochim. biophys. Acta (Amst.) *202* (1970) 192.
Baulieu E.-E., Sasnitzki I. & Robel P.: Biochem. Biophys. Res. Comm. *32* (1968) 575.
Cohen S., O'Malley B. W. & Stastny M.: Science *170* (1970) 336.
Corner G. W.: The Hormones in Human Reproduction. Princeton University Press, Princeton (1947) 281.
Delange R. J., Fambrough D. M., Smith E. L. & Bonner J.: J. biol. Chem. *244* (1969) 319.
Farnsworth W.: Biochim. biophys. Acta (Amst.) *117* (1967) 247.
Farnsworth W.: Biochim. biophys. Acta (Amst.) *150* (1968) 446.
Folley S. J. & Malpress F. H. In: Pincus G. and Thimann K. V., Eds. The Hormones, Academic Press, New York (1948) 708.
Hnilica L. S.: Prog. Nucleic Acid. Res. Mol. Biol. 7 (1967) 25.
Kohler P. O. & O'Malley B. W.: Endocrinology *81* (1967) 1422.
Korenman S. G. & O'Malley B. W.: Biochim. biophys. Acta (Amst.) *140* (1967) 174.
Libby P. R.: Biochem. Biophys. Res. Comm. *31* (1968) 59.
Lostroh A. J.: Proc. Natl. Acad. Sci. (U. S.) *60* (1968) 1312.

Mann T. In: Rosemberg E. and Paulsen C. A., Eds. The Human Testis. Plenum Press, New York (1970) 469.

Means A. R., Hall P. F., Nicol L. W., Sawyer W. H. & Baker C. A.: Biochemistry 8 (1969) 1488.

Nordqvist S.: J. Endocr. 48 (1970) 17.

O'Malley B. W. In: Salhanick H. A., Kipnis D. M. & Vande Wiele R. L., Eds. Metabolic Effects of Gonadal Hormones and Contraceptive Steroids. Plenum Press, New York (1969) 339.

O'Malley B. W. & Means A. R. In: Proc. Breast Cancer Workshop, Roswell Park Memorial Institute. Chicago Press, Chicago (1970).

O'Malley B. W., McGuire W. L., Kohler P. O. & Korenman S. G.: Recent Progr. Hormone Res. 25 (1969) 105.

Prichard P. M., Gilbert J. M., Schafritz D. A. & Anderson W. F.: Nature (Lond.) 226 (1970) 511.

Raynaud-Jammet C. & Baulieu E.-E.: C. R. Acad. Sci. (Paris) 268 (1969) 3211.

Seshadri B. & Warren J. C.: Biochim. biophys. Acta (Amst.) 195 (1969) 566.

Sluyser M.: Biochem. Biophys. Res. Comm. 22 (1966a) 336.

Sluyser M.: J. Mol. Biol. 22 (1966b) 411.

Stastny M. & Cohen S.: Biochim. biophys. Acta (Amst.) 204 (1970) 578.

Turkington R. W. & Hill R. L.: Science 160 (1969) 1457.

Williams-Ashman H. G. & Shimazaki J. In: Diamond M., Ed. Perspectives in Reproduction and Sexual Behavior. Indiana University Press, Bloomington (1968) 241.

DISCUSSION

Kohler: You say that you hope that you have synthesized ovalbumin *in vitro*. You obviously didn't think the immunological criteria for purity were sufficient. Second, I wonder if you could give more information about characterization of the material in the high salt wash.

Means: It is not that I didn't like the immunological criteria. The problem is that this does not demonstrate whether you have synthesized the whole protein. It just shows that there is some material in the reaction medium, that is probably ovalbumin, but it may only have 3 or 4 terminal amino acids labelled. That is the reason for trying to go through the more sophisticated methods, to try to demonstrate that we are specifically labelling the material. Concerning the high salt wash, Dr. *John Comstock* in our laboratory is in the process of doing the same sorts of things that were done with the reticulocyte system, that is, using DEAE chromatography, Sephadex chromatography and calcium phosphate gel absorption techniques to purify these stimulatory factors. We know that they are proteins, or at least, they are inactivated by pronase, heat and N ethyl maleimide but not by RNase. They also require a minimum of 0.3 M salt for activity.

Kohler: Can you not combine your affinity chromatography with fingerprinting and answer the question now as to whether you incorporated label throughout the protein?

Means: Absolutely. That is just a long and laborious procedure. We are working on it and Dr. *Ben Leung* in our laboratory is doing a good job, but it is going to take some time.

Lee: In your polysomal cell-free system, I am sure you have tRNA in the system.

Mean: That's correct.

Lee: Have you ever tried the tRNA from oestrogen treated animals? There is a dramatic change of tRNA after oestrogen treatment (*O'Malley et al.* 1968).

Means: No, we have not. However, with the exception of that final little piece of data I just sort of threw in, this has all been done with animals stimulated for 15 days. We have not gotten to the point where we are really ready to assess changes during oestrogen action. The salt wash factors may indeed change. The tRNA certainly changes. Again, Dr. Comstock, who had been working in Dr. F. Anderson's laboratory at the NIH, has worked specifically on oviduct lysyl tRNA and showed quite dramatic differences at various times after oestrogen administration. However, the stimulatory factors in the salt wash are not destroyed by RNase.

Lee: A number of reports indicate the N-formylmethionyl-tRNA is required for initiation of protein synthesis. By any chance the protein you synthesized in the cell-free system has methionine at N-terminal end. Of course, it is possible that the methionine is clipped off after the chain initiation.

Means: That is what usually happens if it is an acetylated or cyclased amino acid. However, we really have no data on this point.

Lee: Have you tried to add the N-formylmethionyl-tRNA to your cell-free system?

Means: No, we have not.

Graham: In relation to your provocative experiment at the end, I was not quite clear what you are adding to the incubation. I think you said that it was extracted from the nucleus?

Means: That is right.

Graham: I wondered why you extracted it from the nucleus and not from the whole cell? The second part of my question is, what would happen if you added a similar fraction from the cytoplasm?

Means: The answer would be the same. First of all and best of all would be what we are attempting now. One of the fellows, Dr. Gary Rosenfeld, is working on extracting the messenger RNA off the ribosomes. If you extract from the whole cell, you have all sorts of transfer RNA and ribosomal RNAs, which would presumably mask or dilute the »message«. As controls, we purified ribosomal RNA and purified transfer RNA; they have absolutely no effect in this system.

Graham: It is just a way of cleaning up the system?

Means: That's all.

Lee: Can you tell us a little more about the stimulation in the salt wash? Is there any evidence in your hand that they are initiation factors? Are they destroyed by heat or by protease? What I am driving at is, are they proteins?

Means: We feel that they are proteins. We have not yet gone so far as to say that there are one, two or three factors. The fact that they are heat labile and inactivated by pronase or N-ethyl maleimide would so indicate. I will not commit myself by saying that these are initiating factors. I would like very much to be able to say that, but we are not yet ready.

Lunenfeld: Dr. Lee, have you any information that would help to elucidate the nature of the »initiating factor«?

Lee: No, I have no information. What interested me is the possibility that the active component in high salt wash could be tRNA. Washing ribosome with high salt solution certainly will strip off the tRNA from the ribosome.

Hansel: Dr. Means, why did you use stilboestrol and not oestradiol?

Means: It is the least expensive, most potent and longest acting of the most readily available oestrogenic substances. Similar responses can be obtained with 17β-oestradiol or any other biologically active oestrogen.

Eshkol: Since the oviducts were removed 15 days after initiation of the treatment, are you sure that the initiation of these specific polyribosomes can be ascribed to the diethyl stilboestrol, or is it a secondary effect?

Means: If we don't use oestrogen to induce differentiation of the tubular gland cells, we do not have any ovalbumin synthesized. Furthermore, it is clear that oestrogen initiates the synthesis of this substance *in vivo*. The only information that we have specifically from the *in vitro* polysome system is the fact that there is no anti-ovalbumin-precipitable material synthesized by particles isolated from unstimulated animals.

Reference:

O'Malley B. W., Aronow A., Peacock A. G. & Dingman C. W.: Science *162* (1968) 567.

National Institutes of Health, Bethesda, Maryland, U. S. A.

IN VITRO ASSAYS OF ADENYL CYCLASE

By

Martin Rodbell

ABSTRACT

A brief review of the properties and current knowledge of the components of adenyl cyclase systems in animal cells is presented, followed by some general remarks on the problems of assaying adenyl cyclase. Recent techniques developed for the assay of adenyl cyclase in broken cell preparations are described. Methods which determine the levels of cyclic 3′5′AMP in intact cells or tissues are also presented, with particular emphasis on the use of binding of the nucleotide to cyclic 3′5′AMP dependent protein kinases and radioimmunoassays of the cyclic nucleotide.

Adenyl cyclase plays a central role in mediating the actions of a variety of peptide hormones and catecholamines (*Robinson et al.* 1968). Although it has been shown by several authors (*Marsh et al.* 1966; *Franks & Stansfield* 1970) that LH stimulates the activity of the enzyme system in corpus luteum, much of our knowledge of mammalian adenyl cyclase systems stems from studies of tissues or cells other than reproductive tissues. In this paper, recent information on the properties of adenyl cyclase systems in adipose and liver cells, and description of some of the recent methods for assaying adenyl cyclase activity and levels of cyclic 3′5′AMP (cyclic AMP) will be described with the aim of supplying background information to investigators in the field of reproductive biology.

PROPERTIES OF ADENYL CYCLASE SYSTEMS

Adenyl cyclase systems are membrane-bound in all animal cells examined and have been localized in the surface or plasma membrane of liver cells (*Pohl et al.* 1969), adipose cells (*Rodbell* 1967), and red cells (*Devoren & Suther-*

337

land 1963). It is likely that adenyl cyclase is localized primarily in plasma membranes of cells sensitive to peptide hormones, which are excluded from the cell because of their size and charge. »Ghosts« of fat cells, which are sacs of plasma membrane prepared from isolated fat cells (*Rodbell* 1967), contain a single adenyl cyclase system that is activated by at least six hormones – ACTH, glucagon, secretin, LH, thyrotrophin, and catecholamines (*Birnbaumer & Rodbell* 1969; *Bär & Hechter* 1969a; *Rodbell et al.* 1970a). The six hormones act initially through sites, termed »discriminators« (*Rodbell et al.* 1970b) which selectively react with their respective hormone and which, in turn, translate this reaction into activation of adenyl cyclase. Several points of evidence, recently reviewed (*Rodbell et al.* 1970b), suggest that the discriminators are separate molecular entities from the enzyme adenyl cyclase and are localized on the outer surface of the plasma membrane where they are in direct contact with the hormones. Adenyl cyclase may be located at the inner surface where it is in contact with its substrate, ATP. Lipids, particularly phospholipids, appear also to play an important role in hormone action on the system possibly by coupling discriminator and enzyme within the membrane. The discriminator for glucagon in the plasma membrane of rat liver cells seems to be a lipoprotein since binding of glucagon to the glucagon-sensitive adenyl cyclase system in these membranes is abolished by neutral detergents and phospholipase A under conditions in which adenyl cyclase activity is unaffected (*Rodbell et al.* 1970b). It should be emphasized that isolation and characterization of the components of adenyl cyclase systems have not been accomplished.

Recent studies with the glucagon-sensitive adenyl cyclase system in rat liver membranes (*Rodbell et al.* 1970b), suggests that binding of glucagon with its discriminator converts the discriminator into a structure that regulates the activity of adenyl cyclase provided that GTP or GDP, at concentrations as low as 5 nM, are present in the system. The guanyl nucleotides act through binding at a separate site in the system from the site of binding of glucagon and cause rapid changes in the binding of the hormone as well as in the activity of adenyl cyclase. Such findings indicate that there are two regulatory sites in the glucagon-sensitive adenyl cyclase system, involving the binding respectively of glucagon and guanyl nucleotides, which are responsible for hormonal activation of adenyl cyclase. It is not known whether other hormone-sensitive adenyl cyclase systems contain similar regulatory sites for guanyl nucleotides. At least for the glucagon-sensitive system, it seems possible that factors that control the binding and actions of guanyl nucleotides on this system could play an important role in regulating the response of the target cell to its hormone at the receptor or primary site of action of the hormone. The main point of relating these findings is that regulation of adenyl cyclase activity by hormones is not a simple function of circulating hormone concentration.

Sutherland et al. (1962) were the first to establish that fluoride ion stimulates a number of adenyl cyclase systems. Fluoride ion does not activate the enzyme through the same process as hormones. For example, destruction of the binding sites for glucagon by detergent or phospholipase A treatment of liver or fat cell membranes does not alter the response of adenyl cyclase to fluoride ion (Rodbell et al. 1970b). Thus, measurement of adenyl cyclase activity in the presence of fluoride ion provides a means of assaying the enzyme independently of hormone action and even when the hormonal response has been abolished. The mode of action of fluoride ion remains obscure. Indeed, the stimulatory action of fluoride ion has been observed only in broken cell preparations containing adenyl cyclase. Fluoride ion does not increase levels of cyclic AMP in intact cells (Oye & Sutherland 1966) and does not mimic the action of hormones.

There are other factors involved in the activity and response of adenyl cyclase to hormones. Magnesium ion is required for enzyme activity (Sutherland et al. 1962); manganous ion causes selective enhancement of fluoride response in fat and liver cells (Birnbaumer et al. 1969; Pohl et al. 1971). Magnesium ion, in heart (Drummond & Duncan 1970) and in fat cell (Birnbaumer et al. 1969) adenyl cyclase systems also regulates the response of the enzyme to fluoride and hormones at site(s) separate from the catalytic site. Calcium ion inhibits adenyl cyclase activity, possibly by competing with magnesium ion at the putative regulation site (Drummond & Duncan 1970; Birnbaumer et al. 1969). Monovalent cations also affect adenyl cyclase systems. For example, potassium ion enhances the response of fat cell adenyl cyclase to ACTH (Birnbaumer et al. 1969), a hormone which requires uniquely the presence of calcium ion (10^{-6} M) for its action (Bär & Hechter 1969b; Birnbaumer & Rodbell 1969).

Some of the actions of ions on adenyl cyclase systems may reflect their effects on the structure of the microenvironment in which the enzyme system is embedded. Indeed, one of the more interesting aspects of investigating adenyl cyclase systems is that such studies may reveal as much about membrane structure as about regulation of this important enzyme system. In this regard, it should be noted that surface active agents, such as pentothiazines, affect the activity and response of a number of adenyl cyclase systems to fluoride ion and hormones (Wolff & Jones 1970).

In summary, our present knowledge of adenyl cyclase systems indicates that they are multi-component, membrane-bound systems that are influenced by their microenvironment, ions, and nucleotides. Specificity of hormone action is expressed through components that are separate from the enzyme or catalytic component, to this extent adenyl cyclase per se is not the receptor or initial site of action of hormones.

Discussion of the physiological role of cyclic AMP, the product of the reaction of adenyl cyclase with ATP, as the chemical mediator of hormone action is unnecessary; a recent, excellent review of this subject is available (*Robinson et al.* 1968). The levels of the nucleotide are controlled by the activity of adenyl cyclase and that of specific phosphodiesterases. Methyl xanthines inhibit phosphodiesterases and mimic many of the actions of hormones. *Beavo et al.* (1970) have reported that cyclic 3'5' GMP stimulates the activity of a cyclic AMP-phosphodiesterase in rat liver extracts. This finding raises the possibility that production of cyclic GMP controls the levels of cyclic AMP and thus the response of target cells to hormones. For this reason, studies of guanyl cyclase activity (*White & Aurbach* 1969; *Hardman et al.* 1969) may reveal new insights into the regulation of cyclic AMP mediated processes.

METHODOLOGY

The activity and hormonal response of adenyl cyclase have been assessed in purified membranes, homogenates, and intact cells and tissues. Before outlining some of the assay procedures used, it should be emphasized that one of the most important aspects of studying these systems is to know the cell type containing the adenyl cyclase system in question. Tissues consist of many cell types each of which may contain a separate adenyl cyclase system for each hormone acting on the tissue. A notable example of this is kidney which contains in its medullar cells a vasopressin-sensitive adenyl cyclase whereas its cortical cells contain a parathyroid hormone-sensitive system (*Chase & Aurbach* 1968). *Reik et al.* (1970), using a histochemical technique for assaying adenyl cyclase, reported that rat liver contains glucagon-sensitive adenyl cyclase systems in both reticulo-endothelial and parenchymal cells. Obviously, studies of adenyl cyclase response to glucagon in homogenates will express activities given by both cell types.

Another complication involved in studying effects of agents affecting cyclic AMP levels is exemplified by the effects of prostaglandins in rat adipose tissue compared to isolated fat cells. Prostaglandin increases cyclic AMP levels in whole tissue, but decreases the levels in isolated fat cells which is reflected both in intact tissue and isolated fat cells by a decrease response to lipolytic hormones (*Butcher & Baird* 1968). Clearly, more than one cell type is involved in the actions of prostaglandins on adipose tissue.

Measurements of adenyl cyclase in homogenates or purified membranes

In measuring adenyl cyclase activity, one is confronted with the following problems: (1) Maintenance of substrate (ATP) concentrations sufficient to provide continuous maximum rates of cyclic AMP formation; (2) Inhibition of hydrolysis of cyclic AMP by phosphodiesterases without interfering with its formation; and (3) Identification and quantitation of the cyclic nucleotide in the presence of a number of related nucleotides.

1. *Maintenance of substrate concentration.* Since membrane systems containing adenyl cyclase also contain very active ATPases, it is difficult to maintain concentrations of ATP for maximal rates of activity, particularly since most adenyl cyclase systems investigated have Michaelis constants in the range of 0.1 – 1.0 mM and utilize only a fraction of the ATP. One means is to add large concentrations of ATP (3 mM or higher). However, high concentrations of ATP have effects on the system other than as substrate (*Rodbell et al.* 1970*b*) and can alter the free magnesium ion concentration sufficiently to alter hormone response. ATP regenerating systems have been employed in a large number of studies, although our recent investigations indicate that such systems are not efficient when concentrations of ATP are below 0.5 mM. Recently, the problem of maintaining ATP concentrations, even at initial concentrations of 0.1 mM, has been solved by the use of the diphosphoimide analogue (AMP-PNP) of ATP in which nitrogen is substituted for oxygen between the terminal phosphates. AMP-PNP is only slowly hydrolyzed by nucleotide pyrophosphohydrolases in membranes, is not hydrolyzed by ATPases, and is a substrate for adenyl cyclase (*Rodbell et al.* 1971).

2. *Prevention of destruction of newly-formed cyclic AMP.* Inhibition of cyclic AMP hydrolysis by phosphodiesterases can be accomplished by the addition of methyl xanthines (*Butcher & Sutherland* 1962). However, this complicates the system since another drug has been added which may have other possible actions. If one is measuring the production of radioactive cyclic AMP, unlabelled cyclic AMP can be added during incubation as a means of impeding the destruction of the labelled material; cyclic AMP does not inhibit adenyl cyclase even at high concentrations (*Birnbaumer et al.* 1969). The only precaution with this procedure is that 5'AMP, the product of phosphodiesterase action, may be converted to ATP, thus diluting the specific activity of the labelled ATP in the assay medium.

3. *Isolation of cyclic AMP in biological samples.* The remaining and most difficult problem to overcome is the separation and quantitation of cyclic AMP from a mixture contaminated with large quantities of structurally similar compounds. If cyclic AMP is unlabelled it must not only be purified but also be assayed, either chemically or biologically. If, on the other hand, the substrate is radioactive the problems are reduced to isolating and separating the radioactive cyclic AMP from all other radioactive contaminants. The methods described below are by no means the only methods available but are selected because they are the most sensitive, are widely used, and are most applicable

341

for studies not only for adenyl cyclase activity measurements but also for determining levels of cyclic AMP produced in intact cells or tissues.

(a) *Isolation of radio-labelled cyclic AMP*. A simple, sensitive and rapid method for determining adenyl cyclase activity has been reported by *Krishna et al.* (1968). This procedure is based on the observation that with the exception of cyclic AMP, all nucleotides examined are completely precipitated with zinc sulphate and barium hydroxide solutions. After passage through Dowex 50 ion exchange columns, the cyclic AMP fraction is collected, and trace contaminants precipitated with solutions of $Ba(OH)_2$ and $ZnSO_4$. The supernatant fluid is then added to counting vials and counted in an appropriate scintillation fluid. The method is sensitive enough to determine adenyl cyclase activity in less than 1 mg of tissue or with 20 μg of isolated membrane protein, and the entire procedure can be completed in less than 3 hours. With standardization of equipment, as many as 150 samples can be assayed by one person in this time period. A complete account of the method and some of the problems encountered have been published recently (*Krishna & Birnbaumer* 1970). Applications of this method can be seen in our own work with fat cell ghosts (*Birnbaumer et al.* 1969) and liver membranes (*Pohl et al.* 1970).

(b) *Protein kinase binding assay*. *Gilman* (1970) has published a simple and rapid method for assaying cyclic AMP levels in cells or tissues. Binding of the nucleotide to cyclic AMP-specific protein kinases is employed. Preparations of protein kinases having high affinity for cyclic AMP are readily made from bovine muscle extracts and are stable when stored frozen. The method depends upon dilution of binding of ^{3}H-cyclic AMP, under equilibrium conditions, to protein kinase with cyclic AMP present in tissue extracts. The complex formed between protein kinase and the nucleotide is retained on cellulose acetate (Millipore) filters which, after washing, are counted in a scintillation counter. The method is sensitive to 0.05–0.10 pmoles of cyclic AMP. The simplicity and sensitivity of this method makes it the method of choice for assaying levels of cyclic AMP in tissues. It has not been applied for direct measurements of adenyl cyclase activity, however. In most tissue studies, interference by other cyclic nucleotides, particularly cyclic GMP, seems not to be a problem. However, the method is not absolutely specific for cyclic AMP; purification of cyclic AMP is required if high levels of cyclic GMP are present.

(c) *Radioimmunoassay of cyclic AMP*. Like the binding assay described above, radioimmunoassay of cyclic AMP depends on the binding of cyclic AMP, but in the procedure developed by *Steiner et al.* (1969) antibodies specific for cyclic AMP are employed. The advantage of this method over the protein kinase assay method is that it is even more specific for cyclic AMP, the antibodies being produced against cyclic AMP coupled covalently to proteins. The only disadvantage of this method is that it requires synthesis of the antigen and collection of sufficiently high titers of serum-containing antibodies. However, once set up it is a simple and sensitive method for assaying cyclic AMP levels in tissues or cells. The reported sensitivity is 2–40 pmoles of cyclic AMP.

Measurements of adenyl cyclase activity in tissues or cells

Because of problems of permeability of cells to ATP and losses of substrate due to breakdown and binding by other materials in intact tissues, it is not feasible to analyze adenyl cyclase activity in whole tissue or isolated cells. One approach, which circumvents the problem of adding ATP, is to allow the cells to synthesize labelled ATP from appropriately labelled precursors such as adenine and adenosine. This approach has been used successfully in fat cells (*Kuo & DeRenzo* 1969) and with slices of brain tissue (*Shimizu et al.* 1970). The labelled pool(s) of ATP are formed rapidly. After addition of hormones or other agents that stimulate cyclic AMP production, labelled cyclic AMP formed from intracellular pools of the nucleotide is isolated (the method of *Krishna et al.* (1968), described above, is normally used) and counted. This procedure does not give the quantity of cyclic AMP formed since the labelled cyclic AMP may not be formed from the total pool of ATP. Indeed, evidence from studies with brain slices indicate that only a fraction of the intracellular ATP is used in the production of cyclic AMP. Nevertheless, this approach gives information regarding the sensitivity of the adenyl cyclase system to hormones and permits an evaluation of the various factors that influence the enzyme's activity in a rapid and relatively simple manner.

Binding of labelled hormones to cell particles or membranes

Another approach to studies of adenyl cyclase systems *in vitro* is to investigate the specific binding of labelled hormones to target cell membranes. This approach is still in its initial phase but seems sufficiently provocative to report. *Lefkowitz et al.* (1970) labelled ACTH with ^{125}I and showed that the labelled ACTH binds specifically to particles prepared from homogenates of adrenal cell tumours that respond uniquely to ACTH and which have an adenyl cyclase in their membranes that is stimulated only by ACTH. Assuming that the adenyl cyclase is the unique »receptor« for ACTH, these workers have concluded that ACTH binding reflects the content of adenyl cyclase in the membranes.

A similar approach has been made with [125I] glucagon, which has been shown to bind specifically to highly purified plasma membrane preparations from rat liver (*Rodbell et al.* 1970*b*). A number of correlations were made between binding of hormone and activation of adenyl cyclase in these membranes by glucagon. From such studies it was concluded that the binding sites for glucagon represent the primary site, termed discriminator, of action of glucagon on the adenyl cyclase system in rat liver parenchymal cells. The role of guanyl nucleotides in regulating the activity and response of liver adenyl cyclase to glucagon, reported above, was derived from these binding studies.

CONCLUSION

The methodology for investigating the actions of hormones on adenyl cyclase systems is now in its well-developed stage. Each investigator will naturally choose his method of approach according to the information desired. In this brief report, an attempt has been made to provide current concepts relating to the actions of hormones on these systems. It has been evident for some time that adenyl cyclase systems provide a useful means of investigating the actions of hormones. More detailed investigations of adenyl cyclase systems in reproductive tissues, a relatively neglected subject in this steroid-oriented field, seems long overdue.

REFERENCES

Bär H. P. & Hechter O.: Proc. nat. Acad. Sci. USA *63* (1969*a*) 350.
Bär H. P. & Hechter O.: Biochim. biophys. res. comm. *35* (1969*b*) 681.
Beavo J. A., Hardman J. G. & Sutherland E. W.: J. biol. Chem. *245* (1970) 5649.
Birnbaumer L. & Rodbell M.: J. biol. Chem. *244* (1969) 3477.
Birnbaumer L., Pohl S. L. & Rodbell M.: J. biol. Chem. *244* (1969) 3468.
Butcher R. W. & Baird C. E.: J. biol. Chem. *243* (1968) 1713.
Butcheh R. W. & Sutherland E. W.: J. biol. Chem. *237* (1962) 1244.
Chase L. R. & Aurbach G. D.: Science *159* (1968) 545.
Davoren P. R. & Sutherland E. W.: J. biol. Chem. *238* (1963) 3016.
Drummond G. I. & Duncan L.: J. biol. Chem. *245* (1970) 976.
Franks D. J. & Stansfield D. A.: Biochem. J. *117* (1970) 25p.
Gilman A. G.: Proc. nat. Acad. Sci. USA *67* (1970) 305.
Hardman J. G., Davis J. W. & Sutherland E. W.: J. biol. Chem. *244* (1969) 6354.
Krishna G. & Birnbaumer L.: Anal. Biochem. *35* (1970) 393.
Krishna G., Weiss B. & Brodie B. B.: J. Pharmacol. exp. Ther. *163* (1968) 379.
Kuo J. F. & DeRenzo E. C.: J. biol. Chem. *244* (1969) 2252.
Lefkowitz R. J., Roth J., Pricer W. & Pastan I.: Proc. nat. Acad. Sci. USA *65* (1970) 745.
Marsh J. M., Butcher R. N., Savard K. & Sutherland E. W.: J. biol. Chem. *241* (1966) 5436.

Oye I. & Sutherland E. W.: Biochim. biophys. Acta (Amst.) *127* (1966) 347.

Pohl S. L., Birnbaumer L. & Rodbell M.: Science *164* (1969) 566.

Pohl S. L., Birnbaumer L. & Rodbell M.: J. biol. Chem. (1971) in press.

Reik L., Petzold G. L., Higgins J. A., Greengard P. & Barrnett R. J.: Science *168* (1970) 382.

Robinson G. A., Butcher R. W. & Sutherland E. W.: Ann. Rev. Biochem. *34* (1968) 149.

Rodbell M.: J. biol. Chem. *242* (1967) 5744.

Rodbell M., Birnbaumer L. & Pohl S. L.: J. biol. Chem. *245* (1970*a*) 718.

Rodbell M., Birnbaumer L., Pohl S. L. & Krans H. M. J. In: Luft R. & Randle P. J., Eds. Proceedings of the IV Capri Conference on Diabetes. Acta Diabetologica Latina, vol. VII. Il Ponte: Milan (1970*b*) 9.

Rodbell M., Birnbaumer L., Pohl S. L. & Krans H. M. J.: J. biol. Chem. (1971) in press.

Shimizu H., Creveling C. R. & Daly J.: Proc. nat. Acad. Sci. USA *65* (1970) 1033.

Steiner A. L.. Kipnis D., Utiger R. & Parker C. W.: Proc. nat. Acad. Sci. USA *64* (1969) 367.

Sutherland E. W., Rall T. W. & Menon T.: J. biol. Chem. *237* (1962) 1220.

White A. A. & Aurbach G. D.: Biochim. biophys. Acta (Amst.) *191* (1969) 686.

Wolff J. & Jones A. B.: Proc. nat. Acad. Sci. USA *65* (1970) 454.

DISCUSSION

Nakane: You didn't mention another approach that has been reported by *Reik et al.* (1970).

Rodbell: Unfortunately, I failed to point out in my paper that a histochemical procedure has been described for assaying the effects of hormones on adenyl cyclase in intact liver (*Reik et al.* 1970). In this procedure, blocks of liver tissue are treated with glutaraldehyde, after which they are incubated in the presence of ATP and lead nitrate, the lead being used to precipitate *in situ* pyrophosphate liberated during the reaction. The lead precipitate is subsequently visualized in osmium-fixed sections under the electron microscope. With this procedure, they report that glucagon stimulates the appearance of lead deposits on the membranes of Kupfer cells, but only slightly stimulates the appearance of the deposits in parenchymal cells. On the other hand, epinephrine, which we know has a much lower effect on the physiology of parenchymal cells than does glucagon, stimulated the appearance of lead deposits on the membranes of parenchymal cells more than did glucagon. Although I am disturbed, because of the unexpected different effects of glucagon and epinephrine on the parenchymal cells, their controls seemed adequate. The only reservation I have about this method is that we have found that glutaraldehyde used under identical conditions causes complete loss of adenyl cyclase activity in purified liver membranes.

Hamberger: If I understood you right, you consider the discriminator and the transducer as the receptor itself, and that would mean that all the hormonal effects that you have demonstrated in your slides, or more specifically, the metabolic effects of various kinds you obtain by these hormones are transmitted over this system. I think there are quite a lot of data showing that some of the effects you can obtain with

345

the hormones you cannot obtain with cyclic AMP. So, do you want to state that *all* these hormones give rise to *all* the metabolic effects you can register over this system?

Rodbell: That is a very good question. The finding that the receptors for various lipolytic hormones are separate from the enzyme that forms cyclic AMP raises the question of whether there may not be other amplifiers or enzymes in the membranes that may also receive information from the receptor and thereby generate chemical signals that modify the physiology of the cell. In other words, we must keep an open mind with regard to whether cyclic AMP is the unique mediator of the actions of hormones that stimulate adenyl cyclase activity.

Sato: Glucagon has to act on the parenchymal cell. Did the people who used the lead nitrate-glutaraldehyde procedure include GTP, which you found to be highly stimulatory in parenchymal cells? Is it possible that they would have found these granules in the right place with GTP?

Rodbell: I hadn't thought of that possibility. They only used ATP as substrate. I should have also stated that fluoride ion stimulates the appearance of lead grains in the liver.

Sato: In the Kupfer cells?

Rodbell: Yes, in both cell types. With few exceptions, fluoride ion does not stimulate the production of cyclic AMP in intact cells, possibly because it does not penetrate or traverse the membrane. Perhaps glutaraldehyde treatment permitted access of fluoride to the enzyme system.

Rochefort: Do you have any evidence of the reversibility of the binding of glucagon to the discriminator, that is, without adding GTP or without metabolism of the glucagon?

Rodbell: The apparent affinity constant of glucagon for the liver membrane discriminator is about 4×10^{-9} M. After pre-labelling the membranes with labelled glucagon, less than 5 per cent of the labelled hormone dissociates from the membrane even at 30°C. GTP or GDP, 2 M urea, phospholipase A, and various detergents cause release of the hormone. Using 2 M urea, we have found that the hormone is liberated in its active form.

Based on several considerations, it would appear that glucagon binds to the discriminator *via* hydrophobic-type forces. The C-terminal region of glucagon (residues 20–27) is intensely hydrophobic. Recently, Drs. *Bornet* and *Edelhoch* (1971) have found that certain detergents alter the structure of glucagon from a random coil to one having helical structure. At least one region of change is in the C-terminal portion of the hormone. Parathyroid hormone and thyrocalcitonin, but not ACTH, exhibit the same behaviour. We now believe that the binding of glucagon to its discriminator involves interaction between the C-terminal portion of glucagon and hydrophobic regions in the discriminator. We have also found recently that histidine (the N-terminal amino acid) in glucagon is essential for the biological activity of the hormone, whereas the C-terminal region is essential for binding. Thus, essentially the entire molecule is required for the biological activity of glucagon.

Nakane: How stable is this binding site to the glucagon? Can you freeze it? Thaw it?

Rodbell: Binding of glucagon to the discriminator is very tight. Incubation for long periods and freezing do not appear to cause dissociation of the hormone from its binding site.

Nakane: In other words, if I can label this membrane fragment, I would be able to localize the hormone at the synthetic site?

Rodbell: It should be possible with your technique to localize glucagon at its binding site in liver membranes.

References:

Bornet H. & Edelhoch H.: J. biol. Chem. *246* (1971) 459.
Reik L., Petzold G. L., Higgins J. A., Greengard P. & Barrnett R. J.: Science *168* (1970) 382.

Baulieu: There are many aspects of the techniques, methods and concepts reviewed in this meeting which deserve a sort of evaluation. This evaluation may be of interest to young and/or new investigators in reproductive biology. One can divide them into three broad categories. The *first one* concerns mostly the technical problems attached to the isolated systems already known. The *second* is somewhat more prospective, since it is to estimate the possibilities for obtaining new isolated systems, pertinent to the topic of these symposia, in other words, to the concrete problems of reproductive biology. The *third* group of problems concern, in more general terms, the concepts and advances in the understanding of regulatory mechanisms and especially of hormone action.

Technical assessment of isolated systems. Problems concerning particularly the specificity and the sensitivity of the various assays.

Eshkol: When we speak about specificity, we have to keep in mind that a protein hormone cannot be considered as one antigenic entity, but is composed of several antigenic entities. Any antiserum will, therefore, contain different antibodies against the various antigenic regions of the same molecule. This is quite evident also from the presentations which we heard here, and pertinent to them is the fact that there are systems which can detect cross reactions and others which cannot. I would like to point out particularly that immunohistochemical or immunocytochemical methods detect cells which contain and are in the process of synthesizing hormones; that means that the cells contain complete protein hormone chains and also parts of the same protein chain. Antiserum produced against an extracted hormone preparation contains also antibodies against degraded parts of the hormone molecule. Cross reactions can sometimes probably occur between fragments of the hormone and not between whole molecules, because some antigenic sites present in a certain peptide chain being synthesized, or peptide chain which has been degraded from a whole molecule, can be masked in the entire molecule. This might sound very hypothetical and theoretical, but actually is not. *Ishizaka et al.* (1960) pointed out that rabbit antisera, made against unaltered bovine serum albumin (BSA) contained antibodies to buried determinants present in pepsin degraded BSA but not in the unaltered BSA. The degree to which such antibodies, or heterogeneity of antibodies in general, will interfere with specificity depends largely on the system in which they are used.

Nakane: As I pointed out in the discussion of my paper, the age is rapidly passing when we use naturally available hormones as antigens. The majority of the anti-ACTH antigens are now made against synthetic polypeptides. When the complete sequence of the hormones becomes available, I believe that one will be able to selectively pick areas of the differences and then prepare antisera against them. Then I think the method becomes even more specific.

Lunenfeld: Dr. Nakane, do antisera raised against synthetic ACTH also react with shorter peptide chains of ACTH, or only with the entire molecule? If they react even with parts of the chain, your approach would not solve the problem.

Nakane: I am not quite sure whether it is a part or the whole molecule which is reacting. However, when one uses smaller and smaller polypeptide units, at some stage it should become non-specific as antigen and no longer be a specific immunologic system.

Robyn: Several factors contribute to the difficulties in obtaining specific antisera against the protein hormones of the pituitary and therefore in avoiding the cross reactions between STH and prolactin, between ACTH and MSH, and between LH. FSH and TSH.

Even highly purified preparations are heterogeneous. They contain molecules exhibiting, at best, similar biological activities but differing more or less in their physico-chemical and (or) antigenic properties.

The molecules of pituitary hormones naturally available have a very complex polypeptide structure with several antigenic sites. Cross reacting hormones have in common one (or several) antigenic site(s).

The heterogeneity of the hormonal preparations used for immunization is reflected by the heterogeneity of the antisera. The individual variation in the antibody production by the immunized animals is reputed to be an additional source of heterogeneity.

Another source of difficulties is the fact that protein hormones are still defined by their biological effects. Little is known about the relationship existing between the antigenic sites of such hormones and the sites responsible for their biological activity. Bioimmunoassay methods have recently been proposed to investigate this relationship (*Petrusz et al.* 1971).

The specificity of the antisera can be improved by absorption procedures using serum proteins and (or) some hormonal preparations to remove undesirable antibodies.

In radioimmunoassays, the specificity is improved by the selection of highly purified hormonal preparations for labelling with the radioisotopes. Under such conditions, the specificity of the assay is rather uninfluenced by the specificity of the antisera. However, this type of solution cannot be extended to other immunological systems.

It appears that each protein hormone of the pituitary, exhibiting a specific biological activity, possesses antigenic site(s) identical or very similar in several, if not all, mammalian species.

The use of such interspecies cross reactions seems to improve significantly the specificity of the immunological reactions (*Midgley et al.* 1971).

As indicated by Dr. Nakane, another simplification is the use of synthetic polypeptide hormones as antigens.

Sayers: A most attractive feature of the radioimmunoassay methods is their sensitivity, but lately there have been doubts in regard to the matter of specificity. I have hopes that biological assays may return to popularity. I believe that, at least with certain cell systems, sensitivity matches that of radioimmunoassay. I think it is too early yet to make a final statement, but I am encouraged to say that it looks as if the biological assays may be more specific than the radioimmunoassays.

Ryan: It is not enough just to say that assays are not specific. There are other criteria that can be applied, that would allow some appreciation for the amount of non-discrimination that occurs; immunological techniques perhaps, which can tell you how specific your antigen-antibody reactions are.

Eshkol: With respect to *in vitro* methods based on competition, like the radioimmuno-assay, specificity can be largely controlled by the use of a highly purified labelled hormone and antigenic similarity of unknown preparations can be assessed by comparing parallelism in such systems.

For identification of hormone producing cells, by immunohistochemical or immuno-cytochemical techniques, the use of antisera absorbed with soluble antigens should be avoided. Though, by such procedures, antibodies against the adsorbent proteins are removed, the residual antibodies are not well characterized. For such studies, antibodies which have been absorbed onto solid antigens (hormones) and then dissociated should be used. In such a way, antibodies which have been selected and characterized by their capacity to react with a preselected hormone population can be obtained.

Baulieu: I would like to know more precisely if one can calculate the number of reactive molecules you can pick up with different methods, as, for instance, the immuno-enzyme assay and the autoradiographic method?

Nakane: When you talk about the sensitivity of the method itself, especially for the immunochemistry, you must divide it into two different categories, one at their electron microscopic level, and another one at light microscopic level. Not only the method of detection is different, but also the level of resolution. If all these antibodies are labelled in an ideal condition, *i. e.*, no destruction of antibody activity and no destruction of label takes place, I do not think there is any difference from one method to another at an ultrastructural level. Now, at the light microscopic level you get a difficulty of detection; with the fluorescin isocyanate labelled antibody the difficulty does not lie in the fluorescence of the material, but in its background level. If you can reduce the background level to zero, then theoretically, one should be able to see two fluorescent molecules. With regard to the enzyme antibody method we have not yet in practice come upon a situation where you cannot detect with fluorescence but you can detect with enzyme, in other words, the situation is identical.

Stumpf: I am surprised to hear that you could detect two fluorescent molecules with the light microscope. In the microscopic studies of catecholamine fluorescence, the sensitivity is much lower than in autoradiography. In autoradiography it is possible to assess statistically how many molecules are represented by a silver grain, provided one knows the specific sensitivity of the emulsion, that is, how many disintegrations are necessary in order to obtain a silver grain. This has been investigated under various conditions, by a number of investigators. If one knows what the silver grain stands for, one is able to calculate, for instance, how many oestradiol molecules occupy one nucleus.

Nakane: I would like to point out that the fluorescence of catecholamines is quite different, in sensitivity, from that of immunofluorescence. In the case of the catecholamines, it is an induced chemical change with formalin, and you can vary this considerably from one specimen to another, whereas the immunofluorescence method uses a highly fluorescent compound attached to it.

Baulieu: What is the present state of affairs concerning quantitative morphology?

Haumont: I think that much research work will be improved by stereological morphometric studies. At the moment I can just say a few words about the principles of this technique.

Stereological techniques permit to evaluate quantitatively, on morphological preparations, the volumes and surfaces of different components of an organ, a tissue or a cell. Most of these techniques are based on the old principle of Delesse. They have been used by *Weibel* (*Weibel & Elias* 1967) and others for volumetric studies of lung, kidney, liver and brain cells. The technical application of the method is relatively simple, but must be adapted to each problem. For light microscopy, pieces are cut serially and the thickness of the sections is carefully controlled. The sections are taken at random, or systematically. After being treated by routine colouring techniques, they are placed on the Weibel microscope. This microscope is provided with automatic stage, each field taken again at random or following a preset program. It is projected on a mathematical grid. The grid is a square which contains 42 equidistal points and 24 equal lines in a known area. Points and intersections of lines are counted in each field for each component. The results are pooled and treated mathematically and statistically, manually in the simplest case, or better, with a computer program A more elaborate mathematical technique, useful in the study of mitochondria or other organelles, is the analysis of particles based on the study of profiles. This approach to morphological problems can give us quantitative results, and, from a description, give a real quantitative knowledge of a process with morphological techniques.

Baulieu: The use of such technology may be possible in connection with the biochemical evaluation of processes in the tissue. Maybe Dr. Milner would comment on a possible correlation between quantitative morphology and biochemical evaluation.

Milner: I agree with Dr. Haumont that morphometric studies on cellular organelles would be very useful. By combining this type of quantitative information with biochemical studies it should be possible to define more precisely the nature of the correlation between the morphology and functional activity of a cell. For example, the proliferation of the smooth endoplasmic reticulum in steroid synthesizing cells may directly affect the activity of associated enzymes (by the accommodation of an increased amount of enzyme or substrate, etc.). It is also possible that the high smooth membrane volume in these cells may serve to dilute the intracellular concentration of steroid molecules: it has been shown in other systems that steroids stabilise membrane structure and that this results in an inhibition of the functional activity of the membrane (*Hubble et al.* 1970).

Johannisson: I am sure that it would be interesting to follow the changes of the nuclear volume, for instance, after administration of different hormones. We carried out a study – and others have done similar studies – on the changes of the nuclear volume in the endometrium. There are obviously changes of the volume during the menstrual cycle. However, I think that from the light microscopic point of view, there are also other methods which can be useful in the determination of volume, for instance the technique of microinterferometry, which can be used for the estimation of mass in isolated nuclei.

Baulieu: Biochemical or biophysical determinations should be not only accurate, but also evaluated »qualitatively«, in other words, in terms of biological significance. This is the case for binding techniques (*Baulieu et al.* 1970).

Rochefort: I would like to answer Dr. Ryan's question about the choice of method to

351

measure steroid binding *in vitro*. First of all, I think a distinction should be made between the organized systems, such as cells, tissue or subcellular particles, and the soluble systems, such as a cytosol or a nuclear extract. In the organized systems, one measures the uptake or incorporation of the labelled steroid into organite but not binding. In these cases, the compartmentalization and transport across the cell membranes of hormone and/or protein increase the complexity of these systems and it is very difficult to quantitate the steroid reversibly bound to a macromolecule. Therefore, I only wish to discuss the choice of method in a soluble system.

The ideal method should be able to measure, at equilibrium, the specific and reversible complex formed between the hormone and its native cellular binding protein. So you need *first* an equilibrium technique, such as equilibrium dialysis; the charcoal adsorption technique, for instance, is not valuable in this respect, because the equilibrium is broken. *Second*, you have to distinguish between the specific and the non-specific complexes. As the purified »receptor« is not yet available, the steroid specific protein complex has to be measured in a crude extract containing several binding proteins. For this purpose, the charcoal adsorption and the Sephadex column techniques based on the principle of differential dissociation, as already described by Dr. Wira, give better results than the equilibrium dialysis. The *third point* concerns the integrity of the binding proteins, as the »receptors« are known to be very fragile. In order to prevent the denaturation or proteolysis of the specific binding protein, you can use some protective agents or work at low temperature; in addition, the choice of a very rapid measuring method might be valuable. The usual equilibrium dialysis technique is too long in reaching equilibrium, whereas the Sephadex column, the hydroxyapatite adsorption technique of *Erdos et al.* (1970) and the rapid equilibrium dialysis technique described by *Gilbert & Müller-Hill* (1967) seem valuable in this respect.

Baulieu: Development of new isolated systems. There are two correlated aspects: How to obtain good systems and how to assay the tissue or cell integrity.

Sayers: I could just briefly review the situation with regard to isolated cell preparations. I am speaking of isolated cell preparations in which the cells are prepared from organs freshly removed from the animal. Perhaps Dr. Sato will comment on the situation with regard to cultured cells. The great advantage of having free cells in suspension is elimination of problems of diffusion characteristic of the tissue slice. This is reflected in sensitivity to the trophic hormone, ACTH. Sensitivity to ACTH is increased by a factor of 10 000 by going from the adrenal slice or fragment to the isolated adrenal cell preparation. Now as to the techniques that are available for dispersion, it seems to me that that is still a matter of the state of the art. There is not much in the way of theoretical constructs from which to develop new or to improve old techniques.

Baulieu: Could I push you a little further – for instance, you test your cells for corticosteroid production and effect of ACTH. Have you tested their metabolic integrity? Could they be useful for some other purpose, for instance, metabolic events, ascorbic acid state, etc.?

Sayers: It seems to me that we already have cells of high quality. They respond to ACTH at concentrations of 10^{-13}, 10^{-12} molar. Secondly, it would seem to me an excellent system for uncovering energy sources for the secretory activity of the cells.

We must push ahead with the business of »cleaning up« the cells. I am sure that the sensitivity of isolated adrenal cells to ACTH is determined in some measure by the contamination of the isolated cell preparation with cell fragments.

Baulieu: Dr. Rodbell, could you generalize on the enzymatic procedure for obtaining cells? Is it possible at this point?

Hansel: I would like to ask another question. On the basis of what has been said here and before, everyone is attempting to develop assays, for all kinds of hormones, based on their binding to cell membranes. Is the specificity all that good? What other pitfalls are likely to be encountered? Perhaps Dr. Rodbell could best comment on this.

Rodbell: There are procedures other than enzymatic for obtaining isolated cells. In the case of the rat liver, for example, agents that deplete the tissue of potassium or calcium (perchlorate and citrate, respectively) are capable of producing »isolated cells«, although often with harmful metabolic consequences. By virtue of their specific actions, enzymes are more advantageous, provided that the enzymes do not have deleterious actions on the cell membrane. Since we have shown that trypsin can modify or destroy the receptors for various lipolytic hormones (*Rodbell et al.* 1970), its use for obtaining isolated cells must take these observations in mind. Collagenase has been used successfully for containing hormone-responsive fat cells. However, commercial collagenase contains several peptidases and possibly phospholipases which have harmful effects on the integrity of the cell membrane. *Kono* (1969) in a very elegant study, actually separated some of the enzymes from crude collagenase that are responsible for digestion of adipose tissue. Using a mixture of the purified enzymes, he was able to obtain much greater responses to insulin with isolated fat cells. I bring up these points to show that there are a number of techniques available, each of them having certain pitfalls. Isolation of cells is still in the stage of being an art rather than a science.

Concerning Dr. Hansels questions, it is still too early in the game to give definitive answers to these. To establish specificity of hormone interaction, it is necessary not only to show that a specific hormone binds to the membrane in question, but that the hormone will not bind to other membranes from cells which are known not to respond to this hormone. The latter point is to be stressed, since many of the peptide hormones have the intrinsic property of binding to many types of surfaces. For example, plastic is one of the best receptors for glucagon that I know of, which means that some caution must be used in the handling of hormones for studies of binding to membranes.

Baulieu: Steroid people have obviously the same problem. Every steroid binds to every protein.

Could somebody try to elaborate somewhat more on the selection of cells?

Sato: I have been very impressed by the range of *in vitro* systems that have been displayed here. We have covered perfused glands, freshly isolated cells, organ cultures, dispersed cell cultures, isolated membrane systems, dissociated membrane systems, etc., and each of these is contributing something. Cell culture systems offer the advantage of technical ease of handling and the retention of sufficient organization to display complicated behaviour of biological interest. They are useful for furnishing clues as how to proceed to more defined subcellular systems to get at biochemical detail. Aside from the technical ease with which culture systems can be handled, culture systems allow us to look at a few selected cells when there is a complex mixture and to put together combinations of cells to study interactions. One of the best examples of the usefulness of resolving cell mixtures comes from immunology. In this case, cloning is achieved not in cell culture, but by the induction of a tumour of gamma globulin producing cells. These myelomas produce gamma globulins with a single amino acid sequence that can be analyzed. This is a sort of advance that could be made by looking at just a few cells of a great mixture. Probably the best example of the use of cell cultures for analyzing the interactions of cell mixture comes from immunology. Immunologically competent cell cultures can be made from a mixture of cells of bone marrow origin, of thymus origin or probably stromal elements of spleen. In my own laboratory, we are looking at a few selected cell types from the great mixture found in the pituitary. Cell culture techniques enable us to select out only that cell which responds to TRF by secreting TSH. This is a necessary step for understanding the difficult action of TRF.

Baulieu: Is there anybody who would like to comment on the following question: Do you see that hybridization cell techniques could be of utility for the selection of certain new hybrids which could be of interest for the studies in which we are involved?

Graham: There was, in the past, a mistaken belief that when you fused a differentiated cell with fibroblast or »undifferentiated« cell, then the differentiated function was always lost. Recent unpublished studies have shown that differentiated function can be maintained. So, I don't think people should hesitate to use the cell fusion technique because of the initially disappointing results in maintaining differentiated function.

Rodbell: It seems from what we have heard at this meeting that a greater effort should be made to understand the process of fusion and fission of biological membranes. The actions of viruses on isolated membrane vesicles, for example, could tell us something of the nature of secretory processes which appear to involve both fusion and fission of secretory vesicle membranes.

Baulieu: I see also a great potential for studying hormone action in those systems in which there is not much success with hormone response, for instance in adult tissues *in vitro*.

Besides isolated cell systems, we have also to assess other *in vitro* systems. For instance, one may compare the perfusion system with the culture system.

Gurpide: I believe that the correct attitude is to consider that tissue slices retain all the capabilities of the tissues *in situ*, unless otherwise demonstrated. Some differences in behaviour of tissue *in vitro* and *in vivo* are due to changes in the environment rather than to cell damage. One may question, for instance, whether the need for high concentration of some drugs and hormones to elicit an *in vitro* response which can be observed *in vivo* at much lower concentration in plasma is due to a lack in the culture medium of agents which normally facilitate entry of the compounds into cells rather than to basic alterations in the incubated tissue.

Ryan: Although I have spent my life doing *in vitro* work, I don't think we ought to try to use the word »physiological« for *in vitro* studies. I don't think we should use it for tissue cultures either. We should instead try to learn what information we can obtain from these mehods and try to quantitate as much as possible, so that we can, at least, intelligently present what we are observing. I think it is foolhardy to try and say that this is physiological and something else is not, if we mean by physiological, something which is in the body and functioning in a specific way. In the organ explant, one has to use higher oxygen concentrations, for instance, and we don't know the significance of this. This does not, however, mean that the system cannot give us a tremendous amount of information which is potentially useful.

I would like to hear Dr. Lee's, and perhaps Dr. Sato's comments about tissue culture in general.

Lee: Concerning the tyrosine transaminase induction by steroids, I am not going to say that this is the primary action of steroid hormone on liver cells. But this is one of the hormone actions on the liver. The enzyme concentration is affected by the hormone, then we can ask what are the molecular events after the hormone enters the cell and before the change of the enzyme concentration. The methods developed to probe these molecular events should be of value in the assessment of similar aspects of hormone actions in a more complicated system. As far as the cell culture is concerned, we can maintain our cells viable in a serum-free medium, which contains essential amino acids, vitamins, glucose and salts for 4 to 5 days. The cells maintained under these conditions will resume growth after the addition of serum. We routinely carry out experiments with cells maintained in serum-free medium. Cultured cells can be synchronized, then we can ask what is the role of cells in different phases of the cell cycle in relation to hormone action. Hydrocortisone apparently cannot induce the transaminase in mitotic cells, while insulin can.

Baulieu: I would like a comment by Dr. Stumpf about tissue incubation experiments. The autoradiographic pattern and the amount of labelling of the nuclei, and the eventual transfer of labelling into nuclei are just similar to what is observed *in vivo*. However, we know that in this incubation system there has been, until now, no demonstration of an effect of oestrogen.

Stumpf: I just don't know why we get the binding and concentration pattern and don't get an effect. This may simply demonstrate that the localization of oestradiol in the nucleus, the biochemically assessed binding to the 8 S protein, does *not* represent the active step; nothing has happened to the receptor yet. Why not? Is energy missing to maintain the action sequence or is some component missing in the incubation fluid?

May I add something else to this – it may not contradict Dr. Ryan's remark. In general, the *in vitro* manipulation should be related to *in vivo* experiments in so far that whatever data we obtain, one should be able to correlate them in some sense. There are so many publications about data from *in vitro* studies that apparently have no meaning for *in vivo* events, and one could do all kinds of manipulations, obtain certain effects, and then determine why it is so. This is maybe a waste of resources.

Means: I think the problem of sex steroids not having any effect *in vitro* is a crucial one and that we have to find out what is going on in relation to what Dr. Stumpf just said. One system that has not been mentioned much today is the system of *O'Malley* and collaborators (*O'Malley et al.* 1970; *Sherman et al.* 1970). That is the chick oviduct progesterone binding protein. They have been able very clearly to demonstrate binding to a cytoplasmic protein and subsequent transfer into the nucleus. The nuclear receptor, or the nuclear binding protein hormone complex binds very tenaciously to chromatin, and it is species specific. Moreover, they can demonstrate that if they remove histones from the chromatin material, it still binds and the binding is specific to the acidic protein DNA complex. Furthermore, if one adds progesterone to a mince of oviduct tissue, one can demonstrate synthesis of avidin (an oviduct specific gene product). So, I think that looking at binding in a nucleus, whether by radioautography or something else, appears to reflect an action of the hormone *in vivo*.

Graham: I would like to mention a problem which was encountered while culturing one cell eggs. The necessary condition was to distil the water for the tissue culture medium at least four times, and preferably six times; and the elements of the still should be covered with glass. After one distillation, the eggs die within 12 hours and you obtain an increasing success rate up to 6 distillations. This does not only apply to mammalian eggs. The cloning efficiency of embryonic fibroblasts increases ten times, if ordinary tissue culture medium is made up with this very clean water. Many problems in *in vitro* work would disappear if people used clean water for their culture media.

Sato: I am just raising to the bait offered by Dr. Ryan. I don't think any discussion here is going to stop some reckless people from rushing to extrapolate their *in vitro* results to the *in vivo* condition. Nor do I think that anything we can say here is going to encourage some people, who are too timid to leave the whole animal, to come into more biochemical aspects of hormone action. I think that what we are going to do is rely on the good sense of the scientific community, and here I have confidence that these cases are going to be judged one by one, and good sense will prevail.

Baulieu: I believe that people are concerned with the possible generalization of the concept that hormone metabolism in target tissue may be directly implicated in hormone action.

Robel: Obviously, progesterone is the second candidate. First, progesterone is extensively metabolized in utero to 5α-reduced compounds. Moreover, recently it has been proposed that in chick oviduct nuclei, and also in rat uterus nuclei, there is a 5α-reductase which can reduce progesterone, and also the 5α-reduced metabolite of progesterone, pregnanedione, accumulates somehow in nuclei. However, the direct demonstration of such reduced compounds being active by local assays is still lacking, and I think that before such a demonstration is presented it is very difficult to accept progesterone metabolites as the active compounds. There are many arguments too, which demonstrate that progesterone is directly related to progestational activity and, for instance, the binding to receptors shows that progesterone is much more strongly bound in guinea pig cytosol receptor than its metabolites, which is the reverse in the androgen story.

Ryan: You know, it is interesting that when a new theory becomes available, everyone wants to apply that same process to other examples. These will have to be very critically evaluated with respect to the 5α-reductase which, as we know, occurs in many many tissues.

The suggestion I wanted to make, Dr. Baulieu, was that perhaps if you are going to consider a new nomenclature for testosterone, that prohormone might be appropriate. From the suggestion of Dr. Stumpf, in pharmacological nomenclature, the term prohormone, rather than prehormone, is used for a substance that is active locally, but which inside the cell is converted to another compound, that is the active species.

References:

Baulieu E. E., Raynaud J. P. & Milgrom E.: Acta endocr. (Kbh.) Suppl. 147
 64 (1970) 104.

Erdos T., Best-Belpomme M. & Bessada R.: Analyt. Biochem. *37* (1970) 244.

Gilbert W. & Müller-Hill B.: Proc. Nat. Acad. Sci. (U.S.A.) *58* (1967) 2415.

Hubble W. L., Metcalfe J. C., Metcalfe S. M. & McConnell H. M.: Biochim. biophys.
 Acta (Amst.) *219* (1970) 415.

Kono T.: J. biol. Chem. *244* (1969) 1772.

Midgley A. R., Niswender G. D., Gay V. L. & Reichert L. E.: Recent Progr. Hormone
 Res. 27 (1971) in press.

O'Malley B. W., Sherman M. R. & Toft D. O.: Proc. Nat. Acad. Sci. (U. S. A.) *67*
 (1970) 501.

Petrusz P., Diczfalusy E. & Finney D. J.: Acta endocr. (Kbh.) *67* (1971) 40.

Rodbell M., Birnbaumer L. & Pohl S. L.: J. biol. Chem. *245* (1970) 718.

Sherman M. R., Corvol P. L. & O'Malley B. W.: J. biol. Chem. *245* (1970) 6085.

Weibel E. R. & Elias H.: Quantitative Methods in Morphology, Springer Verlag,
 Berlin (1970) p. 278.

ACKNOWLEDGMENTS

For permission to reproduce original illustrative material published elsewhere the Editor is indebted to doctors

E. V. Jensen & H. I. Jacobson
P. O. Kohler & W. E. Bridson
E. Moody & W. Hansel
A. Munck, D. A. Young, K. Mazur & C. R. Wira

as well as to the Editors of

Acta physiologica scandinavica, Stockholm, Sweden
Endocrinologia Japonica, Tokyo, Japan
Endocrinology, Bethesda, Md., U. S. A.
Journal of Biological Chemistry, Bethesda, Md., U. S. A.
Journal of Clinical Endocrinology and Metabolism, Bethesda, Md., U. S. A.
Journal of Dairy Science, Bloomington, Indiana, U. S. A.

to

Drs. G. L. Wied & G. F. Bahr, Editors of Introduction to Quantitative Cytochemistry II (Academic Press, New York)

and to

Academic Press, Inc., New York, N. Y., U. S. A.
Appleton-Century-Crofts, Inc., New York, N. Y., U. S. A.
Excerpta Medica Foundation, Amsterdam, The Netherlands
J. B. Lippincott Co., Philadelphia, Pa., U. S. A.